The Wholesale Bargains & Free Stuff Guide

The Wholesale Bargains & Free Stuff Guide

ISBN
1-884350-50-X

Library of Congress Catalog No.

93-073408

ALPHA SELF-HELP BOOKS

THE
WHOLESALE BARGAINS
&
FREE STUFF
GUIDE

By

Frank J. Simpson
Susan Applegate

 Alpha Publishing, Inc.

WHOLESALERS & OUTLETS

If you would like to be listed in this guide, please send details of product, discounts, etc. on your letterhead to:

The Editor
Wholesale Bargains & Free Stuff Guide
Post Office Box 747
Walnut, CA 91789

TABLE OF CONTENTS

I

Introduction

Forget the middleman and go straight for the savings! That's what this new edition of *The Wholesale Bargains And Free Stuff Guide* is all about. It's a consumer's guide to eliminating middlemen and their sky-high mark-ups by buying directly from manufacturers or producers of goods and services.

Listed on the following pages are over 500 carefully chosen companies that sell top-quality, brand-name merchandise at 30% to 90% off average retail prices. Whatever you need, from apparel to wallpaper, is available by mail- order at wholesale prices. You don't have to pay middlemen. You don't have to wait for sales events. You don't have to battle the crowds and confusion and pay outlandish prices at shopping malls. From the convenience of your own home, you can save hundreds, even thousands of dollars.

All you need to do is follow the easy directions in *The Wholesale Bargains And Free Stuff Guide* . You'll find hundreds of firms' names, addresses and toll- free numbers. The listings also let you know what each company sells and how much you can expect to save. Simply contact the firms that interest you, by mail or by toll-free phone, and request their latest catalogs, savings brochures, bargain sheets, direct-to-consumer advance savings notices, and more. You won't be obligated to buy a single thing, but you will get catalogs and brochures, jam-packed with unbeatable wholesale savings.

While most companies send their catalogs free upon request, a few firms charge nominal fees ($1 to $5) which are usually refundable or redeemable upon ordering. However, before you send for a catalog or place an order, you should read the section titled, "How To Shop By Mail: A comprehensive guide to saving hundreds of dollars on mail order values" thoroughly. You'll find out how to shop by mail and find the quality merchandise you want at the greatest savings. You'll also learn all the do's and don'ts of mail-order shopping.

Shopping by mail can result in substantial savings, and it's fun! We're sure this new edition of *The Wholesale Bargains And Free Stuff Guide* will prove to be an invaluable reference/guide-book to help you find super mail-order bargains. Happy shopping!

The Wholesale Bargains And Free Stuff Guide is intended as a consumer's reference/guide-book only. While each company listed herein has been chosen carefully for quality merchandise, bargain prices and reputable service, users should never order directly from this book. Make sure you contact the companies first and request catalogs or current price quotes. Also take care to follow specific instructions for ordering and making payment. *The Wholesale Bargains And Free Stuff Guide* is not intended as an endorsement for any specific company or product. Prices, available merchandise, and other information given in this catalog's listings are subject to change.

II

A Guide To The Listings

E
ach Listing in this catalog provides specific information about companies that accept mail orders. The information is designed to to lead you to the companies that stock the products you wish to buy. The information presented in each listing, generally, is as follows:

1) The company name, mailing address, phone number, and FAX number (when applicable)

2) What goods a company sells and has in stock

3) The type(s) of information a company publishes—catalog, brochure, price list, etc.—and whether the information is free or requires a minimal fee. Many companies that charge a small fee for their literature, make the cost "refundable" or "deductible" if an order is placed.

Most companies require that you include a self-addressed, stamped envelope (#10) when you send for a catalog and/or price list. Many companies also give price quotes and/or information by phone.
Companies frequently revise their literature so you may have to wait a few weeks for a catalog to arrive. Most compa-

---

nies advise potential customers to allow six to eight weeks for delivery of catalogs and/or other literature.

Firms without catalogs usually have a price quote system. When requesting a price quote, give the company the exact make and model number of the item you want.

4) The percentage of savings you may expect from a company— please remember that this percentage (when included in a listing) pertains to how much savings you may expect on the suggested list or comparable retail prices of specific products and/or services. This percentage should not be deducted from the total order. Always rely on a company's price quote to determine the actual total cost of an order.

5) The method of payment accepted by a company— check, money order, certified check, and major credit card (MasterCard, VISA, American Express, etc.).

6) Minimum orders— some companies require a minimum order in dollars or goods. Make sure you are familiar with a company's policies before you order.

III

How To Shop By Mail:

A Comprehensive Guide To Saving Hundreds Of Dollars On Mail-Order Values

The end of the 1980s saw a marked increase in the number of consumers who made major purchases while "shopping at home". According to the Direct Marketing Association (DMA), over 90 million Americans ordered products and services by mail or by phone in 1989. That number has grown considerably over the past couple of years with "saving" a major priority of the 1990s. The millions of consumers who have discovered the convenience of shopping at home are taking advantage of the great bargains offered through mail-order catalogs, toll-free order lines, magazine subscription services, and other direct marketing services.

Most people (around 90% , according to some recent studies) report satisfaction with their shop-at-home experiences— merchandise and service. However, mail-order and telephone shopping can be confusing, and less than satisfactory for the "uninitiated". Every consumer needs to know exactly what he/she is getting into before placing an order. With the necessary information, an understanding of the shop-at-home process, and a little patience, you'll be able to take advantage of the bargains offered to mail-order and telephone shoppers.

This section of the Wholesale Bargains & Free Stuff Guide provides valuable information on how you can shop at home virtually risk free. You should be armed with this information before you order any catalogs or call for any price quotes.

Catalogs, Brochures, and Price Lists

Before you order anything from any company, you should do some "comparison" shopping. Most mail-order companies publish catalogs, brochures or price lists which provide representative selections of goods, services, and prices offered. You should get as many catalogs, brochures, etc. as you can and compare what each company has to offer.

Many companies provide their catalogs and other literature free upon request. A phone call or a written request is often all it takes to get a catalog and/or to get on a company's mailing list. Some companies request a fee (typically, $1 to $6) for their catalogs and brochures. In some instances, the price of the catalog is "refundable" upon placing an order. Other companies may require that you send a #10 (business-sized) self-addressed, stamped envelope (SASE).

When you request a catalog by mail, be as specific as possible. Some mail- order companies have more than one catalog (depending on the product line) so you should be clear as to the products you are interested in. If the company has a toll-free information line, you may call and inquire about the availability of a catalog. (Please note that you should never call a company's toll-free "order" line to request a catalog. And don't call non-toll-free numbers collect.)

For catalogs that cost $1.00 or more, you should send a check or money order. After ordering or requesting a catalog, be patient. You may receive some catalogs within a few days, while others may take weeks to arrive. As a general rule, you should allow 6 to 8 weeks for shipment of catalogs.

Price Quotes

Some mail-order firms offer their products by way of price-quotes. In most cases, the company will carry name-brand merchandise which can be identified readily by manufacturers' name, model or stock number, and color or pattern name or code. When you call or write a firm to request a price quote on a particular item, you should be able to supply the identifying information. The information can be found on factory packaging or tags on products in stores. You can also get brochures and/or specification sheets which provide product identification by writing to the manufacturer's customer service department.

The price quote you get from a company is simply "its" price on the goods in question. It's a good idea to request that the tax, shipping charges, insurance, and handling be itemized separately instead of as part of the price quote. This will make matters less confusing should you have to return the merchandise for a refund. Also ask the company how long they will guarantee the price it quotes. Some companies guarantee price quotes for a limited time only.

Most price quotes by mail require a SASE. However, price quotes by mail often cost less than phone calls, and allow you to have a "written" record of the quote. If you phone for a price quote, take down the complete name of the person who provides you with the quote. Inform that person that you are keeping a record of all the information he or she gives you. This may help avoid problems later on.

Ordering

After you've received (and reviewed) catalogs and price quotes, and you've compared quality of goods, service, return policies, fees and surcharges, length of time for delivery, methods of delivery, and prices, you should be able to get the best possible bargain. Don't forget to compare your catalog and price quotes with prices on the same product(s) at a local retailer. You should also consider the time it takes to order compared with the time it takes to purchase the item from a local retailer.

Once you've made your decision, you can order by mail, using the order form from your catalog. Be sure to fill out the form(s) carefully and completely. You should also make a photocopy of the order form, and your check or money order. If you don't have access to a copier, write down the company's name, address, and phone number; and all pertinent information from the order form— item inventory number or code, size and color, the date of order, method of payment, etc.

Most catalogs will indicate that the prices listed therein are in effect until a certain date only, and that prices are subject to change without notice. You should try to place your order, using a "current" catalog. If you order from an "out-of-date" catalog, you'll most likely be billed for the difference between the old and new price. You should also be sure to meet the minimum order requirement, if one is required.

Many mail-order companies offer toll-free (800 number) ordering lines. You can often save time and money by using such lines. You'll also be able to find out immediately if the item you are interested in is in stock or not. If you don't know whether or not the company you wish to call has a toll-free number, you can check an 800 directory (found in most public libraries), or you can call the toll-free information number, 1-800-555-1212.

If you call to place an order, make sure you have your credit card handy. You should also have all necessary ordering information in front of you, as well as the catalog from which you are ordering. It is important (for your own protection) that you keep a written record, including the name of the person to whom you speak. Also have your order, name, address, etc. read back to you and/or confirmed in writing.

Regardless of how you order—by mail or by phone—you should keep all information pertaining to your order, including the catalog, brochure, price list, or advertisement; and your canceled check or charge account records, until the order has been delivered in satisfactory condition.

Making Payment

The first thing to remember is "never send cash through the mail". The listings in this catalog, and the companies' catalogs themselves, provide instructions for paying by check, money order, or credit card. You should also keep in mind that some firms have minimum-order requirements for credit card orders which are typically higher than those required on pre-paid (check, money order) orders. Make sure you are aware of the minimum order requirement before you order.

Guarantee and Return Policies

While most mail-order firms promise "satisfaction", and accept returns, actual policies will differ considerably from one company to the next. You should understand the company's policies regarding product guarantees and returns before you place an order. Guarantee and return policy information can usually be found in the customer service section near the order form in a catalog. You can also get information by calling or writing the mail-order company and requesting copies of product warranties before you order.

It's a good idea to open and inspect merchandise immediately upon receipt (or as soon as possible) to confirm that the item is what you ordered and that it is in satisfactory condition. If there is a problem, and you wish to return a product, you should follow the company's return policy exactly. If the return information is unavailable, write the company with a clear and concise explanation of what you wish to return, and why. Be sure to supply all pertinent information about the merchandise, reason for return, method of payment, and your name and address. Keep a copy of the letter for your records.

"30-Day Rule"

The Federal Trade Commission (FTC) Mail-Order Merchandise Rule offers some protection for consumers against late delivery and/or nondelivery of merchandise. The FTC rule requires mail-order firms to ship goods to the buyer within the time period specified in their catalogs, brochures, ad, etc.. If no shipping date is given, the firm is required to ship the merchandise within 30 days of the receipt of payment and a "properly completed order form".

The firm must notify you if it cannot meet its shipment date, and ask you to agree to a specified delay (up to 30 days). You don't have to agree to the delay— you can, instead, cancel your order and receive a full refund. When the company notifies you of a delay in shipment, it is obligated to provide return postage for your reply. If you do not respond to the notice, your order is considered still in effect. If the firm cannot meet the new shipping date, it must send a second notice. If you do not sign and return this notice within the specified time period, your order is considered canceled.

If your order is canceled because of delayed shipment, the firm must send you a check or money order within 7 business days or, for credit card orders, credit your charge account within one billing cycle. It is worth noting that some states and/or counties have enacted laws similar to the FTC's Mail-Order Merchandise Rule but which may offer more protection. If that is the case, these state and local laws take precedence. This could be especially important to give consumers further protection on phone orders if their states have strong laws protecting such transactions.

Filing A Complaint

Since studies indicate that most mail-order shoppers are satisfied with their shop-at-home experiences, it is evident that the mail-order industry does a good job in meeting consumer expectations. However, nobody or no business is perfect all the time. If problems should occur—products fail or service is inadequate—there are certain things you can do to receive satisfaction.

The first thing you should do is identify the problem accurately, and decide what you think would be an appropriate settlement— exchange, repair, or refund. You should then contact the company (and salesperson) who sold you the item or performed the service. Explain the problem and what action you would like taken (according to the company's return policy, outlined in their catalog or brochure). If, after informing the company of a problem, there is still no resolution, you should consider filing a formal complaint.

Such a complaint should be lodged in a letter written to the company. The letter should be brief and to the point. It should also be business-like, rather than angry and threatening. Your letter should include your name and address, all pertinent ordering information regarding the product (serial number, model number, etc.), and your method of payment— check, money order, credit card. You should also tell the company what you want done about the problem, and give them a reasonable period of time (usually 30 days), you are willing to wait for a resolution. It's best that you type your letter and keep a copy of it and all additional correspondence to and from the company.

If your complaint letter does not result in a satisfactory resolution, the following organizations and agencies may be able to offer assistance:

The Direct Marketing Association
Action Line 11 West 42nd Street
P.O. Box 3861
New York, NY 10163-3861

The DMA is the largest organization of direct marketers worldwide, and may be of help solving problems that occur when your order by mail or by phone. The DMA's Mail Order Action Line (MOAL) will contact the mail-order firm directly (after receiving a copy of your written complaint) in an effort to help reach a resolution.

You may also get help from a Better Business Bureau agency. BBBs are self- regulatory agencies which are funded by business and professional firms. They monitor selling and advertising practices, maintain files on firms, and help consumers resolve complaints. If you wish to enlist the aid of the BBB (either before you order, or after you have filed a complaint), you must contact a bureau nearest the mail-order company in question. Do not contact the BBB in your area, unless the company you are dealing with is in your BBB office area. You can find a directory of BBBs at your local library. Find the address of the appropriate office and send a written request for an "inquiry" or "complaint" form, whichever you need. (The best advice is to check out an unfamiliar company with the Better Business Bureau before you place an order.)

The U.S. Postal Inspection Service may also be able to help. Contact your local post office and get the name and address of the nearest postal inspector. The Inspection

Service may contact the company in question and attempt to help you reach a resolution. It may also investigate if the case appears to involve mail fraud.

The Federal Trade Commission
6th & Pennsylvania Avenue
N.W. Washington, D.C. 20580

If the case involves widespread mail fraud, the FTC may get involved and be able to help. The FTC does not act on individual complaints, but it does compile complaints to build files on firms. When a company's file becomes filled with complaints, an investigation by the FTC may take place.

Whenever you enlist the aid of any organization or agencies, such as those listed above, be sure to put your complaint in writing and specify the merchandise or service ordered. You should include the date of the order, and all other pertinent information. Also include photocopies of any correspondence and documents which will backup your complaint.

IV
Animal Supplies:

Pet and livestock supplies, equipment, medicines, and services at incredible mail-order prices

f you are a pet and/or livestock owner, you're one of millions of Americans who spend almost $2 billion a year on their animals. Shopping by mail for animal supplies can mean a considerable savings. The firms listed in this chapter offer a wide assortment of pet and livestock products and supplies, from special foods and toys to medication, at wholesale prices.

It should be noted that when you order medical supplies for your animals, you are required, by law, to state that such purchases (needles, antibiotics, etc.) are for use on animals only. You'll also have to send a veterinarian's prescription with your order. These are Food and Drug Administration (FDA) requirements with which you must comply every time you order animal medical supplies. You should also check with your local health department before you order such medical supplies to make sure there are no local regulations banning the receipt of such items.

Animal City

P.O. Box 269024
San Diego, CA 92126-9024
Phone: 800-237-Pets (7387)

Animal City is the mail-order division of Petco and has been in business since the mid 1960's. Animal City's mail-order inventory includes a wide assortment of brand name pet, kennel, and veterinary supplies for most pets, including cats, dogs, birds, hamsters, gerbils, and fish.

Animal City's catalog, which is free upon request, displays everything from horse tack to litter pans at a savings of up to 30%. Pet owners can choose from a selection of pet doors, scooper sets and litter pans, cages, carriers, beds, toys, animal doors, collars, leashes, treats, and other items. Brand names offered include American Leather, Ames, Dexol, Farnam, Norden, St. Aubrey, and others.

Animal City guarantees satisfaction with your order. Medical supplies are sent where local laws allow. Payment can be made with check, money order or major credit cards (Master Card, Visa). Discounts can be obtained when buying in quantity. Returns (except for vaccines and instruments) are accepted for refund or credit on another order.

Care-A-Lot

1617 Diamond Springs Road
Virginia Beach, VA 23455.
Phone: (804) 460-9771

Dog owners can find a complete line of pet supplies offered at excellent savings in Care-A-Lot's free catalog. The catalog lists everything from flea and tick products to cages, collars, shampoos, leads, and treats, to a full range of books. The company specializes in show-training and professional grooming supplies and also has in stock many hard-to-find items.

Most orders are shipped the same day. Payment is accepted by check, money order, MasterCard or VISA.

Dairy Association Co., Inc.
Lyndonville, VT 05851-0145.
Phone:(802) 626-3610

The Dairy Association Co., Inc. has been in business for over 100 years. The firm offers an assortment of livestock treatments and leather balm at savings ranging up to 35%. Products include Bag Balm ointment for use on cows, sheep, goats, dogs and cats with a variety of ailments; Hoof Softener, and Tackmaster leather conditioner.

The Dairy Association Co., Inc. will provide a brochure, free upon request. Price quotes can be obtained by written request with a SASE or by phone. Payment for purchases can be made by check or money order. Orders made by phone will be accepted for C.O.D. payment.

For prices and other information in Canada write to:

Dr. A.D. Daniels Co. Ltd.,
North Rock Island, Canada.

The Dog's Outfitter
P.O. Box 2010
Hazelton, PA 18201.
Phone:(717) 384-3257

While there is a $75 minimum order requirement, The Dog's Outfitter does offer savings of up to 50% on a full assortment of pet, kennel, groomer, and veterinary supplies. The company's name can be misleading since it also sells a full range of products for cats and other pets.

Pet owners can find grooming tools, flea and tick collars, shampoos, insecticides, feeders, vitamins and minerals, collars and leads, pet beds, gates, cages, carriers, and many other related items. There's also a selection of books for pet owners.. Name brands include Bio- Groom, General Cage, Oster, Ring 5, Twinco, Zodiac, and others.

The Dog's Outfitter—in business for over 20 years—will send a free catalog upon request. You can get a price quote by phone or by mail with a SASE. Payment can be made by check, money order, or most major credit cards. C.O.D orders are accepted. All orders must be $75 or more.

Echo Discount Aquarium & Pet Supply
Box 145, Department
Westland, MI 48185
Phone:(313) 453-3131

For 30 years Echo Discount Aquarium & Pet Supply has offered mail-order fish and pet supplies at excellent savings. Although the company's specialty is tropical and saltwater fish products, it also sells supplies for dogs, cats, hamsters, gerbils, birds, and other pets as well.

Echo features savings of up to 70% on complete aquarium outfits and supplies, fish food, medication, and pet supplies. The company's catalog costs $1 and is published twice a year. The catalog lists everything you need to start and maintain your own aquarium, including air pumps, filters, water pumps, mini reef systems, lighting, and heaters, as well as complete aquarium outfits. The catalog is packed with valuable information and discounts on thousands of brand name supplies.

You can get a price quote by mail with a SASE or by phone. There is a 15% restocking fee in effect on the return of unused purchases. Payment can be made by check, money order or major credit card.

Mail Order Pet Shop (California & New York)
1338 North Market Blvd.
Sacramento, CA 95834 (Western Region) or

250 Executive Drive Edgewood,
NY 11717 (Eastern Region)
Phone:800-366-7387 FAX: 800-877-3834

The Mail Order Pet Shop has both East and West coast warehouses for mail-order convenience. Pet owners will find a full range of pet supplies for dogs and cats, birds, hamsters, and other pets, as well as aquariums and accessories in the companies free catalogs. The company invites customers to compare its selection of pet supplies, prices, and service with other firms selling comparable goods.

The Mail Order Pet Shop's dog and cat catalog lists over 4,000 items for dog and cat care. The stock includes many items for dogs, including leads, harnesses and muzzles, collars and chokes, out chains and stakes, travel cages, dishes and feeders, clothes by Dogie Duds, dental kits, scrapers and breath sprays, cologne and deodorant, beds and cushions, clippers, vitamins and minerals, chews, toys, treats, and shampoos, conditioners and rinses. There are also medications for dogs, including earmite powders, drops and lotions; wormers; eye washes; diarrhea treatments; hot spot lotion; and medicated sprays, lotions and ointments. Regular and electronic flea and tick collars, powders and sprays, grooming equipment, and a huge selection of educational "dog books" are also available.

Cat owners will find an assortment of automatic feeders and bowls, odor free litter boxes, grooming and health supplies (wormers, hairball remedies, ear mite remedies, vitamins and supplements, shampoos, dental kits and scrapers, brushes, claw clippers), catnip and regular toys, flea and tick collars, transportation boxes, scratching posts, and treats. There's also a good selection of cat leads, collars and harnesses, and informative books about cats.

The Mail Order Pet Shop's "Dog & Cat Catalog", as well as it's "Aquarium" and "Birds & Small Animals" catalogs, is free upon request. Every product is factory new and fully guaranteed. Orders are shipped quickly from New York and California warehouses. Pay by check, money order or major credit card.

Master Animal Care
411 Seventh Avenue
Two Harbors, MN 55616
Phone:(218) 834-3200

Master Animal care has become one of the most trusted sources for dog and cat products. Pet owners will find Master Animal Care's free 72-page catalog full of mail-order savings on dog and cat supplies and biologicals. The catalog also features health care tips and information.

Master Animal Care offers savings of up to 50% off average retail prices on a full range of health-care items, grooming aids, leashes and leads, feeders, training aids,cages and carriers, flea and tick collars, and other pet supplies. This company also sells hard-to-find items such as electronic training devices and hot-oil skin treatment for dogs and cats.

Satisfaction on every order is guaranteed. Returns (everything but vaccines) are accepted within 30 days for exchange, credit, or refund. Pay by check, money order or major credit card.

Northern Wholesale Veterinary Supply, Inc.
P.O. Box 7526
Omaha, NE 68107 8

Phone:800-356-5852

Northern Wholesale's free catalog lists savings of up to 50% on a wide assortment of veterinary, kennel, and pet supplies. The company has supplied livestock farmers, veterinarians, breeders, and pet owners with quality animal supplies for over 20 years.

The products listed in Northern Wholesale's catalog include nutritional supplements, vaccines, biologicals, horse tack, pest treatments, leashes, cages and carriers, flea and tick remedies, feeding equipment, and other related items. There's also a selection of books available. Brand names include Absorbine, Orvus, Oster, Rubbermaid, Sunbeam, and others. The catalog is geared toward livestock owners and professionals and the pet supplies offered are mostly healthcare products.

Northern Wholesale provides quantity discounts on some items. Payment is accepted by check, money order or major credit card.

Western Suppliers
P.O. Box 791 Pilot Point,
TX 76258
Phone: (817) 686-2251

Western Suppliers offers savings of up to 50% on a complete line of saddles and tack. Their discount price list is available upon request.

Western's free catalog features an excellent selection of western and show saddles, with prices ranging from under $100 to several hundred dollars. Also featured in the catalog are harnesses, saddlebags, bridles, stirrups, reins, feed buckets, lariats, beautiful tack decorations, and many other equine- related items. Western has stocked quality goods for horse owners for 20 years. You can get a price quote from Western Suppliers by phone or by mail with a SASE. Pay by check, money order or major credit card.

J.B. Wholesale Pet Supplies, Inc.
289 Wagaraw Rd., Hawthorne, NJ 07506
Phone: (201) 423-2222; (800) 526-0388

For over a decade, J.B. Wholesale has been offering wholesale bargains on pet supplies. All sorts of supplies for dogs and cats, including grooming, showing, and training items are available. You'll find feeding equipment, leashes and leads, carriers and cages, flea and tick products, toys and treats, shampoos, and many other pet care items.

A catalog is available free upon request. Pay by check, money order or major credit card.

New England Serum Company
U.S. Rte. 1, P.O. Box 128
Topsfield, MA 09183
Phone: (508) 887-2368; (800) NES-SERUM [637-3786]

New England Serum began selling pet care products and supplies when Dwight D. Eisenhower was president. The company is still providing pet owners with quality products, many at below wholesale prices. New England Serum has over 10,000 products in stock.

A product catalog is available free upon request. Pay by check, money order or major credit card.

Omaha Vaccine Co.
3030 "L" St., Omaha, NE 68107
Phone: (402) 731-9600; (800) 367-4444

Savings of 25% - 50% off typical retail prices are available from the Omaha Vaccine Co. Omaha Vaccine has been in business for over 25 years, offering a wide assortment of kennel, equine, and pet supplies.

Omaha Vaccines "Best Care Catalog" is chock full of bargain items for your pet. There are 14,000 products for dogs, cats and horses, including vaccines (sent where ordinances permit), flea products, wormers, clippers, cages, halters, saddles, toys, and treats. These are the same name brand products you've seen in pet stores, grooming shops, and at the Vet's office, but at much lower prices.

Call or write the co. to request the "Best Care Catalog". It's free. A minimum order of $10 is required. Pay by check, money order or major credit card.

Pet Warehouse
P.O. Box 310, Xenia, OH 45385-0301
Phone: (800) 443-1160 [Daytime, 9-5 EST];
(800) 443-1176 [evenings & weekends]
FAX: (513) 374- 9800

The Pet Warehouse takes great pride in its "service, selection, and customer satisfaction". The company's service includes trained representatives to help make selecting and ordering as easy as possible; 24-hour-a-day, 7-days-a-week, toll-free ordering; fast shipping; and few backorders. The selection of pet products

and supplies includes everything from bird baths to videos. Savings are available on almost any pet product imaginable.

A recent 133-page, color Pet Warehouse catalog listed hundreds of items for every type of pet. For cat lovers, the stock includes beds, collars, dishes, feeders, toys, cat "condos", litter boxes, training devices, flea and tick products, and many other items.

There's even a product called Allerpet/C (sold for $5.57) which is for people who are allergic to pets. It's a non-toxic grooming emolient that cleanses your pet's coat of antigens which can cause allergic reactions in many people.

If your pet is a dog, the Pet Warehouse carries a complete selection of supplies, including beds and cushions, choke chains, collars, dishes, deodorizers, feeders and waterers, flea and tick products, shampoos, toys, sweaters, carriers, and much more. Also in stock is a large inventory of fish supplies, bird supplies, and rabbit, reptile and other small animal supplies. Books such as "Owning The Right Dog", and training videos are also available. The best thing to do, is to call or write the company and request that your name be placed on their mailing list.

Within a few weeks, you'll begin receiving (free) catalogs which provide graphic descriptions of the Pet Warehouse inventory.

Customer satisfaction is guaranteed with returns of unused items accepted for a refund, exchange, or credit. Some returned items may be subject to a minimal restocking fee. All items in stock are usually shipped within 18 hours. Payment may be made by check, money order or major credit card.

R.C. Steele Co.
Sporting Dog Specialties
1989 Transit Way, Brockport, NY 14420-0910
Phone: (800) 872-3773

The R.C. Steele Co. is a division of Sporting Dog Specialties and specializes in pet supplies at wholesale prices. Save as much as 50% off typical retail prices on some items. The company has been providing quality pet supplies and pet care products since the late 1950s.

A recent R.C. Steele catalog listed hundreds of wholesale bargains including feeding equipment, leashes, leads, grooming products, rawhide bones, carriers, cages, pet doors, flea and tick products, and much more. There's also an outstanding

selection of training devices, books, and videos. R.C.

Steele also sells pet care products and supplies for "the cat of the house".

A catalog is available free upon request. Satisfaction is guaranteed. Authorized returns are accepted. The minimum order is $50. Pay by check, money order or major credit card.

Wholesale Veterinary Supply
P.O. Box 2256, Rockford, IL 61131
Phone: (815) 877-0209; (800) 435 6940

For over 20 years, Wholesale Veterinary Supply has been providing pet supplies and animal care products at savings of up to 50%. Past catalogs have featured thousands of items for dogs, cats, horses, rabbits, and cattle.

Wholesale Veterinary Supply's inventory includes an assortment of cages and carriers, leashes, leads, flea and tick products, feeding equipment, toys, grooming tools and preparations, and many other pet care products. There's also a selection of veterinary equipment, including vaccines (sent where ordinances allow), surgical instruments, and nutritional supplements. Brand name products in stock include Oster, Sergeants, Absorbine, Farnam, Fortex, Shaw's, Roche, Holiday, and many others.

Call or write the company to request a free catalog. Price quotes are also available by phone or by mail (with SASE). Authorized returns are accepted within 30 days. The minimum order is $30. Pay by check, money order or major credit card.

V
Appliances:

Big and small personal care and kitchen appliances at super mail-order savings

The companies listed in this section offer a full assortment of household appliances to meet every consumer need. Whether you are in the market for a new washer, dryer, refrigerator, range, air conditioner, sewing machine, vacuum cleaner, or floor machine, these firms have them at discounts averaging up to 40%. The listings also include a full complement of personal care and small kitchen appliances at wholesale savings.

ABC Vacuum Warehouse
6720 Burnet RD.
Austin, TX 78757
Phone: (512) 459-7643

Here's your chance to save up to 50% on top-quality vacuum cleaners. ABC's selection of brand name vacuum cleaners comes from purchases made from distributors who are overstocked. The quality is the best, with no seconds or rebuilt models sold. ABC has been offering consumers substantial savings on vacuum cleaners for over 15 years.

Brand name vacuum cleaners in stock include Kirby, Rexair's Rainbow, Filter Queen, Hoover, Royal, Tri-Star, and others. Both upright and canister models are available, as are bags, filters and accessories. Send for ABC's free price list. You can also get a price quote by phone. Pay by check, money order or major credit card.

Bernie's Discount Center, Inc.
821 Sixth Ave.
New York, NY 10001
Phone: (212) 564-8758

For over 40 years, Bernie's Discount Center has been selling appliances and other goods at discounts of up to 40%. The company sells first-quality merchandise only, and no grey-market goods.

Bernie's has an outstanding selection of small appliances (toasters, food processors, coffee-makers, can openers, blenders) by Black & Decker, Braun, Bunn, Clairol, Eureka, G.E., Hamilton Beach, Hitachi, Hoover, KitchenAid, Mr. Coffee, Norelco, Panasonic, Remington, West Bend, and many other manufacturers. Microwave ovens are also available at discount prices. These items are shipped nationwide. Larger items—washers, dryers, refrigerators, TVs, air conditioners, etc.—are shipped in the New York City area only.

Bernie's also sells electronic equipment (audio, TV, video) by Fisher, Hitachi, Mitsubishi, Panasonic, RCA, Sony, Sylvania, Toshiba, and others. No catalog is available, but you can get a price quote by phone or by mail with a SASE. Payment can be made by check, money order or major credit card.

Derry's Sewing Center
430 St. Ferdinand
Florissant, MO 63031
Phone: (314) 837-6103

Top brand name sewing machines and vacuum cleaners are offered by Dewey's at savings of up to 35%. A good selection of parts for both new and older model sewing machines is also available. Brand names include Singer, Simplicity and Necchi.

Derry's offers a brochure for $1 and a SASE. The brochure displays new sewing machines by Simplicity and Singer. The company also has in stock vacuum cleaners by Panasonic and a good selection of bags which fit most models. Derry's has been in business for over 10 years and sells only top-of-the-line products.

You can get a price quote by phone or by mail with $1 and a SASE. There is a minimum order of $5 required. Pay by money order or major credit card.

E.B.A. Wholesale Corporation
2361 Nostrand Ave.
Brooklyn, NY 11210.
 Phone: (718) 252-3400

E.B.A. carries an excellent selection of large appliances (refrigerators, washers, dryers, dishwashers, ranges) at savings of up to 40%. The company sells only top quality brands such as Amana, Frigidaire, G.E., Hotpoint, Jenn- Air, Kitchen Aid, Magic Chef, Whirlpool, and others. There's also a good selection of TV's and video equipment by Magnavox, Panasonic, Quasar, RCA, Sony, Sylvania, G.E., Zenith, and other manufacturers.

No catalog is available but you can get a price quote by phone or by mail with a SASE. Items can be returned but a 20% restocking fee may be imposed. Pay by by check, money order, MasterCard or VISA.

Foto Electric Supply Co., Inc.
31 Essex Street
New York, NY 10002.
 Phone: (212) 673-5222

If you need white goods (washers, dryers, refrigerators, and ranges), Foto Electric Supply can save you 30% and more. The company has been in business for 30 years, selling top quality brand names such as Amana, G.E., Magic Chef, Maytag, White-Westinghouse, Whirlpool, and others. Shipment is made nationwide.

Foto also has in stock mid- to high-end audio equipment (stereo systems, components, etc.), video equipment, phone machines, cameras and film (by Kodak, Fuji, Agfa, and Polaroid), and other brand-name products. To get a price quote, contact Foto Electric Supply by mail only with a SASE. Payment is accepted by check, money order or major credit card.

LVT Price Quote Hotline, Inc.
Box 444
Commack, NY 11725-0444.
 Phone: (516) 234-8884

In business since 1976, LVT offers over 4000 products by brand-name manufacturers. You can save up to 30% on suggested list or full retail prices on microwave ovens, bread-making machines, air conditioners, vacuum cleaners, washers and dryers, and hundreds of other products. Brands in stock include Amana, Bearcat, Caloric, Electrolux, Eureka, G.E., Hoover, JVC, Jenn-Air, Maytag, Sony, and many others.

Besides appliances, LVT also sells electronics and office machines (type writers, copiers, fax machines, word processors, computers) at great savings. Also in stock are TV's, video equipment, phone machines, and calculators.

The first thing to do is to send for LVT's free brochure which provides details on ordering and shipping procedures. You can then phone and get a price quote on any product as long as you provide the brand name and model number. You can also get a price quote by mail with a SASE. Payment is made by check, money order or certified check.

Percy's Inc.
19 Glennie
St. Worcester, MA 01605
Phone: (508) 755-5269 FAX: (508) 797-5578

With over 50 years of experience, Percy's has the reputation of offering quality merchandise at great savings. The company has in stock a full line of large appliances (does not sell small appliances), including dishwashers, refrigerators, ranges, freezers, and standard and microwave ovens. Dehumidifiers and disposals are also available. Brands sold include Bose, Fisher, G.E., Hitachi, Litton, Thermador, Toshiba, and others. Prices are as much as 40% below list.

Also in stock at Percy's is a good selection of video equipment and tapes, audio components, TV's, and office machines.

No catalog is available but you can call the company and get a price quote or send a letter with a SASE. Payment can be made by check, money order, certified check, or major credit card.

Sewin' In Vermont
84 Concord Ave.
St. Johnsbury, Vt 05819.
Phone: (802) 748-3803

Here's a company that specializes in selling name-brand sewing machines and accessories at great savings. Sewin' In Vermont offers savings from 15% to 40% below list prices on quality American and European products. In stock are sewing machines by Viking, Sergers, Bernina, and others. Replacement parts and a full line of accessories are also available. The company also stocks a selection of professional-quality sergers, presses, and irons.

You can get Sewin' In Vermont's brochure and price list free by mail with a SASE. You can also get a price quote by phone. Pay by check, money order or major credit card.

Singer Sewing Center
1669 Texas Ave.
College Station, TX 77840.
 Phone: 800-338-5672

Singer, Necchi, Elna, and Pfaff are among the name-brand sewing machines, sergers, and vacuum cleaners sold by Singer Sewing Center at average savings of 33%. This company also has a layaway plan available upon request.

Phone or send a letter with a SASE for a price quote. If ordering parts, the minimum order is $25. Pay by check, money order or major credit card.

Irv Wolfson Company
3321 W. Irving Park Road
Chicago, IL 60618.
Phone: (312) 267-7828 FAX: (312) 267-7154

This company has been selling appliances and electronics since the early 1950's at prices ranging up to 40% below average retail.

Among the many name-brand products in stock are refrigerators, ranges, washers, dryers, microwave ovens, kitchen appliances (blenders, food processors, toasters, can openers), air conditioners, electric blankets, and other personal use products. Brands offered by Irv Wolfson

Company include Amana, Carrier, Eureka, Gaggenau, G.E., Oster, Sharp, Speed Queen, Tappan, and others. Video equipment and foreign current TV's are also available. Current converters, "stepdown" transformers, plug adaptors, and other electronics and supplies in stock, as well.

To get a price quote on an Irv Wolfson product, phone or send a letter with a SASE. Payment may be by check, money order or certified check.

AAA All Factory, Inc.
1230 N. 3rd St., Abilene, TX 79601-5726
Phone: (915) 677-1311

AAA All Factory is America's "largest discount vacuum cleaner store". The company has been in business since 1965, offering name brand vacuum cleaners, supplies and accessories. Savings range up to 75% off typical list prices.

In stock at AAA All Factory are brand name products such as Eureka, Hoover, Tri-Star, Filter Queen, Rexair, and many others. All models are available, including upright, convertible, canister, and mini vacuums.

A catalog is available for $2.00 (refundable with first order). Call or write the company. Pay by check, money order or major credit card.

VI
Crafts & Hobby
Material and Supplies:

Everything needed for fine and appplied arts, crafts and hobbies

Buying art materials and supplies by mail can mean a savings of 20% or more on name-brand goods. Mail-order shoppers can also save on private-label goods. These products may be made by well-known manufacturers but identified as "house brands", and are usually less expensive than their name-brand counterparts. The companies listed in this section offer both name-brand and proprietary art materials, tools, equipment and supplies for fine and applied arts.

Also listed in this section are companies which offer a full range of craft materials and supplies. Beginners and experienced craftsmen and hobbyists can find savings of 20% to 70% on woodworking, needlecraft, leathercraft, basketry, silk fabric for home sewing, radio-controlled cars, boats, airplanes, and trains; and many other craft and hobby needs.

America's Hobby Center
146-K W. 22nd St.
New York, NY 10011-2466 (
Phone: 212) 675-8922 FAX: (212) 633-2754

If your hobby involves radio-controlled airplanes, cars, boats, trains, or helicopters, America's Hobby Center can supply all your needs. In business since 1931, this company offers savings of up to 40% on a wide range of vehicular hobby items.

You'll not only find the above models, but a selection of tools, materials, and supplies needed to put them together and get them running. There's also a series of books and manuals which provide valuable instruction and advice.

You can get free sample copies of the company's two brochures dealing with model airplanes, boats, cars, and trains. A subscription to 12 issues of both brochures is $10. A price quote on any item not listed in the brochures is available by phone or by mail with a SASE. Pay by check or money order.

Annie's Attic

1 Annie Lane,
Box 212 Big Sandy, TX 75755
Phone: 800-582-6643 FAX: 800-882-6643

You can save up to 50% on crochet patterns and supplies and other craft needs when you order from Annie's Attic. Annie's needlecraft catalog features 42 pages of savings on yarn, patterns, and other craft supplies.

Among the crochet patterns available from Annie's Attic are antique booties and bibs, little-miss dresses, hair bows, Irish crochet jewelry, pincushions, pullovers, skirts, jackets, camisoles, slippers, and doll house decor. Over 500 colors and sizes of yarn are available, as well as aluminum hook sets, bone rings, craft glue, fabric stiffener, plastic canvas, scissors, canvas markers, tapestry needles, and magnetic needle cases.

Call or write the company for more information and/or to

inquire about the needlecraft catalog. Satisfaction is guaranteed. Returns are accepted for full refund. Pay by check, money order or major credit card.

Art Supply Warehouse
360 Main Ave.
Norwalk, CT 06851
Phone: 800-995-6788 FAX: (203) 849-0845

The Art Supply Warehouse catalog promises low discount prices on a full range of art supplies. The company has been in business since 1979 and offers everything from airbrushes to watercolor crayons at a savings of up to 60% off typical retail prices.

The catalog lists a selection of oil and acrylic paints, pigments, and watercolors by Liquitex, Golden, Windsor & Newton, Createx, Shiva, Winton, Rembrandt, Rowney, Blockx, Grumbacher, Holbein, Sennelier, and other top manufacturers. You'll also find a wide assortment of tools and supplies such as colored pencils, brushes, painting knives, markers, ink, chalk, palette, frames, mixing cups, charcoal, cleaning supplies, aprons and smocks, paper and board, and acid-free tape. Brand names include D'Arches, Bob Ross, Gary Jenkins, Sumi-E, and others.

The company also has in stock compressors and air brush supplies, sculpture supplies (oven bake clay, modeling clay), drawing boards, tables, chairs, portfolios, lamps, easels, and a selection of Northlight "how-to" manuals.

The Art Supply Warehouse catalog is free upon request. Satisfaction is guaranteed. There is no shipping charge on orders shipped within the continental U.S., and no handling charge on orders over $150. Pay by check, money order, MasterCard or VISA. C.O.D. orders are accepted.

The Country Seat, Inc.
Box 24 A, RD 2 Kempton,
PA 19529-9411

The Country Seat is a small company but it offers a complete line of basketry and chair seating supplies at reasonable prices. The company's catalog lists a selection of oval reeds, hoops, handles, kits, and over 100 different instruction books. All goods are top-quality and available at the lowest possible prices.

To get the catalog, send a large 65 cent postage SASE. Pay by check, money order, MasterCard or VISA.

Craft King
P.O. Box 90637, Department WBFG
Lakeland, FL 33804.
Phone: (813) 686-9600

Since 1969 Craft King has been selling general project and craft supplies at average savings of 30% to 60%. Top quality, name brand and fast, friendly services are hallmarks of Craft King.

The company's discount mail-order catalog lists a wide array of craft supplies, such as paints, brushes, beads, Plastic canvas patterns, macrame, wreaths, flowers, glue, pins, doll parts, miniatures, Christmas ornaments, crosstitch, and instruction books for all types of crafts. Name brands in stock include Maxi, Darice, Simmons, Delta, Scribbles, Fairfield, The Beadery, Fibre-Craft, Forster, and many others.

The discount catalog is available for $2.00 (refundable). A price quote is available by phone or by mail with a SASE. Satisfaction is guaranteed. Pay by check or money order.

Dharma Trading Company
P.O. Box 150916

San Rafael, CA 94915.
Phone: 800-542-5227

Dharma Trading Company started doing business in 1969 and almost 25 years later "the beat goes on".The company offers fiber arts supplies for artists, craftpersons, and industry. Dharma keeps its prices low by discounting from list prices and then adding further discounts for quantity orders.

The 111-page "Fiber-Arts Supplies Catalog" shows a large selection of tools and materials for fiber arts. The products include fiber reactive dyes, paints, resists, fabrics, chemicals (thickener, wetting agent, water and textile softener), plastic storage jars, rubber gloves, dust masks, fabric glue, silk dye, mixing palette, mist sprayers, brushes, fabric pens and markers, and bottles and droppers for mixing and applying dye. Brand names include Procion, Dyehouse, Deka, Versatex, Pebeo, Jacquard, Sennelier, Dupont, Peintex, Visionart, and others.

Dharma also sells clothing for infants, children and adults. For infants and toddlers you'll find cotton jumpsuits, fun suits, jumpers, booties, T-shirts, and rompers. Children's clothing includes cotton dresses, California Baggyz, socks, shorts, T-shirts, and jams. Adults can select from jackets, baseball shirts, tunics, tank tops, T-shirt dresses, jams, shorts, and rompers. Some hand and shoulder bags are also available.

Dharma's comprehensive catalog is free upon request. Quantity discounts are available. Returns are accepted within 30 days for exchange or refund (a 20% restocking fee may be applied). Pay by check, money order or major credit card. C.O.D. orders are accepted.

Dick Blick Company
P.O. Box 1267 Galesburg, IL 61401.
Phone: (309) 343-6181

This company's catalog features over 400 pages of general art and craft supplies at savings of up to 30%. The Blick Co. offers a selection of paints by Liquitex, pigments by Shiva, paint brushes, crayons and finger paints, drawing tables, canvas, paper, scissors, adhesives, and transfer letters by Alfac.

Also in stock are wood-carving tools, kilns, molding materials, silk-screening materials, leatherworking kits, macrame, and an assortment of dyes. There's also a good selection of videotapes, slides, films and manuals on arts and crafts.

The catalog is available for $3.00. Get a price quote on quantity orders by phone or by mail with a SASE. Pay by check, money order or major credit card (there is a minimum order of $10 required with credit cards).

Herrschners, Inc.
Hoover Road Stevens Point, WI 54492
Phone: 800-441-0838 (orders) (715) 341-0560 (customer service) FAX: (715) 341-2250

Herrschners has been providing quality needlecrafts and supplies since 1899. The company's annual yarn catalog lists a good selection of patterns, materials, and supplies for knitting, crocheting, and crosstitching. Herrschners' prices are competitive with other firms selling comparable goods.

Herrschners' patterns include afghans, teddy bears, Victorian tablecovers, sweaters for kids, potholders, floral bath sets, dolls, bookmarks, doilies, floor coverings, baby clothes, and many more. A good selection of yarn—in over 70 different colors—is also available. Other supplies listed in the catalog include crochet hooks, knitting needles, storage bags, plastic canvas kits, scissors, embroidery needles, totes for crosstitch and needlework, floss and yarn caddies, and hobby lights.

The company's catalog is free upon request. Satisfaction is guaranteed. Returns are accepted for exchange or refund. Pay by check, money order or major credit card.

Home-Sew Bethlehem
PA 18018
Phone: (215) 867-3833

Home sewers will delight in Home-Sew's sewing and craft supplies catalog. The catalog lists savings of up to 65% on thousands of items, including ribbons, flat and ruffled laces, eyelets, elastic, thread (spools and cones), muslin, barrettes, zippers, snaps, buttons, belts and buckles, pins, needles, scissors, and other related items.

Home-Sew has been in business for over 30 years and guarantees satisfaction with every order. Returns are accepted for exchange, refund, or credit. The catalog is available for $1.00. Pay by check, money order or major credit card.

Leather Unlimited Corp.
7155City Highway
Belgium, WI 53004-9990
Phone: (414) 994-9464

Even if you're a beginner, Leather Unlimited's guide and wholesale savings catalog offers leathercraft supplies and equipment you can use. The company has established a reputation for quality goods and dependable service over the past 20 plus years.

Mail-order shoppers can expect savings of up to 50% on leather (sold by the hide or piece) and findings for garments, handbags, belts, and wallets. Also available are finished leather goods (purses, wallets, belts, and sheepskin accessories), leathercraft tools (punches, carvers, screws, snaps, zippers, mallets, needles), patterns, dyes, buckles,

Indian lore items, and much more. Leather Unlimited also sells leather brief cases, attache cases, portfolios, doctors' bags, and other small leather goods.

The catalog is available for $2.00 (refundable). Price quotes are available by phone or by letter with a SASE. Satisfaction is guaranteed. Authorized returns are accepted within 10 days. Pay by check, money order, MasterCard or VISA. There is a minimum order requirement of $30.

National Thread & Supply Corp.
695 Red Oak Road Stockbridge, GA 30281
Phone: 800-331-7600 FAX: (404) 389-9202

This is one of the nation's oldest and largest sewing supply companies, having been in business since 1948. You can buy direct from National Thread & Supply and save up to 50% off typical retail prices.

Savings are available on superior quality serging thread, nylon thread, applique scissors by Gingher, cutting mats, rotary cutters, general dress- making scissors, electric shears, dress forms, household irons, work tables, and "how-to" sewing books by Singer.

Call the company to inquire about available literature. Pay by check, money order or major credit card.

Pearl Paint Company
308 Canal Street New York, NY 10013
Phone: 800-221-6845

Discount prices of up to 70% off average retail on art and craft supplies await mail-order shoppers at Pearl Paint. The company, founded in the early 1930s, has a large stock of goods, some of which are shown in its free catalog.

Past catalogs have shown a representative selection of

items for every craft. You'll find pigments, brushes, solvents, canvas, papers, studio furniture, stretchers, and much more. In stock are such top-quality name brands as Lascaux, Bellini, Bainbridge, Liquitex, Pantone, Pelikan, Alvin, Robert Simmons, Windsor & Newton, Sennelier, and Sculpture House.

Call or write the company to request a free catalog. Quantity discounts are available. Pay by check, money order or major credit card. The company requires a minimum order of $50.

Thai Silks
252- W. State St. Los Altos, CA 94022
Phone: (415) 948-8611

If you've had trouble finding silk fabric for home sewing, decorating, etc., at affordable prices, you'll want to check out Thai Silks. The company got its start in 1964 and continues to offer imported silk fabrics and yardage and piece goods at an average savings of 30% to 50% off typical retail prices.

Thai Silks has in stock a selection of beautiful silk from Thailand, India, Japan, China, and Italy. The silks include cotton-backed silk corduroy, jacquard weaves, pongee, raw silk, silk satin, silk velvet, silk taffeta, upholstery weights, and many others. The company also sells wool gabardine and Challis, Irish linen, and hand-loomed cottons.

A brochure is available free upon request. Price quotes are available by phone or by mail with a SASE. Satisfaction is guaranteed. Returns are accepted. There is a minimum order of one half yard of fabric. Pay by check, money order or major credit card.

Wicker Warehouse, Inc.
195 South River St. Hackensack, NJ 07601
Phone: (201) 342-6709 FAX: (201) 342-1495

Beautiful wicker for every project is available from the Wicker Warehouse. The company offers savings of 30% to 50% off list prices on national brands (Lane, Link, Ficks) and hand-picked imported wicker. The company's 64-page catalog ($5.00) shows a selection of wicker for bedroom, dinette sets, bathroom accessories, and even baby carriages.

Send $5.00 for the catalog (receive $5.00 credit). Pay by check, money order or major credit card.

The Winfield Collection
1450 Torrey Road Fenton, MI 48430
Phone: 800-466-7712

Woodcraft enthusiasts will find over 1000 full size woodcraft patterns featured in The Winfield Collection's free catalog. The company specializes in easy-to-make woodcraft projects at reasonable prices.

You'll find patterns for furniture for dolls and teddy bears (swing, buggy, bench, cradle, stroller), 3-D layered animals (rabbit, sheep, cow, goose, cat, squirrel, pony, deer), country and folk art (Amish designs, old fashioned signs, cats, dogs), and yard decor (butterflies, Bo Peep and sheep, lifesize geese). The catalog also shows holiday designs and pattern transfer paper for smudgeproof tracing of patterns onto wood. Easy-to-follow assembly guidelines are included with each design.

Call or write the company to request a free catalog. Satisfaction is guaranteed. Pay by check. money order or major credit card. There is a minimum order of $25 required.

Cherry Tree Toys, Inc.
P.O. Box 369, Belmont, OH 43718
Phone: (800) 848-4363
FAX: (614) 484-4388

Cherry Tree has been in business since 1980 and provides a craft catalog full of woodworking and crafting ideas and supplies. The company's inventory includes toys, wood parts, models, clocks, plans, tools, and craft supplies. Whether you are involved in woodworking or crafting strictly as a hobby or you sell your creations on the craft fair circuit full or part time, Cherry Tree can supply you with everything you need. A wholesale catalog is available for customers who wish to take advantage of the lowest possible prices on large quantity orders.

A recent catalog featured a selection of wood turning and other special wood parts including pegs, flat wheels, spoked wheels, thick and thin wheels, specialty wood shapes (people, smokestacks), mushroom head plugs, spindles, finials, pull knobs, and hundreds of other parts. Also in stock are scale model covered wagon and stagecoach kits, Finnish Birch plywood, watches, weather stations (thermometers, barometers, and hygrometers), desk accessories, Bostich staplers, drill bits, sanding drums, needle file sets, paint brushes, paint, oil, glue and hundreds of other items. There's also an assortment of plans for easy to build projects and "how to" books.

Satisfaction with every order is guaranteed. Returns are accepted for exchange or refund. Lowest prices are on larger quantity orders. Call the toll-free number listed above and request a wholesale catalog. There is a minimum credit card order of $20.00. Pay by check, money order or major credit card.

Co-Op Artists' Materials, Inc.
P.O. Box 53097
Atlanta, GA 30355
Phone:(800) 877-3242

Co-op Artists's Materials offers savings of up to 70% off

typical retail on a wide selection of art materials. Everything needed for graphic and fine arts is available, including paints, brushes, canvas, papers, and frames. Brand name products in stock include Mont Blanc, Grumbacher, Fabriano, Strathmore, Pentel, Neolt, D'Arches, Liquitex, Badger, Windsor & Newton, and other famous manufacturers.

Call or write the company to get a catalog ($3.50). Satisfaction is guaranteed. Pay by check, money order or major credit card.

Enterprise Art
P.O. Box 2918, Largo, FL 34649
Phone: (813) 536-1492

Enterprise Art's 80-page catalog features a good selection of bulk-priced beads and jewelry. In business since 1970, Enterprise Art has everything you need, including hard-to-find beads, rhinestones, jewelry findings, doll supplies, wearable art, miniatures, plastic canvas, and many other items. Bulk prices are available on most of the supplies.

Call or write to request a catalog. Pay by check, money order or major credit card.

Factory Direct Craft Supply
440 Conover, Franklin, OH 45005
Phone: (513) 743-5855

Whatever your craft, Factory Direct Craft Supply can supply you with everything you need at wholesale prices. You can order factory direct lace, baskets, hats, and hundreds of other craft supply items. The company has a 6000 sq. ft. showroom filled with every type of craft supply item imaginable.

Send $2.00 for the Factory Direct wholesale craft supply catalog. Pay by check, money order or major credit card.

Fashion Fabrics Club,
10490 Bauer Blvd.,
St. Louis, MO 63132 Phone: (314) 993-1464

You can expect savings of 20% to 50% or more on designer fabrics when you join the Fashion Fabrics Club. The club offers over 30 years of experience and a membership fee of only $10.00. Membership entitles you to savings on a big selection of designer fabrics, free monthly swatch kits (featuring top-quality fabrics from world-famous designers and mills), free frequent buyer's plan (the more you buy, the more you save), and a free gift certificate.

The Fashion Fabrics Club offers savings on the top names in fashion including Liz Claiborne, J.G. Hook, Evan Picone, Polo, Jones NY, Koret, Villager, Leslie Fay, Blassport, Herman Geist, and Alexander Julian.

Satisfaction is guaranteed. Returns are accepted for a full refund. Call or write the company for information about joining and services offered. Pay by check, money order or major credit card.

Glass Crafters
369 Plandome Rd., Manhasset, NY 11030-1940
Phone: (800) 422-4552

Stained glass crafting can be a fun and easy hobby. It can also be profitable. Since 1975, Glass Crafters has been providing beginning and expert crafters a complete line of stained glass supplies at discount prices. The company's catalog also features hundreds of patterns and project kits for creating your own Tiffany heirlooms.

The Glass Crafters discount catalog, which features stained glass supplies, patterns, and a line of instructive videos and books, is free upon request. Monthly sales flyers are also available for additional money-saving values.

Hudson Glass Co., Inc.
219 N. Division St., Peekskill, NY 10566-2700
Phone: (914) 737-2124; (800) 444-2748

The Hudson Glass Co. offers everything for the novice or professional stained glass crafter. For over 65 years, Hudson Glass has been selling stained glass supplies, patterns, and instructional books at competitive prices. The company offers a large inventory of quality products, guaranteed to help you make beautiful stained glass items for fun and/or profit. Discounts are available on many items.

Send $3.00 for Hudson's complete supply catalog, "The Source". The catalog price is refundable with your first order. Satisfaction is guaranteed. Pay by check, money order or major credit card.

Maplewood Industries, Inc.
P.O. Box 2010, Hazelton, PA 18201
Phone: (717) 384-1111

The Maplewood Crafts catalog provides family fun for all seasons. The company offers low prices on craft ideas and supplies for the entire family. Past catalogs have featured paint-on clothing, needlework, beaded doll and ornament kits, latch hook, woodworking kits, and tools. Also in stock are beads, sequins, and many other hard-to-find craft supplies.

The Maplewood Crafts catalog is available for $1.00. Call or write the company. Pay by check, money order or major credit card.

Nancy's Notions
P.O. Box 683, Beaver Dam, WI 53916-0683
Phone: (414) 887-0391; (800) 833-0690 [orders]

Home sewers will enjoy browsing through the Nancy's Notions catalog. It features over 140 pages of sewing and quilting supplies, fashion fabrics, and educational books and videos. Items are available at "everyday discounts".

Nancy's Notions has been in business since 1979. Call or write the company to request a free catalog. Pay by check, money order or major credit card.

Patterncrafts

P.O. Box 25639, Colorado Springs, CO 80936-5639
Phone: (719) 574-2007

Patterncrafts has been in business since 1986, providing patterns for make-your-own crafts, sewing, and woodworking. The company offers "the worlds largest selection" of patterns for wood, crafts, and creative sewing. All patterns are full size, high quality, and easy to use. Competitive prices on all items, plus free patterns on large orders.

Patterncrafts catalog is available for $2.00. Satisfaction is guaranteed. All orders are shipped within 24 hours. Pay by check, money order or major credit card.

Roussels

107 Dow Ave., Arlington, MA 02174
Phone: (508) 443-8888

In business since 1989, Roussels offers a wide range of wholesale craft supplies and jewelry findings. Past catalogs have featured jewelry at closeout prices (some items as low as 55 cents a dozen); neckchains for 11 cents; 2" x 3" poly bags, $3.00 for 400, and many other items at wholesale prices.

Roussels catalog is available for .50. Pay by check, money order or major credit card.

Zimmerman's

2884-34 Street N., St. Petersburg, FL 33713

Phone: (813) 526-4880

For over 31 years Zimmerman's has been selling quality craft supplies of all kinds. The company features Ben Franklin discount craft supplies including macrame, dolls, doll making supplies, wood products, sewing aids, miniatures, knitting and crochet implements, plastic canvas, and flowers and flower parts. There's also a good selection of beads, ribbons, yarns, crochet threads, and craft books.

Zimmerman's latest catalog is available for $2.00. Orders may be paid by check, money order or major credit card.

VII

Art And Antique Values:

Fine art, antiques, porcelain, collectables, tableware, and handcrafts

Mail-order shoppers can find substantial savings on quality tableware, crystal, and silver pieces by picking up the telephone and calling many of the firms listed in this section. If you're not sure what place-setting pattern you want, get as many catalogs as you can—most companies provide catalogs free upon request.

Buying antiques and collectables can be a money-saving proposition when you buy by mail, but it can also be risky. You should know exactly what you want before you buy, because you'll usually have only a photograph of the goods from which to make your evaluation. You should also take care to purchase from companies that accept returns. Experienced collectors know the "antiquing" and collecting markets, and are able to find the best pieces at bargain prices. If you're a novice, several hours spent in research at your public library may save you a good bit of money in the long-run.

Antiques Imports Unlimited
P.O. Box 2978 Covington, LA 70434-2978
Phone: (504) 892-0014

Antique Imports offers "dealer" prices on antiques and

collectables. Mail- order shoppers can expect savings of as much as 50% less than retail prices on comparable goods.

Antique Imports markets its goods by publishing several price lists. Single lists cost $3.00 each with yearly subscription rates also available. The lists include "Antique and Collectible Jewelry" (old jewelry, watches, charms), "Antiques and Collectables", (glassware, china, coins, metalware, stamps), and "Antiquities" (ancient artifacts, including statuary, coins, pottery, and amulets).

Call or write the company for more information. Pay by check, money order or major credit card. The company requires a minimum order of $75 in each category.

Barrons P.O.
Box 994 Novi, MI 48376-0994
Phone: 800-538-6340 (orders) 800-762-7145
(customer service)

Barrons, the "world's largest in-stock dealer", features a good selection from the best names in fine china, flatware and stemware, plus unique gifts and collectables. The company has been in business for 18 years, offering factory- direct prices on china, crystal and silver in over 1500 patterns. Save up to 65% on brand names such as Bernardaud, Block, Dansk, Fitz & Floyd, Gorham, Lenox, Minton, Noritake, Oneida, Mikasa, Reed & Barton, Wallace, Wedgwood, and many other leading manufacturers. Five-piece place settings, sterling silver flatware, stainless flatware, and beautiful stemware are all available.

Barron's collectables and gift selection includes Lenox China Jewels figurines, Mikasa Crystal Candlesticks, mugs, bells, Waterford Crystal Rose Bowl Lamp, Golden Memories figurines, 3-light candelabra, cherry finish silverware chests, Hummel plates, and more. A complete Bridal Registry service is also available.

Call the toll-free number and request this season's free catalog. Instant price quotes are also available by phone. Barrons promises fast, expert service, with most orders processed within 24 hours. Satisfaction is guaranteed. Returns are accepted for a full refund, credit or exchange. Pay by check, money order or major credit card.

The China Warehouse
Box 21797 Cleveland, OH 44121
Phone: 800-321-3212

For over a decade The China Warehouse in Cleveland has been offering savings of 20% to 50% on name brand china, crystal, and flatware. Mail-order shoppers can save by buying direct from the warehouse a selection from manufacturers such as Lenox, LADRO, Royal Doulton, Noritake, Towle, Waterford, Wedgwood, Gorham, Nambe, and many others in all the popular patterns.

The China Warehouse also offers a national bridal and all-occasion registry.

Call the toll-free number for a price quote and order information. Payment can be made by check, money order or major credit card.

Michael C. Fina
580 Fifth Ave./3 West 47th St. New York, NY 10036
Phone: 800-289-3462

Michael C. Fina offers special mail-order values on china, crystal, and sterling and stainless patterns. The company features low prices on quality china by Noritake (Golden Cove, Barrymore, Rothschild), Lenox (Autumn, Charleston, Eternity), Royal Doulton (Biltmore, Princeton), Royal Derby, Mikasa (Royal Glimmer, Garden Harvest), and other manufacturers. Also in stock is crystal by Lenox, Stuart, Gorham, and

Noritake, as well as sterling and stainless patterns by Wallace, International, Reed & Barton, Lunt, Towle, and Kirk-Stieff.

Call the toll-free number for a price quote. Pay by check, money order or major credit card.

Fortunoff
Fifth Ave. at 54th St. and Westbury, NY 11590
Phone: 800-937-4376 Ext. 63LL

Fortunoff has more than 500 patterns of sterling silver, silverplate and stainless in stock for immediate delivery. The company has been in business since 1922. Great savings are available on beautiful place settings by Mikasa, Reed & Barton, Lunt, Gorham, Wallace, Chantilly, and many other leading manufacturers. Silver giftware selections, such as tea and coffee services, ice buckets, chafing dishes, candlesticks, and picture frames, are also available. Fortunoff sells first-quality merchandise only.

Send $2.00 for a catalog. Call the company for a price quote, or send a letter with a SASE. Satisfaction is guaranteed. Pay by check, money order or major credit card.

Heirloom Editions
520B Route. 4 Carthage, MO 64836
Phone: 800-725-0725

Heirloom Edition's big, full-color catalog ($4.00) is packed with lots of old fashioned prints, cards, stationery, calendars, and stickers made from turn- of-the-century originals. Prices are competitive with those of other sources selling comparable goods.

Send $4.00 (check or money order) for the catalog. Call the toll-free number for more information. Pay by check, money order or major credit card.

House of 1776, Inc.
P.O. Box 472927 Garland, TX 75047-2927
Phone: 800-989-1776

The House of 1776 has beautiful 5-piece place settings by Lenox, Noritake, Johnson Bros., Oneida, Villeroy & Boch, Reed & Barton, and Hutschenreuther at competitive mail-order prices. The company sells first-quality goods only.

The 5-piece place settings in stock include Autumn, Eclipse, Charleston, Liberty, Poppies on Blue, and Blue Pinstripes by Lenox; Barrymore, Shenandoah, Ontario, Royal Orchard, Opulence, American Flowers, and Sand n' Sky by Noritake; Juliard, Michelangelo, Dover, Easton, Kenwood, and Affection by Oneida; Regency, Heritage, and Willow Blue by Johnson Bros.; and Baronesse White by Hutschenreuther. Many other beautiful patterns are also in stock.

Call the toll-free number for information and to request a free catalog. Pay by check, money order or major credit card.

The Jompole Company, Inc.
330 Seventh Ave. New York, NY 10001
Phone: (212) 594-0442

Jompole has been in business for 80 years offering a fine selection of figurines, table settings, watches, and writing instruments. Mail-order shoppers can expect to save up to 50% on some items. No catalog is published, but Jompole does provide price quotes by phone or by mail.

The company has in stock a good selection of figurines and collectables by manufacturers such as Llandro, Hummel, Swarovski, Norman Rockwell, Towle, and Waterford. You can also select from the china patterns of Lenox, Mikasa, Minton, Denby, Royal Copenhagen, Spode, Wedgwood, and other quality manufacturers. Jompole also has crystal stemware by Gorham, Rosenthal, Kosta Boda, Baccarat, and Fostoria, as well as flatware from Fraser, International, Kirk-Stieff, Oneida, Lunt, and Reed & Barton. Pens and pencils by Mont Blanc, Parker, and Cross are also in stock.

Call or write (include a SASE) for a price quote. Pay by check, money order or major credit card.

Kenneth Lynch & Sons
84 Danbury Road Wilton, CT 06897
Phone: (203) 762-8363 FAX: (203) 762-2999

Classic sculpture is only one of the more than 2500 unique products listed in Kenneth Lynch & Son's catalog of garden ornaments. Besides sculpture and statuary, the catalog also shows a selection of fountains and pools, planters and urns, sundials, weathervanes, benches, gates, topiary, and more. The catalog also provides specs and sitework suggestions. Everything offered in the catalog is the product of "traditional craftsmanship".

For information about specific products and/or to request a free catalog and current price list, call or write the company. Pay by check, money order or major credit card.

Midas China & Silver
4315 Walney Road Chantilly, VA 22021
Phone: 800-368-3153

Since 1964, Midas has been selling quality china, crystal, and silver giftware at low, "direct-to-the-customer" savings. In stock are products by Gorham, Wedgwood, Stuart, Noritake, International, Mont Blanc, Oneida, Lenox, Royal Doulton, Villeroy & Boch, Mikasa, Baldwin Brass, Wallace, Lunt, Portmeirion, Ladro, Rosenthal, Spode, Baccarat, Christian Dior, and many other top-of-the- line manufacturers.

Midas offers an outstanding selection of china and

sterling silver place settings and crystal stemware at savings of up to 60%. The company's free catalog shows a beautiful collection of Waterford giftware and stemware, elegant 5-piece place settings, fine crystal, and stainless and silverware. Also available are gifts, collectables and accessories such as silver chests and silver bags, David Winter Cottages, cultured pearl sets and solitaire pearls, sterling tea sets, sterling baby cups, jewelry, Kirk Stief giftware, commemorative coins, and Mount Blanc writing instruments.

Midas also offers a computerized bridal registry.

Call the toll-free number for a price quote and/or to request a free catalog. Pay by check, money order or major credit card.

Museum Editions New York LTD.
12 Harrison St., 3rd floor New York, NY 10013
Phone: (212) 431-1913

For over a decade, Museum Editions has been offering fine contemporary art reprints at savings of up to 50%. Both modern and contemporary art are well represented by Museum Edition's reproductions of posters used to announce exhibits in art galleries and museums.

Among the modern reproduction shown in the firm's catalog are masterpieces by Georgia O'Keefe, Ando Hiroshige, David Hockney, Paul Klee, Camille Pissaro, Mark Rothko, and Edward Hopper. The catalog also shows examples of photography, photorealism, and posters. Custom framing is also available.

Send $5.00 (refundable) for the catalog. Call or write the company to inquire for information. Pay by check, money order or major credit card.

Prairie Edge
P.O. Box 8303 Rapid City, SD 57709-8303
Phone: 800-541-2388 FAX: (605) 341-6415

The colorful Prairie Edge catalog shows over 100 examples of beautiful Plains Indian art, crafts, and jewelry. Collectors can browse through the catalog and discover bow and arrow sets, knives, painted buffalo and elk robes, shields, axes, dance sticks, dolls, ceremonial pipes, rattles, shirts, coyote fang necklace, silver jewelry and more unique gifts and collectors items. All are hand made with authentic materials, and are available at reasonable prices.

The catalog also tells the story of each item's place in Sioux heritage. Send $3.00, check or money order, for a copy of the catalog. Pay by check, money order or major credit card.

Ross-Simons Jewelers
9 Ross-Simons Drive Cranston, RI 02920
800-556-7376 FAX: (401) 463-8599

In business for over 40 years, Ross-Simons has in stock over 2,500 flatware, china and crystal patterns. The company's free catalog, "Anticipations", features a representative selection of the goods offered at competitive prices.

Mail-order savings are available on quality patterns by Block, Gorham, Kirk Stieff, Lenox, Lunt, Noritake, Reed & Barton, Wallace, Wedgwood, and many other quality manufacturers. A recent catalog also shows a 7-piece tea service by International Silver, mirrors, candlesticks, bookends, hand-painted porcelain pieces, sterling silver cufflinks, hand-painted earthenware cookie jars, tabletop carousels, showpiece perfume bottles, Royal Doulton collectible figurines at a savings of over 30%, collectible figurines made of hand-painted porcelain by Ladro, decorative collectors' boxes, and other collectables and gift ideas. Ross-Simons also sells a selection of fine jewelry (see "Jewelry" section).

Call the toll-free number for immediate price quotes, to request your free copy of the Ross-Simons catalog, or to register in the company's national bridal registry. Returns are accepted on any used items (except those that have been personalized) within 30 days for a refund, credit or exchange. A gift certificate will be issued if items received as a gift are returned. Pay by check, money order or major credit card.

Nat Schwartz & Co., Inc.
549 Broadway Bayonne, NJ 07002
Phone: 800-526-1440 (201) 437-4443 (in NJ)

The Schwartz catalog—free upon request—features an outstanding selection of tableware and giftware. In business for more then 30 years, this company can provide you with savings of up to 50% on some items.

The company carries the finest brand names in china and giftware including Fritz & Floyd, Royal Doulton, Lenox, Stuart, Waterford, Belleek, Spode, Wedgwood, Royal Crown Derby, Royal Worcester, Pickard, Minton, and Llandro. Fine crystal by Lenox, Stuart, Galway, Miller Rogaska, Mikasa, Atlantis, St. Louis, Gorham, Waterford, and Val St. Lambert is also in stock, as are flatware and hollowware by Kirk-Stieff, Oneida, Ricci, Towle, and Gorham. Schwartz also offers a bridal registry.

Past catalogs have also shown such items as Reed & Barton Silverplate 4 piece coffee and tea sets, candlesticks, mugs and salad plates, cake plates, animal paperweights, Ladro collectables, silver chests, and picture frames.

Call for a price quote and/or to request the free catalog. Satisfaction is guaranteed. Returns are accepted within 30 days. Pay by check, money order or major credit card.

Albert S. Smyth Co., Inc.
29 Greenmeadows Drive Timonium, MD 21093
Phone: 800-638-3333 (301) 252-6666 (in MD)

Tableware, giftware, and jewelry at savings of up to 50% are offered to mail-order shoppers by the Smyth Company. For almost 80 years, this company has provided savings on tableware, figurines, watches, writing instruments, and other gift items.

You can choose from place settings by Gorham, Kirk-Stieff, Aynsley, Lenox, Reed & Barton, Noritake, Royal Doulton, Spode, Towle, Waterford, Wedgwood, and many other top manufacturers. Hummel figurines, pens by Mont Blanc, watches by Pulsar and Seiko, pewter candlesticks, coffee sets, and punch bowl sets are all featured in Smyth's free catalog. The company also offers a bridal registry.

Call or write to request the free catalog. A price quote is also available by phone or by mail with a SASE. Satisfaction is guaranteed. Pay by check, money order or major credit card.

Thurber's
14 Minnesota Ave. Warwick, RI 02888
800-848-7237 FAX: (401) 732-4224

This company carries all the leading manufacturers of sterling silver, hollowware, flatware, and china at competitive mail-order prices. Past catalogs have shown savings of 20% to 50% on fine crystal, china, flatware, and gifts.

Thurber's invites you to compare and save on sterling by Gorham, International, Wallace, Lunt, Reed & Barton, Kirk-Stieff, and Towle. A selection of fine china by Wedgwood, Mikasa, Ansley, Fitz & Floyd, Royal Doulton, Lenox, Noritake, and Royal Albert is also available. Collectables and gift ideas shown in past catalogs include Hummel collectables (figurines, plates, bells), silver candlesticks, bookends, Christmas ornaments, sterling silver baby cups, wooden silver chests, picture frames, and crystal vases.

Call the toll-free number to request Thurber's free, full-color catalog, filled with values and gift ideas. Price quotes are available by phone. Satisfaction is guaranteed. Returns are accepted within 30 days for exchange or refund. Pay by check, money order or major credit card.

Zucker's Fine Gifts
151 West 26th Street New York, NY 10001
Phone: (212) 989-1450 (information only) 800-333-9933 (order only)

Zucker's offers savings of up to 50% on Hummel collectables (plates and figurines). Other fine collectables by David Winter Cottages, Llandro figurines), and Swarovski are also available at huge savings.

Call the information number for complete details. Pay by check, money order or major credit card.

Emperor Clock Co.
Emperor Industrial Park, Fairhope, AL 36532
Phone: (205) 928-2316

The Emeror Clock Co. is the world's largest manufacturer of grandfather, mantle, and wall clocks. The company has been in business since 1969 and offers factory direct prices on clocks and assorted furniture items.

Emperor's clocks feature West German solid brass movements and dials and solid hardwood cases of oak, cherry, and black walnut.The clocks are available completely assembled and finished or as do-it-yourself kits. Furniture in stock includes bookcases, tables, cabinets, and other items.

A color catalog is available for $1.00. Call or write the company. Pay by check, money order or major credit card.

For other listings of firms that sell related goods, see the following sections in this catalog:

"General Merchandise"

Lillian Vernon— sells porcelain dinnerware, flatware, candleholders, figurines, handcrafted stoneware mugs, and hand-painted glazed earthenware bowls.

VIII
Automobile, Marine, and Aviation Equipment:

Auto tires, parts, supplies, and maintenance items

I f you've ever spent days, weeks, or even months searching for automobile parts for an older model or foreign model vehicle, you know what a frustrating experience it can be. This section of the Wholesale Bargains & Free Stuff Guide features listings of firms that offer everything you need to keep your vehicle running, including hard-to-find parts. Savings may be as much as 70% on some items when compared to the prices on new parts. You can save on everything from automobile tires and shocks to mufflers and carburetors. Most of the companies listed are staffed with experienced parts and service people who can provide advice and assistance in getting the right part for your vehicle.

You'll also find mail-order savings on marine supplies in this section. Whether you need maintenance products to keep your boat up and running, electronics, hardware, safety gear, or foul-weather gear, you can find it at average savings of 30% when you shop by mail.

American Marine Electronics and Supply, Inc.
5700 Oleander Dr. Wilmington, NC 28403
Phone: 800-243-0264

For the past 12 years, American Marine has been selling marine electronics for a variety of boating needs. The company's free catalog lists a huge selection of goods, including deep-sea fishing tackle at savings of up to 40%.

Seagoers can find compasses, depth sounders, chart recorders, CB radios, battery chargers, radar equipment, VHF radios, and many more marine items. American Marine's goods are all top-quality, with manufacturers such as Apelco, Bausch & Lomb, Coastal Navigator, Cybernet, Datamarine, Dytek, First Mate, Hull, Intech, Marlin Marine, Ritchie, Texas Instruments, EMS, and other well known brands in stock.

The American Marine catalog is free upon request. A price quote on models not shown in the catalog is available by phone or by letter with a SASE. Authorized returns are accepted. Pay by check, money order or major credit card. There is a minimum order requirement of $25.

Bass Pro Shops
1935 S. Campbell Springfield, MO 65898-0050
Phone: 800-227-7776 FAX: (417) 887-2531

Bass Pro Shops has been outfitting boaters with quality marine products and accessories for over 20 years. The company's selection of goods is outstanding and its prices are competitive with other sources selling comparable goods.

Bass Pro Shops publishes a "Master Catalog" ($3.00, receive credit) which features over 400 full color pages, listing over 22,000 items. The $3.00 also gets you a free year's subscription to Bass Pro Shops seasonal sale catalogs. The company's recent "Marine Catalog" shows personal watercraft covers, battery charging systems just for boats, marine/RV batteries, anchors, safety equipment (chemical fire extinguishers, distress signal packs, boater's vision visors, safety vests, swim ladders), aluminum boat repair kits, nylon rope, boat lights, oars and oar locks, marine jacks, hitches and accessories, bilge pumps, boat motors and engines, meters and gauges, and many other items. Name brands include Teleflex, Airguide, Motorguide, Minn Kota, Evinrude, Johnson, Attwood, Waterspike, Driftmaster, and many others. There's also a selection of boats for fishing, cruising, and skiing, inflatables, and water skis.

Send $3.00 for the master catalog. Satisfaction is guaranteed. Returns are accepted. Pay by check, money order or major credit card.

Cherry Auto Parts

5650 N. Detroit Ave. Toledo, OH 43612
Phone: 800-537-8677 800-472-8639
(in OH) (419) 476-7222

Finding foreign auto parts can be like looking for the proverbial needle in a haystack. If you are lucky enough to find the part(s) you need, the price can take a major bite out of your wallet. Instead of paying high retail prices for new parts, you may be able to find used and rebuilt parts at Cherry Auto parts at considerable savings. The company has been in business for over 40 years and can save you up to 70% less than the cost of new parts for foreign cars.

Cherry Auto Parts has in stock a wide selection of used and rebuilt foreign- car parts, such as rebuilt engines, starters, cylinder heads, alternators, drive axles, calipers, and hard-to-find parts. All parts are in good working condition and can be used on such foreign models as Audi, Austin, Datsun, Fiat, Honda, Isuzu, Jaguar, Mazda, Mercedes, Merkur, MG, Peugeot, Porsche, Saab, Renault, Subaru, Toyota, Volkswagen, Volvo, and others. Parts are also available for Chrysler imports (Arrow, Colt, Champ, and Challenger), and some Ford imports. The company can save you time and money in locating hard-to-find parts.

Cherry Auto parts has a brochure available free upon request. You can get a price quote by mail with a SASE or by phone. Pay by check, money order or major credit card . The company requires a minimum order of $15.

Defender Industries, Inc.
255 Main St. New Rochelle, NY 10801
Phone: (914) 632-3001 FAX: (914) 632-6544

Whether you are an "old salt" or a novice mariner, this company offers all the marine supplies, gear, and equipment you'll need. Defender has been in business for over 50 years and is nationally known for offering quality marine supplies and service at affordable prices. Mail-order shoppers can expect savings of up to 60%.

The company's catalog ($3.00, refundable) features over 200 pages of marine supplies, gear, and equipment, including outboard engines, boat tops and covers, winches, windlasses, sounders, antennas, radios, dinghies, mobile phones, foul-weather gear, vests, boating shoes, resins and coatings, galley fittings, optics, and much more. Name brands include Barlow, Aqua Meter, Evinrude, Lowrance, Shakespeare, Maxxima, Avon, Tasco, Omega, Sebago, Force 10, Taylor, and other manufacturers.

Defender also has in stock such items as sunglasses, first-aid kits, lamps and lanterns, deck coverings and tarps, sailboards, and boat-building supplies (fiberglass, epoxy, etc.). You can also inquire about the company's custom services, which include rigging services, canvas goods made to order, life raft repair, and more.

Send $3.00 for the catalog. A price quote is available by phone or by mail with a SASE. Mail-order returns are accepted within 20 days (A small restocking fee may be required). The company will special-order any marine product. Pay by check, money order or major credit card. A minimum order of $25.00 is required.

E & B Marine Supply, Inc.
201 Meadow Road Edison, NJ 08818
Phone: 800-533-5007

E & B offers a wide range of marine supplies and gear at discount prices, which can be up to 60% less than typical list prices. The company has been in business for over 45 years, and publishes a catalog which is free upon request.

Power boating and/or sailing enthusiasts can get E & B's catalog and look over products for boat navigation, safety, communications, and maintenance and repair. These products are all first-quality by such top-of-the-line manufacturers as Boatlife, Aqua Meter, Apelco, EMS, ICOM, Galaxy, Datamarine, Kohler, Cybernet, Kiode, Ray-Jeff, Sand-Piper, Interlux, Sea Range, Seth Thomas, Stearns, Woolsey, and others.

E & B also has in stock inflatables, water skis, boating apparel, sportswear, safety equipment (vests, etc), hardware, and more. Mail-order shoppers can expect savings of 10% to 60% on some items.

Call or write the company to request a free catalog. The company will accept authorized returns within 90 days. Pay by check, money order or major credit card. There is a minimum order requirement of $15 ($25 on phone orders).

Eastern Cycle Salvage, Inc.
87 Park St. Beverly, MA 01915
(508) 922-3707

Motorcyclists can find a good selection of "used and reconditioned" motorcycle parts at Eastern Cycle. Savings can average up to 50% off typical retail on some items, based on the prices of the same parts, if new.

For over 20 years, Eastern Cycle has been selling motor cycle parts such as engines, mufflers, pipes, kickstands, fenders, handlebars, carburetors, gears, clutches, mirrors, and lights. The company also has a good selection of parts for older model Japanese bikes and British motorcycles. Eastern also sells new parts, but the discounts are available only on the used and reconditioned motorcycle parts.

Call or write (with a SASE) the company for a price quote. Pay by check, money order or major credit card.

E.T. Supply
P.O. Box 78190 Los Angeles, CA 90016-8190
Phone: (213) 734-2430

Aircraft replacement parts and military and commercial surplus are among the goods sold by this firm. Savings can be up to 90% below original selling costs on some items in stock.

The company's free catalog shows a selection of aircraft instruments and replacement parts, along with the necessary maintenance and repair tools— wrench and socket-sets, pliers, etc.). Brand names available include Lear, G.E., Bendix, Kidde, and Weston.

Call or write the company to request a free catalog. The company accepts authorized returns (A small restocking fee may be required). Pay by check, money order or major credit card.

The Tire Rack
771 W. Chippewa Avenue South Bend, IN 46614
Phone: 800-428-8355 FAX: (219) 236-7707

The Tire Rack specializes in performance tires and wheels for all your motoring needs. The company is staffed by experts who can help you match your needs to the correct tire. Prices are competitive with other firms offering comparable goods and services.

The Tire Rack's catalog ($3.00) lists an outstanding selection of tires, in all sizes by top manufacturers such as B.F. Goodrich, Goodyear, Michelin, Yokohama, Bridgestone, Dunlop, Continental, and Pirelli. Light truck tires by most of the same manufacturers are also available. The catalog also shows a representative selection of the Tire Rack's wheels which are available for most cars. Brand names include BBS, Borbet, Ronal, and others. Call for more information about brands and sizes available, and to get a price quote.

Send $3.00 to get a copy of the color catalog. Call or write the company to get details of its "Recommended Installer Program". Pay by check, money order or major credit card.

Titan Rubber International
One Bryan Drive Wheeling, WV 26003-0137
Phone: 800-443-8473

Titan Rubber is also known as "Tire America" and offers a vast selection of performance tires and wheels at savings of up to 50%. The company has been in business for over 30 years.

Titan Rubber has in stock high-performance and RV tires as well as a selection of performance wheels. All goods are first-quality (no seconds or retreads are sold) by such manufacturers as B.F. Goodrich, Goodyear, Michelin, Fittipaldi, Pirelli, Hayashi, Falken, Ronal, Sentry, Stratton, BBS, Cartech, and others. All brand-name tires and wheels are sold with the manufacturers warranties.

No catalog is available, but you can call or write (with a SASE) the company for more information or to request a price quote. Pay by check, money order or major credit card.

For other listings of companies that sell automotive,

marine, and aviation equipment, see the following sections:

"Hardware, etc."

Car/Puter International Corp.
499 Sheridan St., Dania, FL. 33004
Phone: (800) 221-4001

Buying a new car can be confusing as well as expensive. Most people purchase their new automobiles from local dealers, without much "shopping around" for the best buy possible. Considering the expense involved in buying a car, getting the best deal possible should be of primary concern. That's where Car/Puter comes in. It's a company which has helped consumers save thousands of dollars on new car purchases over the past quarter century.

Car/Puter's service includes providing customers with information about where they can save the most money when buying a new car. Here's how it works: you decide on what type of car you want (exact make, model, options, etc.) and then pay Car/Puter a fee for a computer printout of pertinent information regarding the car's availability. The printout features the factory invoice price of that particular car so you'll know exactly how much the dealer paid for it. It also includes the factory prices for all available options. The printout will also give you the name(s) of the dealer(s) in your area who offers the lowest price on the car. If a local or area dealer is not listed on the printout, you may take advantage of Car/Puter's referral service. This service covers most areas of the U.S., and will provide you with the name(s) and location(s) of the closest dealer(s), offering the best deal on the car you are interested in.

By providing you with dealer costs, Car/Puter enables you to deal in a more informed and confident manner. You'll have a much better idea of how much you should pay for the car you want. The service (computer printout) costs $22.00, but has helped many shoppers save anywhere from about $200 to well over $1000 on new car purchases.

Call or write the company for more information.

Lou Fusz Auto Parts Network

Phone: (800) 325-9584 for AMC, Jeep Eagle, Renault.
(800) 451-7783 for Cheverolet Geo and
all GM products.
(800) 325-9584 for Dodge and all Chrysler products.
(800) 533-2175 for Ford, Lincoln, Mercury.
(800) 451-1471 for Isuzu.
(800) 341-5935 for Mazda.
(800) 528-2525 for Mitsubishi.
(800) 392-1372 for Nissan.
(800) 325-1471 for Pontiac and all GM products.
(800) 392-1372 for Rolls Royce, Bentley.
(800) 451-1471 for Subaru/Suzuki.
(800) 358-9873 for Saturn.
(800) 325-9581 for Toyota.

Lou Fusz Auto Parts Network sells an outstanding selection of auto parts wholesale to the public. The Network has in stock, or can get, parts for just about any automobile—American-made or import. You can call any one of the 13 toll-free numbers (depending on the make of your automobile) and find out the availability and wholesale price of the part you need. You can also save time by ordering the part you need by phone. You should be able to locate the "genuine" parts you need and get them at wholesale prices from the Lou Fusz Auto Parts Network.

IX
Books, Periodicals, and Recordings:

Magazine subscriptions; new, used, and out-of print books; films and videotapes; records, CDs and cassettes

---

I f you're an avid reader, you know that the cover prices of many books and magazines can be prohibitive. This section of the Wholesale Bargains & Free Stuff Guide contains listings that could conceivably save you 80% and more on books, magazines, records, CDs, cassette tapes, and videos.

Most of the "booksellers" listed in this section feature books which cater to the interests of readers of all ages. Both hardbound and paperbacks are offered in closeout, remaindered, new, used, and out-of-print books. The video selections are also directed at virtually every interest and age group. Music lovers can find bargains on everything from rock to classical music.

To get the most out of the listings in this section, you should get as many catalogs as you can and then compare products, prices, and services offered. Book buyers are also advised to keep up on book reviews as a means of being

---

more knowledgeable when looking through catalogs for specific books and videos. Some companies also accept written "want lists", and can get a particular book for you, if it isn't already in stock.

Magazine readers should stop paying cover prices for many of their favorite magazines and check out the publications and subscription rates offered by magazine clearing houses. The savings on such subscriptions can amount to 50% and more.

Adventures in Cassettes
5353 Nathan Lane North Plymouth, MN 55442-1978
Phone: 800-328-0108 FAX: (612) 553-0424

Adventures in Cassettes, a division of Metacom, Inc., offers a good selection of audio cassettes full of the "golden age of radio". Savings on some products are up to 30%.

You can order comedy classics, including Abbot & Costello, Amos 'N Andy, Burns & Allen, Duffy's Tavern, Fibber Mcgee & Molly, Jack Benny, The Life of Riley, and many others. Classic mysteries and dramas such as Black Museum, I Love A Mystery, Suspense, Mysterious Traveler, The Whistler, War Of The Worlds, X- Minus One, Sherlock Holmes, Green Hornet, The Lone Ranger, and the Lux Radio Theatre are also in stock.

Adventures in Cassettes also sells music, from rock 'n roll to classical; self-help tapes (stress reduction, weight-loss); children's tapes (sing along, dances and stories); language learning tapes; and "teach-at-home" tapes to help you solve your pet (dog and cat) problems.

The music on tape includes a 5-CD collection of Billboard hits from 1955-1959, featuring classic tunes by such rock legends as Elvis, Buddy Holley, Chuck Berry, and Jerry Lee Lewis. There's also a 2-cassette collection of rock 'n roll chartbusters from the 1950's and 1960's, as well as 50's and 60's dance music. Classical music selections available include the music of Beethoven, Chopin, Tchaikovsky, Brahms, Mozart, Debussy, and other immortal composers.

Country music, Broadway and Big Band, New Age, Easy Listening, and Inspirational music cassettes are also available at economical prices. The company also sells books on tape and readings of classic literature.

Call or write Adventures in Cassettes and request the catalog of your choice— music, language, old time radio, health/wellness, and/or books on tape. Satisfaction is guaranteed. Pay by check, money order or major credit card. No C.O.D. orders are accepted.

American Family Publishers
P.O. Box 30640 Tampa, FL 33662-0640
Phone: 800-237-2400

Magazine buffs can get subscriptions to many of their favorite periodicals through this magazine clearing house at savings of up to 70%. American Family Publishers offers many of the most popular magazines at subscription rates that are often much lower than those offered by individual magazine publishers.

The company has offered low rates on subscriptions to such popular magazines as "TV Guide", "The Atlantic", "Popular Science", "Time", "Jet", and "The Family Handyman", "American Health", "Baseball Digest", "Popular Mechanics", "Field & Stream", "Outdoor Life", "McCall's", and many others.. Call or write the company to request information about current subscriptions available.

Satisfaction is guaranteed. Pay by check or money order. An installment plan is also available.

Anatomical Chart Co.
8221 Kimball Skokie, IL 60076
Phone: 800-621-7500 FAX: (708) 674-0211

This company offers an outstanding selection of books and videos at savings of up to 75%. The Anatomical Chart Company's "BareBones Book Catalog" is free upon request and lists books and videos for every member of the family.

Included in the catalog's listings are coloring books and field guides, children's science books, children's fun books, and children's activity books. Also listed are texts on ecology and environmental awareness, dinosaurs and natural wonders, mammals and nature, science, health, exercise and fitness, medical reference, nutrition, and cooking. Video's available include health, exercise and fitness, massage, childbirth and childcare, and nutrition. There's also a selection of learning videos for children which are designed to make learning subjects such as grammar, math, science, and history, fun and easy.

Write or call the company and request the "BareBones" catalog. The Anatomical "Products" catalog and "Gift" catalog are also available free upon request. Satisfaction is guaranteed. Returns are accepted within 30 days for refund or exchange. Minimum order is $15. Pay by check, money order or major credit card. (no C.O.D. orders)

Barnes & Noble
126 Fifth Ave. New York, NY 10011
Phone: (201) 767-7079 (orders) (201) 767-8844
(customer service)

Barnes & Noble have been "booksellers" since 1873, and offer savings of up to 90%. The free catalog mailing shows savings on over 2000 items, including books, videos, classical music, CDs, and cassettes, wood bookshelves, book stands, bookends, and much more.

The Barnes & Noble catalogs are published on a regular basis and are loaded with values on new book arrivals, best-sellers, paperbacks, reprints, publishers' overstock, and textbooks. Specific areas of interest include history, science, religion, medicine, mystery, literature, reference, arts and crafts, travel and transportation, children's literature, entertainment, humor, hobbies, and self-help. Also available are videos for children, such as the Walt Disney classic "101 Dalmations", as well as drama and family entertainment videos such as "The Great Gatsby" and "The Ten Commandments".

Call or write to get on the Barnes & Noble catalog-mailing list. Satisfaction is guaranteed. Returns are accepted for a full refund. Pay by check, money order or major credit card (there is a $15 minimum order required with credit cards).

Berkshire Record Outlet, Inc
RR1 Lee, MA 01238
Phone: (413) 243-4080

Classical music lovers will appreciate the thousands of classical recordings offered by the Berkshire Record Outlet. The company publishes a free quarterly catalog, which lists over 100 pages of overstocked and remaindered recordings- - most of classical music—at savings of 30% and more.

Berkshire's selection of classical recordings is extensive and features the concertos and movements of every classic composer from Beethoven to Tchaikovsky. Aficionados and novices alike are almost sure to find the classical recordings they're looking for in the Berkshire catalog.

Call or write the company to get on the mailing list and receive a free catalog. You can also get a price quote by phone or letter with a SASE. Some recordings may be in limited supply so customers are advised to order from the catalog without delay. Pay by check, money order or major credit card.

Dover Publications, Inc.
31 East 2nd Street
Mineola, NY 11501

A recent Dover catalog offered over 350 books, most priced from $1.00 to $7.95. The catalog featured 82 "thrift editions" at $1.00 each. Dover has been publishing for over 40 years, and by purchasing direct from the publisher you can save on mystery and detective fiction, works of literature, arts and crafts, educational, history, and a host of great books and cassettes for language learning.

Among Dover's $1.00 thrift editions (paperbacks) are books of poetry by Poe, Longfellow, Milton, Edgar Lee Masters, and Edna St. Vincent Millay. The thrift editions also include classics by Chekhov, Conrad, Crane, Dickens, Dostoyevsky, Doyle, Hawthorne, Joyce, James, London, and others. Also available for $1.00 are children's classics such as "The Story of Peter Pan", "Black Beauty", and "Sleeping Beauty and Other Fairy Tales".

The Dover catalog also offers "listen and enjoy" poetry cassettes; adventure, science fiction and fantasy paperbacks; humor (Bierce, Carrol, Twain, Wilde); language learning books and cassettes; travel paperbacks; historical studies; book marks; bookplates; and much more.

The Dover Publications catalog is free upon request. Write to the above address and request your free copy. All Dover books are unconditionally guaranteed. Returns are accepted within 10 days for a full refund. Pay by check, money order or certified check. (Telephone or credit card orders are not accepted.)

Express Music Catalog

50 W. 17th St. New York, NY 10010
Phone: 800-233-6357

Express Music's catalog costs $6.00 (refundable) but contains over 200 pages of records, audio tapes, CDs, and videotapes at savings of up to 35%. The company has been in business since the mid-1960's and publishes monthly updates to its catalog. The $6.00 cost of the catalog entitles shoppers to a year's subscription of the updates.

The new catalog and updates list pages of new audio and video releases. The company's stock includes pop, rock, gospel, and R & B audio selections, as well as classical, opera, and show tunes— everything from Madonna to Ethel Merman. Rock videos, workout tapes, and movies (both old and new) are also available.

A price quote is available by phone or letter with a SASE. Returns of defective goods are accepted within 10 days. Pay by check, money order or major credit card.

Edward R. Hamilton Bookseller

Falls Village, CT 06031-5000

Hamilton publishes a monthly tabloid which is free upon request. The tabloid lists hundreds of books in every genre and category. The books are publishers closeouts or overstocks, and remainders, and many are in limited supply. At savings which average 50% to 70% off the publishers' prices, mail-order shoppers should not waste any time ordering the books they want. All books listed in the tabloid are new, and are hardbound, unless marked otherwise.

Mr. Hamilton's tabloid lists books of interest to every reader. The listings include bargain-priced texts of biographies, sports, history, politics, archaeology, religion, travel, philosophy, animals, gardening, nature, cooking, art, architecture, crafts, photography, movies, music, humor, poetry, literature, theatre and dance, popular fiction, children's literature, science, psychology, self-help, health, reference, television and more.

Write to Mr. Hamilton and request his monthly listings. Satisfaction with every book ordered is guaranteed. Returns are accepted for a full refund. To offer the lowest possible prices, all orders must be prepaid. Pay by check or money order only.

Wood Knapp's Special Interest Video
100 Enterprise Place P.O. Box 7022
Dover, DE 19903-7022
Phone: 800-336-9660 FAX: (302) 678-9200

Wood Knapp's videos cater to a wide range of interests, including children's entertainment, education, sports, health and fitness, photography, travel history, business, mystery, performance, and more. Over 750 titles are available, many of which are hard to find in other collections. Prices are competitive with other collections with similar titles.

The company's free catalog lists videos for children including the "Maurice Sendak Library". There are also videos on cooking, stress management, flower arranging, language learning, myths and legends, martial arts, bodybuilding, dance, music, animals, games, computers, and much more.

Call or write the company to request the catalog. Satisfaction is guaranteed. Returns are accepted within 30 days for a full refund. Pay by check, money order or major credit card.

The Mind's Eye
Box 1060 Petaluma, CA 94953 800-227-2020 FAX:
Phone: (415) 883-1849

The Mind's Eye began over 20 years ago with a modest stock of 12 dramatized classics on tape. Today, the company publishes a 47-page catalog filled with audio cassettes, books, T-shirts, videos, CDs, music, mystery, dramas, and the BBC Audio Collection.

Among the many "gifts and treasures" in the Mind's Eye catalog are competitively priced audio cassettes such as the 8-tape collection "The Home Front", featuring voices from the past, including those of FDR, Churchill, Tokyo Rose, General MacArthur, and dozens more. J.R.R. Tolken's beloved trilogy "The Lord Of The Rings" (and a complete figurine collection featuring Bilbo, Gandalf, and Thorin), "The Hitcher's Guide To The Galaxy" from the BBC Audio Collection, "Dr. Who", Kipling's "Just So Stories", and many other entertaining audio cassettes are available. Children will love listening to the recorded stories and books of Ronald Dahl, and "The King Arthur Sound Book". Comedy radio classics from Jack Benny to Will Rogers are also in stock, as are radio novels such as "The African Queen", and "It's A Wonderful Life".

The best thing to do is to call or write the company and request your free Mind's Eye catalog. Pay by check, money order or major credit card. No C.O.D. orders are accepted. Gift certificates are available.

Mitchell Books

1395 E. Washington Blvd. Pasadena, CA 91104
Phone: (818) 798-4438

Mitchell Books specializes in out-of-print detective fiction, spy fiction, crime fiction, and mystery fiction. Also available is a large stock of Shadow Pulps, Doc Savage Pulps, and many mystery magazines, all at competitive prices.

Call or write the company for more information on its in-stock selections, or send your "want list". Pay by check or money order.

Old Time Radio
706 North Star Drive
San Antonio, TX 78216

Old Time Radio doesn't publish a full-color catalog describing the goods it has to offer. However, it does provide lists of the old time radio programs it has available upon cassette— and there are hundreds of them. What's more, Old Time Radio's prices may be the lowest around on comparable goods.

The program lists are free upon request and feature classic old time radio programs from Amos 'N Andy to X-Minus One. Remember "The Halls of Ivy", "The Great Gildersleeve", "Suspense", "Lady Ester Screen Guild Players", "The Shadow"? Old Time Radio has them all on cassette, as well as hundreds more.

The program lists provide the title of each program, the name of the episode being offered, and the date the episode first aired. If you're interested in a program not shown in any of the listings, just write to the company and tell them what you are looking for.

Write the company and request a program list. Pay by check or money order. Minimum order is 2 cassettes.

Publishers Clearing House
101 Winners Circle Port Washington, NY 11050
Phone: (516) 883-5432

This popular magazine clearing house offers low rates on subscriptions to a wide selection of popular and special-interest periodicals. By subscribing through Publishers Clearing House, customers can expect savings of as much as 50% on regular subscription rates.

Past Publishers Clearing House mailings have offered subscriptions to "Time", "Discover", "Consumer Reports", "Readers Digest", "Car And Driver", "Mademoiselle", and many other popular magazines. The company also features sweepstakes and provides regular bonuses and premiums.

Call or write the company for information about the subscriptions currently being offered. Satisfaction is guaranteed. Pay by check or money order. An installment plan is also available.

Strand Book Store, Inc.
828 Broadway New York, NY 10003
Phone: (212) 473-1452 FAX: (212) 473-2591

The Strand book store has an enormous selection of new and used books in stock— over 2 million volumes are available. The company, which began in the late 1920's, publishes a catalog, which is free upon request. The catalog could not possibly begin to list every volume available, but it does list a representative selection at savings of up to 80%.

You'll find books in every category, dealing with a multitude of subjects and interests for readers of all ages. Books on art, history, architecture, philosophy, politics, theatre, food, and biographies are just a few of the reading interests covered by the catalog's listings. There's also available an outstanding selection of children's books. The catalog also lists tape and CD recordings of classical (and some jazz) music at competitive prices.

Write the company and request the specific catalog you want— the "general" catalog and/or the "children's" catalog. Get a price quote by phone or letter with a SASE. Returns are accepted. Pay by check, money order or major credit card. (A minimum order of $15 is required with credit card orders.)

Bookrak

PBCA, Inc.
P.O. Box 104353,
Jefferson City, MO 65110-4353
Phone: 9800) 456-1774

Paperback book fans can turn to the Bookrak for the newest titles at discounted prices. The company has been in business since 1987 and provides home shoppers a monthly selection of the newest paperbacks. All major publishers are represented.

The Bookrak's services include a free monthly catalog featuring a complete selection of the newest paperbacks at discount prices, easy shopping, and quick delivery. There's no obligation— this is a "non-club, book club".

Call the toll-free number listed above or write to the company to request a free catalog. Pay by check, money order, or MasterCard or VISA.

Bose Express Music

The Mountain
Framingham, MA 07101-9323
Phone: (800) 451-BOSE [2673]

The Bose Express catalog provides over 250 pages of CDs, cassettes and videos for music lovers of all ages. In business since 1973, Bose has available virtually every style of music, including rock, classical, jazz, blues, country and western, and opera. All major labels are represented. There are also over 1,000 independent labels available, including DMP, Chesky, Alligator, and Pausa. Prices are competitive.

Active Bose customers receive regular, free music updates which feature best sellers, new releases, samples, and recommendations. Catalog coupons are also available for extra savings.

The Bose Express Music catalog is available for $6 [refundable with first purchase of 3 or more CDs from the catalog]. Call or write the company to get the catalog. Pay by check, money order or major credit card.

Dragich Discount Auto Literature
1660 93rd Ln. N.E., Minneapolis, MN 5534
Phone: (612) 786-3925; (800) 328-8484 [order]

Since 1978 Dragich has been selling an incredible selection of automotive books. There are over 4000 titles available at discount prices. Every automotive subject imaginable is represented.

Dragich has a 40-page catalog available for $2.00. Call or write the company. Pay by check, money order or major credit card.

Light Impressions Corp.
439 Monroe Ave., Rochester, NY 14607
Phone: (716) 271-8960; (800) 828-6216

Light Impressions features a good selection of fine art and photography books at up to 15% off list prices. There's also a good selection of videos available. The company has been in business since 1968, and has a catalog available free upon request.

Pay by check, money order or major credit card.

45'S
Box 358
Lemoyne, PA 17043
Phone: (717) 232 4391

45's has been in business since 1979, offering music

buffs a selection of vintage and current 45's and Lps. Most of these recordings are available for $2.00 or below. Rock 'n' Roll, pop, and country and western are all available.

Send $2.00 and a SASE to get a catalog. Call or write the company to get the catalog and ordering information.

Notes

_____

_____

_____

_____

_____

_____

_____

_____

_____

X

Closeout Merchandise and Government Property:

How to find name-brand products at closeout prices, and get savings on government property

O ne of the best ways shoppers can save on virtually anything is by buying closeout merchandise. It doesn't matter what you need—a new TV, radio, toaster, furniture, tableware, jewelry— someone, somewhere has it at closeout prices. If you know where to look, and what to look for, buying closeout merchandise can save you hundreds, even thousands of dollars. That's because typical closeout prices are so low, you can buy first-quality goods in quantity, if you so desire. It's an ideal way to furnish your home or office, get items for personal use, or to get nice gifts for your family and friends.

Quite often in today's climate of progress, manufacturers have to "close out" existing stock in order to make way for new products and innovations. In order to compete in the marketplace, these manufacturers must constantly update old products and create new ones. That means that last year's models, while still perfectly useful, have become outmoded.

In order to make room for new products and updated models, manufacturers must in turn "get rid" of existing unsold products. Simply put, these manufacturers need to make room for new merchandise while turning their existing unsold excess products into "liquid capital". In such instances, the manufacturers will often sell their goods at prices well below their original costs. After all, from a business point of view, settling for a fraction of the original cost of production is better than letting the merchandise gather dust and take up valuable space in warehouses. The result is that buyers get rock-bottom prices on quality goods, and the manufacturers turn previously unsold excess stock into instant cash. Everybody comes out on top.

Any type of product can be considered a closeout if it meets certain conditions. As a general rule, the merchandise must be offered for sale at prices that are below original manufacturing costs. You can forget about paying exorbitant markups and list prices. Closeouts are even better than ordinary discounts because you are getting the product at less than its "original cost", not at a 10%, 20%, 30%, etc., discount off the list price.

In general, closeout goods can be new or used, and smart shoppers will consider not only price, but condition and utility as well. If you're buying in quantity to resell, marketability must also be considered. It doesn't make good business sense to buy a large quantity of items for resale, just because they're dirt-cheap, if the products aren't marketable.

To determine if you are being offered a true closeout, you should try to ascertain the original cost of production. Compare that cost with what you are being asked to pay. You should also try to find out what it would cost to replace the goods. One way to get such information before you buy is to acquire as many catalogs and price lists as you can. This is especially important if you are buying closeouts with the intention of reselling them for a profit. In that case, it's a wise idea to do some research on the items before you buy. Out-dated newspapers, tradepapers, dealer's price books, and even the public library can provide you with information on the original price of the products. Compare those prices with current asking prices.

Of course, you have to find closeouts before you can buy them. If you are shopping for closeout goods as a way to save on items for your own immediate or future personal use, you'll most likely be dealing with companies that specialize in closeout merchandise and some that occasionally offer closeouts. How do you find such closeout traders? Here are several proven methods:

1) Check the Yellow Pages. This is an especially good source if you're looking for a specific item. The Yellow Pages can provide you with the names, phone numbers, and addresses of companies which sell the product(s) you want. Some Yellow Pages ads may also tell if a company offers closeouts. Once you have this information you can contact each company by phone or by mail and request catalogs, price lists, brochures, etc. Such literature will also contain information about any closeout offers. You can also inquire about closeouts. Tell the company exactly what you're looking for. If the company does offer closeouts on the item(s) you want, you're in luck. If it doesn't, keep looking. Shopping for closeouts, while ultimately very rewarding, takes a certain amount of patience and determination.

2) Read trade papers. Again, if you're interested in a specific item, the trade paper in that particular area may provide information about closeouts. You can find a listing of all general trade papers in "Standard Rate & Data", a directory you should be able to find in the reference section of your local library.

Trade magazines are also a potential source of information. Many such trade publications feature classified sections offering closeout goods. Your library should also have a Standard Rate & Data directory for business publications.

3) Try the classified advertising sections of major newspapers. Quite often you'll find a wide assortment of "wholesale" goods offered. Papers such as the "Wall Street Journal" and the "New York Times", should be available at your local library.

Finding closeout bargains requires research. If you are serious about cashing in on closeout merchandise, either for personal use or for resale for profit, you'll have to seek out the sellers of such goods. It takes time and patience. You'll need to get as many company catalogs and price lists as you can, read as many trade publications as you can get your hands on, and utilize sources such as the Yellow Pages and newspapers.

Closeout Samples

In some cases, you can get closeout merchandise free, or at the lowest possible prices. Most companies which specialize in closeout merchandise, provide inspection samples of the closeouts being offered. Usually there is no charge for such inspection samples. Even if you decide not to buy the company's goods, you will probably get to keep the sample. The company may ask you to pay the closeout "unit" price for the sample, but you'll still be getting the unit at well below regular retail and typical discount prices. So it's a good idea to look for companies which provide samples of their closeouts.

There's no doubt that the closeouts are there, it's up to you the "potential buyer" to take advantage of them. You may start out buying closeouts for your own personal use—an item for your home, a gift, etc.—and once you gain experience in the field and have made several contacts, turn to buying for resale. The profits from reselling closeouts can be substantial.

Other closeout sources and factory outlets are provided in Chapter XXIX.

Government Property

Believe it or not, you can "do business" with the U.S. Government and come away with some great bargains. The Government is always offering personal property for sale, and experienced shoppers can often get quality goods at super-low prices. Government property for sale can include hardware, office machines, (typewriters, etc.), furniture, machinery, industrial equipment, motor vehicles, textiles, and even aircraft. This property may be new or used, and in excellent to poor condition. Some items may even need repair, while others can only be sold as scrap.

In order to take advantage of such Government property sales, you'll need to get on several mailing lists. That's because announcements of pending sales are sent to individuals who have expressed an interest in the types of property being offered.

One agency involved in the sale of U.S. Government property is the General Services Administration (GSA). The GSA conducts government sales on personal property, including many personal use items. You can get a mailing-list application by writing to The General Services Administration, Property Management and Disposal Service at the address of the regional office in your area.

The U.S. Department of Defense sells its surplus and foreign excess property (excluding real property), including consumer, commercial, and industrial goods, to individuals, business concerns, and other organizations. The Defense Department's Surplus Sales Office serves as a sales clearinghouse. You'll need to get a "Surplus Bidder Application" for the mailing list in order to take advantage of these sales. Write to:

Department of Defense,
Surplus Sales Division,
Box 1370, Battle Creek, MI 49106.

Two free pamphlets, "How To Buy Surplus Property From The Department of Defense", and "Classes of Surplus Property Sold by the Department of Defense", a list of regional officers and property locations are also available from the Defense Department.

Generally speaking, there are three basic methods of sale involved in buying Government property.

1) Sealed bids— these bids are made on special forms and submitted with a designated deposit. Bids are then opened publicly on an announced date. Successful bidders are then notified by the Government agency.

2) On the spot bids— these bids are turned in "on the spot" during the sale. The bidder writes out his/her bid and turns it in during the course of the sale. Successful bidders are made known from item to item.

3) Public auction— this type of sale is conducted by Government-approved auctioneers, and follows the same basic guidelines of typical commercial auctions.

Detailed description of opportunities for buying in auctions and from government is provided in Chapter XXIX.

XI

Clothing And Accessories:

Men's, women's, and children's clothing; sweaters and knitwear; lingerie; footwear; furs; handbags; leathergoods; and accessories

Regardless of what type of apparel you need, or your taste in fashion, you can buy almost anything to wear through mail-order outlets. Savings can range from 25% to 50% and more on men's, women's, and children's clothing, lingerie, sweaters and knitwear, footwear, jackets, coats, and other clothing items when you shop by mail.

All the firms listed in this section offer a fine selection of clothing and accessories, footwear, handbags, and leather goods at lower-than-average prices. However, before you make any purchases you should get as much information as you can. Send away for as many catalogs and price lists as you can get and compare what each company has to offer. Learn as much as you can about fabrics, and what should go into the manufacture of well-made clothing for every need and occasion.

Here are a few more shopping tips for buying clothing and

accessories through the mail:

Don't rely on last season's measurements. To be certain the goods you order from a catalog will fit properly, use current measurements only.

Make sure you ask about refund and exchange policies before placing an order.

Avoid buying an article of clothing, no matter how "good" the price, if it clashes with everything else in your wardrobe.

Don't go overboard on "one-time-only" outfits. You are better off spending your money on items you'll be able to wear over and over.

Spend time comparison-shopping at home, using catalogs, price lists, and newspaper ads.

Ace Leather Products, Inc.
2211 Ave. U Brooklyn, NY 11229
Phone: 800-342-5223 (718) 891-0713

Ace Leather Products carries a complete line of name brand luggage and leather goods. Some items are available at savings of up to 40% off manufacturers' suggested list prices.

Ace has in stock luggage by American Tourister, Boyt, French, Hartmann, Land, Pegasus, Samsonite, Skyway, Sport Sac, and other top manufacturers. Also available are briefcases, and attache cases by Atlas, Bond Street, Lodis, Scully, and Tumi. A good selection of quality hand bags and small leather goods are also sold to mail-order shoppers.

Call the toll-free number for a price quote or send a letter with a SASE. Payment can be made by check, money order or major credit card.

Baby Clothes Wholesale
60 Ethel Road West Piscataway, NJ 08854
Phone: 800-568-1930 800-568-1940

Baby Clothes Wholesale offers mail-order shoppers a huge selection of clothing for boys and girls in newborn sizes to size seven. The company's wholesale prices range up to 50% off average retail prices of comparable goods.

To get the Baby Clothes Wholesale 44-page, full-color catalog, send a check for $3.00. Pay by check, money order or major credit card.

Chadwick's of Boston, Ltd.
One Chadwick Place Box 1600
Brockton, MA 01240-1600
Phone: (508) 583-7200 (information)
(508) 583-6600 order)

Chadwick's of Boston is "the original off-price fashion catalog", featuring savings of 25% to 50% on quality women's apparel. The company offers the same up-to-the-minute fashions and the quality you would expect to find in major department stores, but at well below average retail prices.

A recent Chadwick's catalog featured Ellen Ashley multi-tiered ruffled blouses, Ease Sport cotton T-shirts, leggings, capri pants, drawstring pants, and cardigans by Abernathy sport, cotton sheeting shorts by Erika and Co., rompers, leather belts, denim dresses, denim skirts by Oleg Cassini, knit dresses, blazers, knit pants sets, and jumpsuits. There's also a selection of beachwear, including one and two piece swim suits by Mainstream, Sassafras, Oscar de la Renta, Beach Bay, Bill Blass, and Barefoot Miss. You'll also find twill trousers, V-neck dresses, cotton knit tank tops, gingham dresses, and cotton knit tunic and skirt sets. The clothing offered is available in a great assortment of both women's and petite sizes.

Chadwick's catalog is available free upon request. Satisfaction is guaranteed and returns are accepted. Pay by check, money order or major credit card.

Chock Catalog Corp.
74 Orchard Street
New York, NY 10002-4594
Phone: (212) 473-1929

Since 1921, the Chock family has been selling the finest first-quality underwear, hosiery, sleepwear, and infant's clothing at discount prices. The Chock catalog ($1.00) lists a wide assortment of products by famous manufacturers such as Burlington, B.V.D., Calvin Klein, Carters, Hanes, Jockey, Munsingwear, Vanity Fair, and many others.

The company's 72-page catalog is "Chock" full of bargains, including women's stockings, panty hose, panties, and slips; and men's underwear, pajamas, robes, and socks. There's also a selection of infant's and children's clothing such as cloth diapers and crib linen, boys underwear by Hanes, underwear and sleepwear for boys and girls by Carter, and socks by Trimfit. Chock also sells umbrellas and accessories.

Send $1.00 for the catalog. Price quotes are available by phone or by mail with a SASE. Satisfaction is guaranteed. Pay by check, money order or major credit card.

Essex Shoe Co.
950 New Durham Road Edison, NJ 08817
Phone: 800-366-9302

Essex Shoe Co., "The Comfortable Shoe Place", offers a good selection of women's comfort shoes at bargain prices. Famous brand names, such as Oldmaine Trotters, Rockport, Clinic, Beacon, Munro, Daniel Green, Soft Spots, Penaljo, and many others are available, most in full and half sizes to 12, in widths 4A to WW. Essex has many styles from which to choose, including leather walking shoes by Soft Spots and Rockport, interwoven handsewn moccasins by Trotters, leather sandals by Clinic, leather casuals by Munro, T-straps by Beacon, and many others.

Call or write for a free catalog. Satisfaction is guaranteed. Returns are accepted for refund within 30 days on unworn shoes. Pay by check, money order or major credit card (no C.O.D. orders).

Huntington Clothiers
1285 Alum Creek Dr. Columbus, OH 43209
Phone: 800-848-6203 (order) 800- 848-6201 (customer service)

The free catalog (available upon request) from Huntington Clothiers, provides mail-order shoppers with an outstanding selection of conservative men's wear. You can save up to 30% on some items.

Huntington has in stock everything from silk ties to bathrobes. Suits for every season and every occasion are available in pure worsted wool gabardine, houndstooth, cotton chambray, and seersucker fabrics. Also in stock are jackets and blazers in silk, Madras, Belgian Linen, and other fabrics. Formal wear—tuxedo, shirt, cummerbund, cuff links, etc.—is also available. There's also a good selection of neckwear, including silk Repp stripes and foulards.

Trousers, walking shorts, cotton and wool sweaters, leather belts, footwear, boxer shorts, and other items of men's apparel are also featured in the Huntington catalog.

As shirtmakers, Huntington has become well-known for its variety of fabrics, including cotton oxford broadcloth, Egyptian cotton broadcloth, cotton denim, Sea Island cotton, and others. Shirts are available in buttondown and/or plain collars.

Monogramming is also available. All Huntington-manufactured shirts (as well as suits, sportcoats, and trousers) are cut true to size. If you aren't sure of your measurements, or don't know how to determine them accurately, you can call and talk to a trained Huntington personal phone shopper and get professional assistance.

Huntington guarantees satisfaction with every order. Returns are accepted (except monogrammed items). Pay by check, money order or major credit card.

Lady George
P.O. Box 128 Malden, MA 02148
Phone: 800-922-0504

For over 50 years, Lady George has offered a superior selection of intimate apparel at mail-order savings. The company sells intimate apparel by every major manufacturer in a complete range of styles and sizes.

Call for a free catalog. Most orders are shipped within 24 hours. Satisfaction is guaranteed. Pay by check, money order or major credit card.

Land's End, Inc.
Land's End Lane Dodgeville, WI 53595-0001
Phone: 800-356-4444 FAX: 800-332-0103 (credit card orders only)

Land's End has been offering a good selection of men's, women's, and children's clothing since the early 1960s. The company provides savings of up to 40% on many items of casual apparel. Color catalogs are available free upon request. The company also offers the "Book of Caring" which tells you how to keep your clothes looking their best. The book is free upon request.

The Land's End catalog for men shows a wide selection

of dress shirts (Oxford, Broadcloth or Blazer), denim and chambray shirts; cotton, denim, and Como Silk ties; tailored clothing (Harris Tweed sportscoats, John Partridge trenchcoats, slacks); sweaters; footwear; underwear; pajamas and robes; belts; socks; swimwear; and other items of apparel. Women will find a selection of dresses, blouses, blazers, jackets, pajamas and robes, skirts, pants, blazers, belts, sweaters, swimwear, shoes and sandals, and shorts.

Land's End will hem your pants free of charge— whether you prefer cuffs or plain bottom, the company will finish your pants with matching color thread at no charge. A monogramming service is also available.

The Land's End "Kid's Catalog" features 60 pages of clothing and accessories for infants, toddlers, boys, girls, and kids of all sizes. For infants, the company has sleepers, coveralls, rompers, hooded cardigans, and a selection of diaper bags. Colorful Tees and knit shorts, cotton dresses, Overalls, and a host of "Britches" are in stock for toddlers. Also available are boys weathered mesh Crew cargo shorts, jeans, chinos, cotton sportshirts, girls dresses, mix and match knits, and swimwear.

The store also has a selection of sneakers, sandals, beach bags, beltpacks and duffles, and bedding for kids of all sizes. Toys and games are also available, including compact chess and backgammon, pocket parafoil kites, and original world map puzzles. Call the toll-free number to request your free catalog(s).

Satisfaction is guaranteed, and returns are accepted. Pay by check, money order or major credit card.

Lane Bryant
P.O. Box 8303 Indianapolis, IN 46283-8303
Phone: 800-477-7030 (information) 800-477-7070 (order)
FAX: 800-456 9838

Lane Bryant publishes a catalog which features an outstanding selection of women's fashions in all sizes. The company offers women's wear in the largest selection of special sizes, including women's 34-54, misses 12-14, halfs 12 1/2- 34 1/2, tall 12-24. There's also footwear in sizes 7-12 AA-EEE. Mail- order shoppers can expect savings of up to 50% on some items.

Past Lane Bryant catalogs have featured women's intimate wear, including panties, bras, slips, stockings and pantyhose, and lace nightwear. Name brands sold include Fruit of the Loom, Berkshire, Playtex, Vanity Fair, Exquisite Form, and other manufacturers. Lane Bryant also offers savings on denim blazers, sweaters, stretch pull-ons, Oxford shirts, sports casuals, T- shirts, stretch-fit jeans, baseball shirts, rompers, pullover shirtdresses, and much more. Footwear bargains include low heel pumps, canvas casuals, sandals, dress shoes, moccassin style oxfords, and others by Soft Spots, Hush Puppies, Beacon, Venezia, and Hunter's Run. The company's fashion consultants are happy to assist you with questions about size, style or fit.

Call or write the company to request a free catalog. Satisfaction is guaranteed. Returns are accepted for exchange or refund. Pay by check, money order or major credit card. (Lane Bryant charge accounts are also available to qualified applicants.)

Lee's Comfort Shoes
P.O. Box 728 Bucyrus, OH 44820
Phone: 800-753-4736

This company specializes in women's comfort shoes, and in hard-to-find sizes. Lee's specially trained staff can help you get a proper fit on any of the styles shown in the company's free catalog.

Lee's has in stock quality footwear by Easy Spirit, Soft Spots, Clinic, Extra Depth, Selby, Cobbie, and other famous manufacturers at competitive prices. You can choose from a selection of comfortable walking shoes, walking pumps, sandals, casuals, oxfords, dress shoes, and other styles. All shoes are designed for comfort and durability.

If you have special foot problems, such as arthritis, diabetes, and bunions, The Extra Depth footwear carried by Lee's is designed to give you the utmost support. These shoes by Extra Depth, including the lightweight "Dancer", "Miss America", and "Snappy", are all made in the U.S. and are available in over 100 sizes.

Lee's catalog is available free upon request. Call the company if you don't see your size listed in the catalog. Returns are accepted within 30 days for exchange or refund. Pay by check, money order or major credit card.

National Wholesale Co., Inc

400 National BLVD. Lexington, NC 27292
Phone: (704) 249-0211

When you buy direct from National Wholesale, you are buying from the "nation's leading supplier" of first-quality hosiery and pantyhose. In business since the early 1950's, National Wholesale offers a large selection of colors and styles. The company's hosiery, loungewear and sleepwear for women are guaranteed to fit, "petite to queen sizes". Also available are name-brand bras, girdles, panties, and body slimmers by Playtex, Exquisite Form, Glamorise, Kayser, and Vassarette. Slips, pants liners, thermal underwear, briefs, and cotton-knit vests are also sold. By ordering direct from National Wholesale, you can expect savings of up to 50% on some items.

Call or write for National's catalog. The company sells first-quality goods only. Satisfaction is guaranteed, and returns are accepted. Pay by check, money order or major credit card.

Okun Brothers Shoes
356 E. South St. Kalamazoo, MI 49007
Phone: (616) 342-1536 800-433-6344

The Okun brothers have been selling quality dress, casual, and work shoes since 1920. The company is independently owned and not part of a chain, so it can provide customers most all of the best brands available at discount prices. Because of the company's large purchasing power, it can buy in quantity and pass the savings on to its customers. Many of the low prices are on brands that aren't often discounted. Discounts vary from item to item, but mail-order shoppers can expect some good bargains. The company's free catalog features an outstanding selection of footwear for men and women in sizes 6-16 with widths from AA to EEEE (men), and 5-12 in widths AAA to EEE (women).

Shoppers can choose from men's dress shoes, casual shoes, plain pumps, nurses' shoes, sandals, loafers, moccasins, boots, and athletic shoes for many types of sporting activities. Brand names in stock include Acme, Auditions, Buster Brown, Carolina Shoe Co., Converse, Dexter, Dingo, Easy Spirit, Extra Depth, Eastland, Hi-Tec, Timberland, Adidas, Reebok, New Balance, Ellesse, Florsheim, Grasshoppers, Minnetonka, Nurse Mates, Penaljo, Pony, Rockport, Soft Spots, Sebago, and many others. Okun Bros. also features a large stock of men's work and safety shoes.

Call or write for the free catalog (Inquire about the availability of any brands and styles not listed in the catalog). A price quote is available by phone or by mail with a SASE. Satisfaction is guaranteed. Returns, if unworn, are accepted for refund, exchange, or credit. Pay by check, money order or MasterCard, VISA or Discover.

Arthur M. Rein

32 New York Ave. Freeport, NY 11520-2017
Phone: (516) 379-6421

This company specializes in custom-made furs. All fur coats are made to customer specifications and are priced as much as 50% below furs from designer furriers.

Arthur M. Rein can custom-make furs from a wide range of pelts, including beaver, fox, chinchilla, marten, ermine, Russian sable, and many others. You can call the company and discuss the particular garment and pelt you have in mind. A sample pelt is available for a refundable deposit. You can also write to the company, sending a description (and a picture, if available) of the garment. The description should include your measurements, height and weight.

Items such as duplicates of designer furs, flings, throws, wall hangings, capes, muffs, boas, scarves, collars, and other accessories can also be made to order. Other services offered include fur remodeling, lengthening, color darkening, and relining. Used furs are also bought and sold.

When you write or call the company, make sure you have a good idea of the type garment and pelt you want. Mr. Rein can also provide you with information and advice. A price quote is available by phone or by mail with a SASE. No catalog is available. Satisfaction is guaranteed. Pay by check, money order or certified check.

Roby's Intimates ("Bras-By-Mail")

121 S. 18th St. Philadelphia, PA 19103
Phone: 800-878-8272 (215) 751-1730 (in PA)

Roby's, also known as "Bras-By-Mail", offers quality women's intimate apparel at a regular savings of 25% off average retail prices. The company has been in business for over two decades. There's a large selection of items in stock, including panties, girdles, bras (over 50 brands in stock), slips, panty hose, and post-surgery garments. Roby's also has a good selection of body control garments for average-size and larger women. Body garments such as waistline panty girdles, waistline pantliners, long torso panty girdles, long torso briefs in firm and moderate control which are not readily available in retail stores.

All goods are by top-of-the-line manufacturers such as Bali, Berkshire, Cannon, Chantelle, Danskin, Christian Dior, Exquisite Form, Jezebel, Lady Marlene, Maidenform, Playtex, Subtract, Warner's, and Olga.

The Roby's price list is available for $1.00. Also available is a full-color "Sexy Lingerie" catalog for average and large size figures. Send $4.00 for the catalog and specify if you want the "large size" catalog. Satisfaction is guaranteed with every order. The company will fill your orders from its stock as well as "special order" requirements. Pay by check, money order, or major credit card.

The Smart Saver
P.O. Box 209 Waso,IL 60183

In business for over 10 years, the Smart Saver offers a good selection of quality women's intimate apparel at "low prices, far below retail". You'll find a good selection of bras, panties, slips, girdles, and nightwear at affordable prices. This family-owned business features Playtex, Vanity Fair, Exquisite Form, Lollipop, and other fine garments at savings up to 30%.

Write the company for a free catalog. The Smart Saver sells first-quality goods only— no seconds or irregulars. Pay by check or money order.

WearGuard Corporation
Box 9105 Hingham, MA 02043-9105
Phone: 800-666-5500 (customer service) 800-388-3300

(order) FAX: (617) 982-9549

For over 40 years, WearGuard has been providing work clothing, casual wear, and accessories for men and women at savings of up to 30%. WearGuard specializes in great looking clothes designed for durability, comfort and style for on-the-job or casual wear.

The company features an outstanding selection of heavy-duty and lightweight workshirts— both long and short sleeves in a full range of sizes. Quality T- shirts, chambray shirts, Western and flannel shirts, button-down Oxford shirts, workpants, Western boots, work boots and shoes, jeans, jumpsuits, coveralls, thermal underwear, jackets, windbreakers, customized caps, canvas work shorts, mesh knit shirts, sweaters, industrial smocks, tech-lab coats, women's smocks and blouses, women's work apparel, and rain gear, are also available.

WearGuard also offers custom logo screen printing and custom logo embroidery on many of its garments. The company will even help you create a design for your business. Call for information.

WearGuard has a catalog available free upon request. Satisfaction is guaranteed with every order. Returns are accepted for full purchase price. Pay by check, money order or major credit card.

Carabella

Hollywood Splash, Inc.
1852 McGraw Ave., Irvine, CA 92714
Phone (714) 434-0472

The Carabella Collection catalog features the most exclusive designs in swimwear at wholesale prices. The company has been in business since 1983 and offers over 100 of the latest styles in the finest quality lycra spandex and swimwear. The swimwear is available in both prints and solids, and in a wide range of sizes.

The Carabella Collection catalog is available for $3.00. Call or write the company. Pay by check, money order or major credit card.

Hanover Shoe Co.
440 N. Madison St., Hanover, PA 17331
Phone: (717) 632-7575; (800) 426-3708

Talk about longevity! The Hanover Shoe Co. has been "America's quality shoemaker" since 1899. A company doesn't stay in business for 95 years unless it provides a quality product, low prices, and excellent service. The Hanover Shoe Co. features all three.

The company provides quality workmanship on a complete line of men's dress,casual, and work shoes at savings of 25% and more. You save because you buy direct from the hanover factory, eliminating the middleman's profit.

Past Hanover catalogs feature well-crafted hand-sewn loafers and slip-ons at prices starting under $70, deerskin golf shoes, and athletic and walking shoes. Brand names include Converse, K-Swiss, Rocky Boots, Clarks, and others. For the finest in dress shoes, Hanover features Shell Cordovan footwear, including Oxfords, penny loafers, classic wing tips, and tasseled slip-ons. All footwear is available in a wide range of sizes. Traditional and contemporary styles are also available.

Hanover's shoe catalog is available for $1.00. Satisfaction is guaranteed. Pay by check, money order or major credit card.

Lingerie Outlet
P.O. Box 63054, Philadelphia, PA 19914

Phone: (800) 245-8659; in (215) area, call 750-4996

The Lingerie Outlet offers an outstanding selection of fine undergarments at savings far below typical retail prices. In stock, are bras and girdles by Exquisite Form, Carnival, Goddess, Playtex, and other brand-name manufacturers. There's also a selection of panties, teddies, hosiery, and other lingerie at discount prices.

Call or write the Lingerie Outlet and request a free catalog. Purchases may be paid for by check, money order or major credit card.

Paul Fredrick Shirt Co.
140 W. Main St., Fleetwood, PA 19522
Phone: (215) 944-0909

For over 35 years the Paul Fredrick Shirt Company has supplied fine quality pure cotton shirts to America's top men's shops. Now, you can buy the same shirts direct from the manufacturer at savings well below typical retail. Save up to 50% on some items.

Paul Fredrick's men's shirt selection includes straight collars, buttondown, tab collars, button or French cuffs, and many other styles. Also available are Italian silk ties in an assortment of patterns and colors, cufflinks, and belts.

Call or write the company to request a color catalog ($1.00). Satisfaction is guaranteed. Pay by check, money order or major credit card.

XII

Computing Needs And Office Equipment And Supplies:

Computers, peripherals, software, supplies, furniture, office machines, and accessories

---

Even when you know what you are doing, buying computers, software and equipment or upgrading your existing system can be a tricky business. Novices should be especially careful. It's not that vendors are out to make a killing off of each customer— actually, computer prices are now lower than ever. The big mistake many first-time buyers make is not knowing their computing requirements before they buy.

Before you buy, you should know what functions you will be performing with your computer. By knowing exactly what you need, you'll be better able to locate and buy the right equipment. If you don't need 150 megabytes, or a laser printer, or a super VGA monitor— don't buy them. When buying software, you should know if the product is compatible with your system. The best way to get what you need and to save money, is to be as "educated" as possible.

A good way to learn about computer systems and

requirements is by taking a beginners computer course. You'll get basic information which will help you when it comes time to make a practical purchase. You can also attend demonstrations of new products and read as much as you can. The "Better Business Bureau A to Z Buying Guide", written by Virginia Schomp (Henry Holt & Company, 1990) can supply you with good information and buying tips. Computer publications such as "Computer Shopper", PC Computing", "Computer Monthly", "PC Sources", and "PC World", are also excellent sources of information. The publications are available at most newsstands. Your public library should also have a good selection of "how to" computer books.

The listings in this section represent firms which offer a full range of quality computing and office needs, from computers and supplies to ergonomic furniture. Get as many catalogs and price lists as you can. Also get as much information as you can, before placing an order. Compare products, services and prices and make your selection as an "informed" shopper.

American Stationery Company, Inc.
100 Park Avenue Peru, IN 46970
Phone: 800-822-2577 FAX: (317) 472-5910

Since 1919 American Stationery has been offering elegant and impressive personalized stationery. The finest standard stationery, embossed notes, calligraphy notes, labels, and memos, are all offered at affordable prices. You can expect savings of up to 40% off typical retail prices on some items.

American Stationery's best value is its popular Standard Box stationery which is available from 100 printed sheets (and envelopes) in the standard box, up to 200 printed sheets (and envelopes) in the deluxe box. The company also offers hand bordered stationery (ivory, white, blue, pink) ornamental calligraphy notes (white, ivory), heavyweight correspondence cards, shell fold notes, typewriter paper in boxes of 100 printed sheets and envelopes, embossed correspondence cards in white and ivory, executive stationery (white, ivory, gray), 25% cotton business stationery, embossed stationery (ivory, pink, blue, white), deckle edge correspondence sheets, children's stationery on recycled paper, and many other selections.

Past catalogs have also featured Cloisonne pens and other writing instruments, gold-plated letter openers, paperweights, personalized memo pads, 3 year calendars, brass desk accessories (letter holder, stamp box, pencil holder), embossers, and shipping and address labels.

The company's catalog is available free upon request. Satisfaction is guaranteed. Returns are accepted for replacement or refund. Pay by check, money order or major credit card.

Lionheart Press, Inc.
P.O. Box 4056 Allentown, PA 18105-4056
Phone: (514) 933-4918 FAX: (514) 939-3087

Lionheart Press offers business and statistical software for personal computer users. Prices are competitive on business statistics, marketing statistics, surveys and questionnaires, inventory, and other software packages. This is numerical analysis software that is easy to use and apply. The company provides full books that help you run the programs right the first time. Only ASCII files are used.

For more information and/or to get the Lionheart Press 30-page free catalog, call or write. The company provides an absolute money-back guarantee that its programs will be compatible with your computer and that they will perform according to specifications. Pay by check, money order or major credit card.

Lyben Computer Systems

5545 Bridgewood P.O. Box 130
Sterling HTS, MI 48311-0130
Phone: (313) 268-8899 FAX: (313) 268-8899

Mail-order shoppers can get on Lyben's mailing list on a one year trial basis. Simply call, write or fax your request and address and you will receive two full 196+ page catalogs and two promotional catalogs during the trial period.

The full-line catalog includes a full range of computer paper, supplies, accessories, boards, cabling, switchboxes, buffers, networking products, and much more. Past catalogs have shown batteries, data cartridges, disk drives, dust covers, joysticks, keyboard protectors, continuous labels, modems, paper shredders, printer stands, ribbons, surge protectors, wrist rests and pads, mice and trackballs, copy holders, memory upgrade chips/modules, disk drive controller cards, diskette drive and video cleaning kits by Perfect Data, and much more.

You can expect savings of up to 50% on some items. Name-brands include Maxell, Sony, Verbatim, Dysan, Exponent, Sony, Curtis, and many others top manufacturers.

Lyben will replace or refund defective or unsatisfactory products that are returned within 30 days of receipt. All returns must be in good condition and in their original packaging. Price quotes are available by mail or by fax. There is a minimum order of $15 for check, VISA, MasterCard, or C.O.D. orders.

National Business Furniture

222 E. Michigan St. Milwaukee, WI 53202
Phone: 800-558-1010

National Business Furniture has been in business since 1975, selling quality office furniture at wholesale prices. You can order everything to furnish your home or business office at a savings of 30% to 60% and more.

National's catalog is available free and features a selection of ergonomics chairs, swivel chairs, recliners, guest chairs, stack chairs, folding chairs, leather chairs, and operator's chairs, by LA-Z-Boy, High Point, Global, Stylex, Harvard, and other manufacturers. You'll also find a good selection of desks, computer furniture (locking rolltop computer desks, mobile units, home- office centers with hutch, desk, printer stand, connector, and chair; bi-level workstations; compact computer stations; printer stands), drafting stools, suspension and flatfiles, chair mats, storage cabinets, bookcases, and tables.

Call or write the company to request a catalog. Volume discounts are available. All goods are guaranteed against defects in the quality of materials or workmanship. Pay by major credit card. A 50% deposit will speed orders to first time customers.

NEBS, Inc.
500 Main Street Groton, MA 01417
Phone: 800-225-6380 FAX: 800-234-4324

The free NEBS catalog, "Computer Forms & Software" has over 50 pages of forms and software values at savings of over 30% on some items. Software compatible forms available include checks, invoices, statements, custom forms and checks, multipurpose forms, and others. The invoice, check, and multipurpose forms are guaranteed compatible with over 1600 software packages, including "Microsoft Money", "Peachtree Software", "MySoftware", "RealWorld", "DAC Easy", "Quicken", "Pacioli", and "Great Plains". The catalog also features a cross- reference guide with a listing of over 750 compatible software programs.

NEBS also offers recycled computer paper, green and blue bar computer paper, colored computer paper, envelopes, labels, laser products (labels, paper), post cards, continuous stationery, and other products to keep your office running smoothly.

The company guarantees satisfaction with all its products and provides a full credit, replacement or refund, including any shipping charges you have paid. The guarantee has no time limit except for software which is limited to 180 days. Write for your free "Computer Forms & Software" catalog. Also available on request are the "Personalized Communications", "Credit & Collections", and "Checkwriting" catalogs. Pay by check, money order, or VISA, MasterCard, or American Express Card.

Paper Direct

P.O. Box 618 205 Chubb Ave. Lyndhurst, NJ 07071-0618
Phone: (201) 507-1996 800-272-7377
FAX: (201) 507-0817

There's no doubt that computer users need an economical source for quality paper and supplies. Paper Direct provides such products at competitive prices.

Mail-order shoppers can choose from a selection of unprinted and preprinted papers for every need (Oriental laser papers, coated laser papers, copier papers, hot colors, white laser papers, cotton rag content laser papers, desktop messages, letterheads, paper frames, certificates), as well as labels, envelopes, designer laser labels, and presentation, mailing and storage products (mailing envelopes, plastic storage boxes, portfolios). The company also has several unique products such as laser note cards, Desktop Color Foil, and Custom Laser Greetings. A selection of Paper Templates for Word Perfect, Microsoft Word, Microsoft Publisher, Page Maker, Lotus Ami Pro, and others are also available.

Paper Direct's "Paper Catalog" is free upon request as is its new "WOW! What a Great Presentation!" catalog. Call the toll free number and ask about the catalogs. Satisfaction is guaranteed. Returns are accepted for a credit, exchange or refund. Minimum order is $30. Pay by check or major credit card.

PC Connection
6 Mill Street Marlow, NH 03456
Phone: 800-800-5555 FAX: 603-446-7791

Since 1982, PC Connection has been providing mail-order values on IBM- compatible hardware and supplies. The company has added the Compaq line of PC- compatibles to their long list of mail-order bargains. The Compaq Prolina, Desktop/i series, Contura notebooks, and the Color Compaq LTE Lite are available from PC Connection. Customizing is also available.

PC Connection also carries the latest versions of popular software by publishers such as Microsoft ("MS Works, Word for Windows, Excel for Windows, Power Point, MS Words, FoxPro for DOS"; Lotus ("AmiPro for Windows, 1-2-3/Windows, 1-2-3/DOS release 3.4"; Microlytics, Inc.; Borland International ("Paradox, Quatro Pro"); Word Perfect (WordPerfect for DOS and Windows"); Xerox; Systematic (Norton Desktop/Windows"); and many others. There's also a bountiful stock of hardware and accessories, from disk drives to multimedia packages. Whether you need a top of the line customized computer, modem, monitor, printer, or word processor, this company is likely to have it in stock at mail-order savings.

Check out the company's ad in computing publications such as PC World and/or write for a free price list. Also ask about their full color catalog.

There's a 3-year limited warranty covering all Compaq parts and labor, and the company also provides warranty backup and support for all the other products it sells. Orders are shipped by first-class mail, with a standard shipping fee of

$5.00 per order. Call for shipping information about orders shipped outside the continental U.S. or to APO and FPO addresses. Pay by check, money order or major credit card.

Penny Wise Office Products
4350 Kenilworth Avenue Edmonston, MD 20781
Phone: 800-942-3311 (301) 699-1000 (Wash., D.C. area)
FAX: 800-622-4411 or (301) 277-6700 (Wash., D.C. area)

If you have an IBM compatible computer and a Hayes compatible modem, you can shop OnLine with Penny Wise and never leave your home or office. The OnLine service is available 24 hours a day so you can shop any time that's convenient for you. The company will deliver your order right to your doorstep within 1 to 3 days. Penny Wise will even send you a free disk for fast, easy access to the OnLine store. To get the free disk, call the toll free number.

Penny Wise offers a full complement of office supplies at low prices. Products include computer accessories (printer stands, keyboard drawers, diskettes by 3M, diskette filing trays, cleaning supplies, workstations) desk organizers, labels and label printers, index cards, printer cartridges, ribbons, copiers, standard and microcassette recorders, dictating cassettes, Hewlett-packard toner cartridges, printer calculators from Texas Instruments, and much more. Available are brand names such as Dennison, Highland, Hammerhill, Texas Instruments, Panasonic, Xerox, Canon Rolodex, and others.

Write or call and request the Penny Wise catalog and/or the free OnLine demo disk. All shipping charges are free within the continental U.S.. Minimum order is $25. Pay by check, money order, or major credit card. The company also offers its own charge accounts contingent upon a satisfactory credit report.

The Reliable Corporation
101 W. Van Buren Chicago, IL 60607
Phone: 800-843-2850 FAX: 800-621-6002

The Reliable Corporation offers savings averaging up to 30% on all your home office needs. The firm's 60-page "Home Office" catalog is free and is jam- packed with discounts on desk accessories and furniture, lighting, and many other products designed to blend with your home decor.

Past catalogs have featured oak computer carts, ergonomic chairs, filing cabinets, fluorescent and halogen floor and desk lamps, bookcases, telephones, wall units, drafting tables, footstools, and many other items. There's even a selection of briefcases and luggage.

Reliable guarantees satisfaction on every purchase. A minimum order of $15 is required with credit cards. Call or write for a free catalog. Pay by check, money order or major credit card.

UARCO Business Products 121 North Ninth Street P.O. BOX 948 Dekalb, IL 60115-9912 800-435-0713 800-435-5555 (customer service) FAX: (815) 756-3219

UARCO features competitive prices on a full line of quality computer supplies and continuous forms at competitive prices. The company's free catalog lists many bargains on forms, printer accessories, diskettes, data cartridges, laser printer accessories and supplies, recycled paper, ribbons, toner cartridges, ergonomic furniture, office panel systems, and many other products. UARCO sells over 10,000 name-brand computer and office supplies.

A recent UARCO catalog features a selection of printers, including Okidata laser printers, Canon Bubble Jet printers, and dot matrix printers by Epson. Computer supplies and accessories in stock include, diskettes, dust covers, font cartridges and toner by Hewlett-Packard, surge supressors, Hayes modems, Samsung monitors, Cyrix FasMath co-processors, tool kits for PC upgrades and repairs, copyholders, keyboard cleaning kits, keyboard drawers, Polaroid anti- glare radiation shields and screen filters, office furniture clusters, personal workstations, computer carts, PC security cabinets, and many other items. There's also a good selection of laser printer and copier paper, continuous mailing labels, and recycled continuous computer paper.

Write to get your free UARCO catalog. Satisfaction on all orders is guaranteed. Returns within 90 days are accepted for exchanges or a refund/credit for the full purchase price. Pay by check, money order, or major credit card. Minimum order is $25.

Computer Clipboard
8309 Linden Oaks Court,
Lorton, VA 22079
FAX: (703) 912-6918

Due to buying power and volume of sales, many manufacturers look to Computer Clipboard to liquidate factory-new or factory- refurbished computer equipment at tremendous savings. Many of the products carry the original manufacturers' warranties, while refurbished products carry a full ninety day repair/replacement warranty. Specials sell quickly and availability cannot be guaranteed.

Past specials have included printers by Hewlett Packard, Apple and Compaq; notebooks by Zenith, Compaq, and Hewlett Packard; and computer systems by Zenith and Apple. The company also sells factory-new and factory refurbished brand-name monitors and peripherals.

Fax Computer Clipboard and ask them to fax you a list of their latest specials and current pricing. Returns are accepted for full refund or credit. Pay by check, money order, or major credit card.

Computer Discount Warehouse (CDW)
2840 Maria Ave., Northbrook, IL 60062
Phone: (800) 726-4239
FAX: (708) 291-1737

CDW is one of the "fastest growing" direct marketing firms in the entire computer industry. The company now carries over 15,000 products, including computer hardware, software and peripherals at discount prices. Some items in the CDW catalog also provide a manufacturer's rebate.

A recent CDW catalog featured desktop computers by NEC, AST, Canon, and DTK. Also available are notebooks by Toshiba, NEC, AST, and Texas Instruments. There are also memory upgrades, monitors (by NEC, Mag, Sony, Panasonic, Magnavox), printers (dot matrix, laser and inkjet by Hewlett Packard, Okidata, Epson, Canon, andPanasonic), hard drives (by Maxtor, Conner, Seagate), internal and externalmultimedia kits, CD-ROM drives by Hitachi; Texel; and Sony; scanners, mice, math co-processors and upgrades, and hundreds of other items at bargain prices.

CDW also offers some of the lowest prices around on quality software. The software selection is quite impressive, and includes Microsoft Excel for Windows, Word for Windows, Works for Windows, and MS-DOS 6.0 upgrade (for under $50, while quantities last). Also available are spreadsheets by Borland, Lotus, Norton, and others. Wordprocessing software available includes Wordperfect and Lotus Ami Pro.

Call or write the company to request a catalog. Pay by cashier or certified check on COD orders, or most major credit cards. You can also apply for CDW credit.

Fidelity Products Co.
5601 International Parkway,

P.O. Box 155, Minneapolis, MN 55440-0155
Phone: (800) 328-3034 [order];
(800) 544-3013 [customer service
hotline]FAX: (800) 842-2725

A recent Fidelity graphic arts catalog lists hundreds of items for architects, artists, designers, and engineers. Fidelity has everything from office furniture to mailing tubes to help keep your office organized and running smoothly. Prices are competitive, with many items priced well below suggested manufacturer's list prices. You can expect savings of 50% and more.

If you are in need of office furniture, you can purchase a multi-task drafting stool for just $99.95 (compare at $169.95). Also in stock are computer workstations by Busch, Budget Steel Blueprint Files, oak taborets, Workmaster drawing tables, wood pc carts, and much more. There's also a selection of computer accessories and supplies including keyboard storage drawers, Wrist-Easy wrist supports, universal anti-static dust covers, desktop printer stands, diskette storage trays, and Dataguard surge suppressors (for under $20).

Fidelity also offers some of the lowest prices around on popular software packages, including Microsoft Windows, Word Perfect, Harvard Graphics, Publish-It, The New Print Shop, and others. Floppy disks by 3M and Sony, continuous forms computer printout paper, computer labels, Panasonic microcassette recorders, 2-line telephone system and answering machine, and hundreds of other quality items are also available from Fidelity.

Call or write the company to request a copy of their latest graphic arts catalog. Pay by check, money order, major credit card, or open a Fidelity 30-day account.

Micro Xperts, Inc.
6230 Cochran Rd., Solon, OH 44139
or 2495 Walden Ave., Buffalo, NY 14225
Phone: (800) 736-4270

Micro Xperts is the "complete computer solution", offering wholesale prices on computer systems and peripherals. Recent catalog listings included a 386SX computer with VGA color monitor for under $700, and a 486SX with a SVGA monitor for under $1000. Also in stock are floppy drives by Teac and Mitsumi. Western Digital and Seagate hard drives, SVGA video cards, multi-media kits, Panasonic Printers, motherboards (386SX, 33 mhz to 486 DX2, 66mhz), and cases (mini- to mega-tower) are all available at wholesale prices. Micro Xperts also sells base system computers (some for under $300).

The company also features a good selection of brand-name, high-quality components. And there's no extra charge for custom configuration. You'll get unlimited, free technical support with your purchase(s), and a one year parts; 5-year labor warranty. There's also a 30-day, money back quarantee. Quantity discounts are available for dealers and consultants. Payment may be made by check, money order or major credit card.

PC Importers
Corporate Headquarters, 8295 Darrow Rd.,
Twinsburg, OH 44087Phone:
(800) 886-5155; FAX: (216) 487-5242

PC Importers offers customers the opportunity to buy high quality computer products direct from the importer. Recent product listings include a 386SX computer with SVGA moniter for $695;and a 486DX power station with SVGA monitor for under $1,500. The company also has a large stock of monitors starting at under $100. Brand name monitors available include Mag and ViewSonic. You can also buy hard drives by such manufacturers as Seagate, Western Digital, Maxtor, Quantum, and Conner.

PC Importers also features floppy drives for under $50. This includes 1.2mb (5.25") and 1.44 mb (3,5") floppy drives. There's also a selection of printers, including Panasonic printers starting at under $200 and up. Also in stock are video cards, keyboards, mice, sound cards, modems, and many other computing needs.

PC Importers accept returns within 30 days for a refund. The company also offers a life-time labor and one year parts warranty, as well as unlimited, toll-free technical support. You can also get custom configuration at no extra charge. Discounts are available for dealers and consultants. Payment may be made by check, money order, or major credit card.

Reasonable Solutions
1221 Disk Drive, Medford, OR 97501
Phone: (503) 776-5777; (800) 876-3475

Easy to use software for IBM PCs and compatibles is the specialty of Reasonable Solutions. The company has over 300 programs available for as low as $3.50 a disk. Call or write to request a catalog. Satisfaction is guaranteed. Pay by check, money order, MasterCard or VISA.

The Software Labs
100 Corporate Pointe, Suite 195, Culver City, CA 90231
Phone: (800) 569-7900
FAX: (310) 410-2044

Computer buffs can save a bundle on software by purchasing shareware from the Software Labs. Shareware is not a specific type of software— it is, instead, "try-before-you-buy" software. The shareware system enables you to choose from a wide variety of high-quality computer programs for as little as $3.79 a disk ($3.29 if you buy 12 or more disks). Once you try a program and find out that it does the job, you can then pay a low registration fee to the author. The registration fee will entitle you to receive all pertinent documentation, technical support, license to use, etc.

For example, a recent Software Labs catalog lists the word processing program "PC-Write Advanced level 4.01. The program comes on 4 disks at $3.79 each, making your cost an extremely low $15.16 for an excellent word processing program. Once you've used the program and found it to your liking you can pay a low registration fee of $89. With this fee you'll get disks, a"Getting Started" booklet, reference manual, license to use, technical support for one year, a quarterly newsletter, and a 20% discount on the author's other products. All Software Labs software is guaranteed 100% virus-free.

The Software Labs catalog lists an impressive selection of software (all priced at just $3.79 a disk, before registration), including games, utilities, word processing, spreadsheets, sports programs, creativity and inspiration, genealogy, world maps, graphics clip art, education, desktop publishing, windows, graphics, and much more. Games include "Wolfenstein 3-D", "Commander Keen", "Jill of the Jungle", "Redhook's Revenge", "Ninja", and many others. There's also a selection of utilities and desktop tools, Word Perfect utilities, database and communications software such as "Professional Librarian"; "Business Plan Master"; "The Modem Doctor"; "EZ-Spreadsheet"; and "PC-File".

The best thing to do is to call or write and request a free Software Labs catalog. The catalog lists thousands of programs for the pc, all priced as low as $3.79 a disk ($3.29 a disk if you buy 12 or more). You also get free disks when you pay for 7 or more disks. Satisfaction is guaranteed. Pay by check, money order or major credit card.

Software Support International
2700 N.E. Anderson Rd., Suite A-10,
Vancouver, WA 98661
Phone: (206) 695- 1393; (800) 356-1179

If quality commercial software is priced a little too steep for your budget, you might give Software Support International a try. While the company does carry the top 100 software programs and a full line of accessories for IBM compatibles, it also specializes in closeouts and liquidations. Past bargains include Treasure Island for $10; Monday Night Football for $13; Blue Max for $15; Time Bandit for $8.00; and Future Wars for $15.

Software Support's catalog is available free upon request. Pay by check, money order or major credit card.

Wholesale Warehouse Computers & Electronics
88-08 4th Ave., Brooklyn, N.Y. 11209
Phone: (800) 782-2885 (Dealers ask for ext. #110)
FAX: (718) 680-4896

The Wholesale Warehouse tries to "match and/or beat all advertised prices" on computer systems, peripherals, and other electronics. Available computer products in stock are from such quality name-brand manufacturers as AST, NEC, IBM, Compaq, Toshiba, Texas Instruments, Altima, Samsung, and others. There's also a
selection of printers by Hewlett Packard, Canon, and Panasonic, as well as popular notebook systems by Sharp, Zenith and Bondwell.

Call the toll-free number for price quotes, and information about any system you have in mind. The company provides free technical support. Pay by check, money order or major credit card.

XIII

Cosmetic & Beauty Needs:

Skin care products, perfumes, toiletries, and accessories

Not many people can afford to spend $100 to $150 an ounce for perfume. The good news is, no one has to. By shopping by mail, you can save 50% to 90% on fragrances (for men and women) as well as cosmetic and beauty needs. Some of the companies listed in this section offer what's known as "copycat" fragrances, which are replicas of famous, name brand, expensive perfumes and colognes. The biggest difference between the copycat versions and the originals is the price. Mail-order shoppers who purchase a copycat fragrance may save as much as 90% when compared with the price of the original. Before you order any of these fragrances, request samples on "scent cards" so you can decide for yourself how closely they duplicate the originals.

Other listings in this section feature companies which also provide mail-order savings on an assortment of cosmetic and beauty needs at savings that average 50% and more below retail prices. You'll find everything from nail conditioner to skin care products, bath products, and makeup.

Beautiful Visions USA, LTD

90 Orville Drive
Bohemia, NY 11716   1-800-645-J113

The free Beautiful Visions catalog shows savings of up to 90% on a wide selection of brand-name cosmetics and toiletries. The company, in business since 1977, also sells grooming tools and some fashion jewelry at moderate prices.

Browsing through the catalog, you'll find an outstanding assortment of skin- care products, cosmetics, and perfumes by such famous manufacturers as Revlon, Coty, Alman, Charles of the Ritz, Diane Von Furstenburg, Jovan, Vidal Sassoon, and Vitabath.

Call or write the company to request the free catalog. Satisfaction is guaranteed on all orders. Returns are accepted. Pay by check, money order or major credit card.

Beauty Boutique

P.O. Box 94520 Cleveland, OH 44101-45202
Phone: (216) 826-3008

Beauty Boutique offers savings of up to 90% on nationally known cosmetics and fragrances. The company's 56-page catalog lists popular cosmetics, toiletries, and perfumes by Max Factor, Gucci, Estee Lauder, Revlon, L' Oreal, Diane Von Furstenburg, Jovan, Prince Matchabelli, Maybelline, Charles of the Ritz, Elizabeth Arden, and other famous manufacturers. Prices are well below what you would expect to pay in retail outlets.

The Beauty Boutique also offers cosmetic accessories, including cases, makeup brushes, and fashion jewelry.

Call or write the company to request the catalog. Satisfaction is guaranteed. Pay by check, money order or major credit card. (the company requires a minimum order of

$10 with credit cards).

Comfortably Yours
2515 East 43rd Street P.O. Box 182216 Chattanooga, TN 37422-7216
Phone: 800-521-0097 (order) (615) 867-9955 (customer service) FAX: (615) 867-5318

Comfortably Yours began operating in the early 1980s, offering a fine selection of ladies intimate wear. The company also features a line of cosmetic and beauty products available to mail-order shoppers at reasonable prices.

Shown in the Comfortably Yours catalog are a selection of unique skin care products, beauty aids and accessories. The products include instant cuticle softener, oil nail conditioner (for dry and brittle nails), cosmetic eye lift, eyelash thickener, Fade Creme (for freckles, age spots, and skin discoloration), Retinol Cream for skin care, natural collagen gel, all-day cover cream, all-day leg-cover, and chemical-free, all natural deodorant.

You'll also find tweezers, tabletop makeup mirrors, hair brushes, and other accessories.

Call or write the company and request a free catalog. Satisfaction is guaranteed. Returns are accepted. Pay by check, money order or major credit card. Minimum order is $25.

Essential Products Co., Inc.
90 Water Street New York, NY 10005-3587
Phone: (212) 344-4288

Essential Products Company began doing business in 1895. The company sells an extensive selection of "copycat" fragrances—its own versions of name-brand and expensive ladies' perfumes and men's colognes—at prices well below those of the originals. You can expect to save up to 90% on Essential's fragrances which are known by the brand name, "Naudet".

In stock are over 40 "copies" of such well-known, expensive perfumes as Giorgio, Coco, Obsession, Opium, Passion, Beautiful, and Poison. Essential also has available several copies of expensive men's colognes including Anteus and Zizanie.

Call or write the company for a price list and to inquire about receiving sample "scent cards". Let Essential know which fragrances you are interested in so you can sample the products before ordering. Even though Essential's Naudet versions duplicate the originals, you should sample the products and make your own evaluation.

The company guarantees satisfaction with all its products. Returns are accepted within 30 days for refund. There is a minimum order requirement of $19. Pay by check or money order.

Lady of the Lake
P.O. Box 341575 Los Angeles, CA 90034
Phone: 800-837-2954 (213) 837-2954

This company offers "herbal products from ancient traditions" for cosmetic and beauty needs at reasonable prices. Lady of the Lake's products, blended from fragrant herbs, are safe and easy to use. A catalog of products and prices, and a sample are available for $2.00 (to cover the cost of postage and handling).

Listed in the catalog are fragrant, herbal bath products, skin care products, herbal teas, and gift baskets which feature an assortment of herbal skin care and bath products. Aromatic oils, creams and lotions are also available. All products are natural and "cruelty free".

Send a letter with $2.00 for P & H to receive your catalog and sample. Pay by check or money order.

Tuli-Latus Perfumes LTD
146-36 13th Ave. P.O. Box 422
Whitestone, NY 11357-0422
Phone: (718) 746-9337

For over 20 years, Tuli-Latus has been selling excellent replications of the most popular and expensive women's perfumes and colognes. Mail-order shoppers can save up to 80% on these "copycat" fragrances compared to the cost of the originals.

Tuli-Latus offers copies of over 30 fragrances for women including copies of Obsession, Opium, Chloe, Joy, Giorgio, L' Air du Temps, and Patous. Available for men are perfume versions of expensive originals such as Russian Leather. The company also has its own fragrant creations for women and men.

Send for a free brochure which lists Tuli-Latus' selection of copycat fragrances, as well as some jewelry (simulated pearls and necklaces). The company accepts returns of "unused" perfume within 15 days for a refund or credit. Pay by check, money order or major credit card (a $15 minimum order is required with credit cards).

For more listings of companies which also sell cosmetics, skin care products and toiletries see the "Health Care" section of this catalog. The listings include:

Action Mail Order Drug— skin care products (aloe vera gel, skin cleanser, bath oil, cocoa butter lotion, hand cream, lubricating lotion, vitamin E cream and oil) and grooming implements (tweezers, nail clippers, emery boards, nail files, scissors).

AARP Pharmacy Service— cosmetics and toiletries (Jean Nate' bath products, moisturizers, aloe vera,baby oil, cleansing lotion, bath soaps, shampoo, lipstick, nail care products, blusher, eyebrow and eyeliner pencils), and fragrances for women and men (Charlie, Tabu, Jean Nate', Jontue, Coty Emeraude, L'Aimant, Ciara, Stetson, and Canoe).

Harvest of Values— skin care and toiletries (hand and body moisture lotion, Vitamin E creme and oil, shampoo, bath and shower products, soap, antiperspirant).

Medi-Mail— toiletries, women's and men's fragrances, skin care products (aloe vera bath/shower gel, body lotion, moisturizer, soap, bath oil, baby oil, cornstarch talc, cocoa butter lotion, women's and men's copycat colognes).

XIV
Entertainment Bonanza:

Audio, TV, And Video Equipment

Shopping for consumer electronics can be a discouraging experience. Whether you are in the market for specific types of audio and video equipment, or a new TV, retail prices can be exorbitant. Mail-order shopping for such goods can bring back your smile because many companies offer well-below-retail prices. It doesn't matter what you're looking for— a big screen TV, camcorder, cassette deck, compact disc player, stereo system, VCR—you can order it at a super-low mail-order price.

Even though price is a major concern with this type of purchase, there are other things to consider before buying. You should never buy electronics without knowing exactly what you want and need. Smart shoppers make it a point to learn as much as they can about specific goods before ordering. The "Better Business Bureau A TO Z Buying Guide" (Henry Holt, 1990) can provide useful information you should consider before buying any consumer electronics product. The book should be available, along with other consumer publications, at your local public library.

Here are some general guidelines and tips for purchasing electronic equipment, such as TVs, video, and audio components:

1) The best way to select the equipment that's right for you is to compromise between the performance and features you want and the price you can realistically afford to pay. Comparison shopping is important in this stage of the decision-making process. Shop for the best prices, but also look for a high-quality picture or sound, easy-to-use controls, and readable displays.

2) Since discounting is common in audio and video products, you should expect to pay 25% and more below list price for most brands. Shop around until you find such discounts.

3) Find out about a store's return policy before you order. Also ask about restocking fees, if returns are accepted.

4) Don't buy "gray market goods". These products, sold by some mail-order companies and retailers, are foreign goods which have been imported through unauthorized channels. While gray market goods are often sold at bargain prices, they may wind up being virtually useless. That's because gray market goods may not operate on standard 110-volt U.S. current. They also may not have safety approval from Underwriters Laboratory (UL). Such goods seldom have a valid manufacturers warranty, and the instruction manual may not be in English.

The Audio Advisor, Inc.
225 Oakes S.W. Grand Rapids, MI 49503
Phone: (616) 451-3868 FAX: (616) 451-0709

If you need high end audio or video components, the Audio Advisor could be the solution. The company works with manufacturers and other retailers to get the goods you want, and then has them shipped directly to you. Mail-order shoppers can save up to 50% on some items. Brand names available, as well as sales policy information can be found in the company's brochure, which is available for $1.00.

You'll find components by Audio Quest, B & K, California Audio, Apogee, ADS, Adcom, dbx, Distech, Grado, Infinity, JVC, Magnavox, Merlin, Proton, Sony, Yamaha, and many other quality manufacturers.

Also available from the Audio Advisor are turntables, tuners, receivers, radios, amps, equalizers, speakers, headphones, cables and connectors, and reel-to-reel tape players, CD players, cassette players, and digital disc players.

Call or write the company (include a SASE) for a price quote and/or to inquire about the brochure. Pay by check, money order or major credit card.

Audio Unlimited

1203 Adams Ave. La Grande, OR 97850
Phone: (503) 963-5731

Since 1976, Audio Unlimited has been selling mid- and high-end home and auto audio components at a savings of from 15% to 25%. The company sells components by Altec, dbx, Advent, DCM, Grado, Infinity, JBL, Onkyo, Sony, Tech, and Pioneer.

In stock are car stereo systems (receivers, speakers, amplifiers, etc.) and home stereo systems, receivers, CD players, cassette decks, speakers, and much more.

No catalog is available but you can call or write for information on any available literature and/or a price quote (include a SASE). Pay by check, money order or major credit card. The company requires a minimum order of $35- - $100 with credit card orders.

Crutchfield Corporation

1 Crutchfield Park Charlottesville, VA 22906-6020
Phone: 800-336-5566

Crutchfield features car and home stereo components and video products at a savings of up to 40%. The company's free, 150-page catalog lists low, discount prices on a fine line of car audio components by Alphasonik, AR, Clarion, Jensen, JVC, Panasonic, Pioneer, Sony, and other top-of-the-line manufacturers. Home audio components by manufacturers such as Advent, AR, Bose, Dual, Infinity, JVC, Kenwood, Proton, and others are also available at low prices.

Crutchfield's stock of car audio components includes in-dash cassette receivers, CD changers, CD players, speakers, amplifiers, installation components (wiring, connectors, fuses, patch cords, cable), and antennas. Home audio equipment includes receivers, CD players, cassette decks, speakers, mini component systems, portables, and accessories (headphones, CD racks, stacked storage racks).

Crutchfield also offers CB radios, scanners, car alarm systems, and camcorders and video equipment (VCRs, laserdisc/CD players, TVs). Brand names in stock include Bel, Whistler, Mitsubishi, Cobra, Akai, Canon, and Sony.

Call the company for information and ask about the catalog. Satisfaction is guaranteed on every order. Returns are accepted within 30 days. Pay by check, money order or major credit card.

Illinois Audio, Inc.
1284 E. Dundee Road Palatine, IL 60067
Phone: (708) 934-9669 800-621-8042

Illinois Audio began selling audio and video equipment and components in the early 1970s. Over 20 years later, the company is still offering quality goods at savings of up to 40%.

Illinois Audio has in stock components and equipment by Shure, JVC, Sony, AIWA, Technics, Koss, Kenwood, Dual, AR, Tech, Discwasher, Maxell, Memorex, Scotch, Senheiser, Sharp, TDK, Toshiba, EPI, Fugi, Panasonic, Sansui, and other famous manufacturers.

You'll find compact disc players and changers, portable compact disc players, cassette decks, receivers, data recorders, turntables, loudspeakers, laser disc players, video tape recorders, stereo headphones, automotive electronics, reel to reel tapes, phono cartridges, and more in the company's free price list.

The price list is available free upon request. A price quote is available by phone or by letter. Authorized returns are accepted within 14 days (a 10% restocking fee is in effect on returns not being repaired or replaced). Pay by check, money order or major credit card.

International Electronic World
Moravia Center Industrial Park
Baltimore, MD 21206
Phone: (301) 448-9600

International Electronic World offers the finest audio and video components at an average savings of 30%. The company has been in business for over 40 years.

International's inventory features a full line of audio and video components by Bose, Advent, Magnavox, JVC, Panasonic, Sony, Onkyo, Harman Kardon, Tech, Infinity, JBL, Audio-Technica, and Zenith. In stock are receivers, speakers, CD players, amplifiers, VCRs, camcorders, cassette decks, and other related items.

Also in stock are audiotape, cables and connectors, and maintenance items (cleaners, tape head demagnetizers).

You can get a catalog free upon request. Get a price quote by phone or by mail with a SASE. Authorized returns are accepted. Pay by check, money order or major credit card.

S & S Sound City
58 W. 45TH St. New York, NY 10036-4280
Phone: (212) 575-0210

As the name implies, S & S sells audio components. The company also offers TVs and video equipment at competitive prices.

Among the items listed in the S & S brochure, you'll find TVs, video, and audio components (receivers, speakers, amplifiers, CD players, cassette decks, VCRs, camcorders) by Hitachi, G.E., NEC, Panasonic, Tech, Sharp, Sony, JVC, Akai, Magnavox, Fisher, RCA, Quasar, Zenith, Toshiba, Sanyo, Vector Research, and other manufacturers. The company also sells tape recorders, phone machines, security and surveillance equipment, and appliances (microwave ovens, air conditioners).

The S & S brochure is available free upon request. Get a price quote by phone or by mail with a SASE. Returns are accepted within 7 days. Pay by check, money order or major credit card.

For other listings of companies which sell audio, TV, and video equipment, see the "Appliances" section in this catalog. The listings include:

Bernie's Discount Center— sells name brand audio, TV, and video equipment.

E.B.A. Wholesale Corp.— sells TVs and video equipment by G.E., RCA, Sony, Sylvania, Sanyo, Quasar, Magnavox, and Zenith.

LVT Price Quote Hotline, Inc.— sells TVs and video equipment by Panasonic, Quasar, G.E., Magnavox, RCA, Sony, Zenith, and other top manufacturers.

Percy's Inc.— sells TVs, video equipment and tapes, and audio components. Name brands available include Magnavox, Panasonic, RCA, Quasar, Sharp, G.E., Zenith, and BOSE.

Irv Wolfson Company— sells TVs and video equipment by G.E., Panasonic, Sharp, and other top-of-the-line manufacturers.

Cambridge Sound Works
154 California St., Suite 200, Newton, MA 02158.
Phone: (800)-FOR-HIFI (307-4434)
FAX: (617) 332-9229

Cambridge Sound Works sells to you factory direct. That means you can save hundreds of dollars on quality entertainment systems. The company manufactures speakers and music systems designed by Henry Kloss (founder of AR, KLH, and Advent). The speakers and music systems are sold to you direct from the factory, cutting out the expence of a middleman.

Cambridge also sells components from Phillips, Pioneer, Denon, and many other famous manufacturers. A recent catalog listing showed an Ensemble II speaker system, factory direct at only $399.

Write or call the company for a free audio catalog. Pay by check, money order or major credit card.

Discount Music Supply
41 Vreeland Ave., Totowa, NJ 07512-1120
Phone: (201) 942-9411

Whether you are an accomplished musician or just a

novice, you'll enjoy browsing through the Discount Music Supply catalog. In it, you'll find name brand guitars, effects, drum machines, cables, strings, tuners, microphones, harmonicas, picks, guitar bags, mixers and speakers, amplifiers, pickups, and much more. If you play guitar, you'll find everything you need in the DMS catalog, and at discount prices. The company has been in business since 1986.

The Discount Music Supply catalog is available free upon request. Pay by check, money order, MasterCard or VISA.

Radar U.S.A.

1749 Golf Road #312, Mt. Prospect, IL 60056
Phone: (800) 777-6570

This company is a division of Landmark Electronics and has "electronics for all your needs". You'll find some of the lowest prices around on Personal stereos, portable CD players, CB radios,Casio car TVs, Southwestern Bell telephones, answering machines, Caller ID phones, and many other electronic goodies.

Of course Radar U.S.A, also features a full stock of radar detectors at "guaranteed lowest prices". In stock are quality products from Bel, Wideband, and Laser. There's also a selection of "undetectable" radar detectors, and you get Radar U.S.A.'s free one year extended warranty.

Call or write the company for a catalog. Returns are accepted within 30 days for a refund or an exchange. Pay by check, money order or major credit card.

Wisconsin Discount Stereo

2417 Badger Rd., Madison, WI 53713
Phone: (800) 356-9514; (608) 271-6889 [in WI]

For over 15 years, Wisconsin Discount Stereo has been providing home shoppers with discount bargains on stereo and video equipment and components. The company carries a large selection of quality brand-name electronics (no grey market items).

In stock at Wisconsin Discount Stereo are audo equipment and components, portable stereos, and video equipment by such quality manufacturers as Panasonic, RCA, JVC, Marantz, Sharp, Sansui, Kenwood, Sony, Teac, Toshiba, dbx, Zenith, and many others. You can expect savings of up to 50% and more on some items.

The company does not publish a regular catalog, but does publish flyers which list special buys. The flyers are free upon request. You can also call for discount price quotes. Satisfaction is guaranteed. Returns are accepted. Pay by check, money order, MasterCard or VISA.

XV
Farm & Garden Supplies and Equipment:

Flower bulbs, plants, seeds, and outdoor supplies

Mail-order shopping for garden seed, bulbs, live plants, supplies, tools, and equipment, can be very rewarding. Local retail outlets usually have a limited selection of standard goods and, of course, charge retail prices. Mail-order companies, however, can provide any type of seed, bulb or plant, and at prices far below average retail rates.

The companies listed in this section offer everything for your gardening and lawn care needs. Every type of seed, bulb, and plant imaginable, as well as fertilizers, soil conditioners, pest controls, tools, and equipment are available by mail-order at a considerable savings. However, before you order exotic seeds, bulbs, or plants, you should be certain they'll be able to survive in your particular climate (outdoor and indoor). Your public library should have several books on gardening which can provide you with valuable information. You can also contact your local extension office for advice and information.

Breck's U.S. Reservation Center
6523 North Galena Road Peoria, ILL 61632
Phone: (309) 689-3855

Since 1818, Breck's has been supplying gardeners with beautiful Dutch flower bulbs. Mail-order shoppers who order by the end of July, in time for fall delivery and planting, can save as much as 50%.

Breck's free, full-color catalog shows a fine selection of tulips (border tulips, white fire, parrot tulips, flaming parrot, pastels, giant tulips, economy tulip mixtures), daffodils, hyacinths, crocuses, amaryllis, lilies, irises, jonquils, and other beautiful flowers.

With every order, Breck's includes a copy of its illustrated Dutch Bulb Handbook. It's an invaluable gardening guide, full of tips from Dutch experts who show how to plant and care for all types of bulbs.

Call or write to request the free catalog. Satisfaction is guaranteed. Returns are accepted for a full refund, replacement or exchange. Pay by check, money order or major credit card.

Central Tractor Farm & Family Center
3915 Delaware Avenue Des Moines, IA 50316
Phone: 800-247-7508 FAX: (515) 266-2952

The Central Tractor Farm & Family Center has been in business since the mid 1930's, providing farm equipment and machine parts at savings of up to 30%. The company's free catalog lists a wide assortment of products for every farming need.

The catalog listings include brand-name goods from manufacturers such as Allis Chalmers, David Brown, John Deere, International Harvester, Case, Massey Ferguson, Oliver, Ford, Minneapolis Moline, White, and Homelite. The company's stock includes used parts for farm machines (new replacement parts are also available), chain saws, shop tools, products for livestock and dairy farmers, air compressors, welding equipment, and much more.

Request your free copy of the company's catalog by phone or by letter. Discounts are available on quantity orders. Pay by check, money order or major credit card.

The Cook's Garden
P.O. Box 535 Londonderry, VT 05148
Phone: (802) 824-3400 FAX: (802) 824-3027

The folks who publish the Cook's Garden catalog maintain trial gardens in order to gain first-hand knowledge of the products they offer. Those products include seeds for vegetables and flowers, and gardening supplies. The company has been in business for ten years and offers competitive prices on its products, and discounts of up to 20% on some quantity purchases.

The comprehensive Cook's Garden catalog lists a wide assortment of family seed packets, including such hard-to-find vegetables as scallions and celeriac, as well as garden regulars such as carrots, corn, beans, kale, lettuce, onions, peas, peppers, potatoes, radishes, spinach, salad greens, squash, tomatoes, turnips, and many others. Also available are seeds for planting cut flowers, everlasting flowers, flowering vines, sunflowers, and edible flowers (Nasturtium, Gem Marigold).

Supplies and tools listed in the catalog include fertilizer, wooden plant tags, seeding mix, rain gauges, harvesting knives, garden scissors, hand-held cultivators, and pocket soil thermometers. There's also a selection of gardening books as well as several tasty, easy-to-prepare recipes.

The Cook's Garden does not sell seed that has been treated with fungicide and insecticide.

Call or write the company to request a free copy of the

catalog. Pay by check, money order or major credit card (minimum order of $20.00 with credit cards).

Dutch Gardens, Inc.
P.O. Box 200 Adelphia, NJ 07710
Phone: (201) 780-2713

The Dutch Gardens catalog features over 100 full-color pages of the world's most beautiful flower bulbs and perennials. The company will ship top quality flower bulbs and perennials directly from Holland to you at close to wholesale prices. You can expect savings of up to 50%.

The catalog shows a selection of tulips, narcissus, daffodils, hyacinths, crocuses, anemone, alliums, amaryllis, and other flower bulbs. Dahlias, begonias, gladiola, and other bulbs are available for spring planting. The catalog also provides information on planting and caring for the bulbs.

Bonuses or discounts are available on quantity orders. Call or write the company to request a free catalog. A minimum order of $20 is required. Pay by check, money order or major credit card.

Gardens Alive!
5100 Schenley Place Lawrenceburg, IN 47025
Phone: (812) 537-8650

Gardens Alive offers "environmentally responsible organic products for a healthy garden". The company features products for organic lawn care, such as Lawns Alive! and Turfs Alive!, which allow you to stop using chemical fertilizers, pesticides, and herbicides.

Other products available from Gardens Alive include Sunspray Ultra-Fine Horticultural Spray Oil, which kills pests but won't harm plants; Beneficial Nematodes Hb to eradicate grubs in your lawn; organic plant food; soil conditioner; row covers; insect barriers; organic rose and flower dust; weed barrier mats; Japanese beetle traps; and birdfeeders. The company also features organic flea and tick spray, pet food supplements, herbal flea collars, shampoo, and soap for pets.

Gardens Alive also offers club membership. The membership includes a free one year subscription to the "Stay Organic Newsletter", and a 10% discount off the catalog price of everything you buy from Gardens Alive. The annual membership fee is $12.50.

Call or write the company to request a catalog. Satisfaction is guaranteed. Pay by check, money order or major credit card.

Gardener's Supply Company
128 Intervale Road Burlington, VT 05401
Phone: 800-444-6417 FAX: (802) 660-4600

Gardener's supply is in its 10th year of providing a full line of gardening equipment and supplies. A recent 63-page catalog lists everything for the garden, from fertilizer to tiller/cultivators. Prices are competitive with those of other companies selling comparable goods.

Gardener's can choose from a selection of garden hose and sprinklers, rain gauges, water garden kits, watering cans, organic fertilizer, spring cover crops (New Zealand White Clover, Buckwheat), hand tools (weeders, trowels, pruners), planters, mulches, bamboo stakes, composters and composting kits, and much more. Gardener's Supply also offers lawn care products, including all-organic lawn fertilizer, Trim-A-Lawn mowers (battery and gas models), reel mowers, leaf rakes, trimmers, edgers, and seed spreaders.

You'll also find an affordably-priced tiller/cultivator, which is versatile and easy to handle. Tools available include garden rakes, forks, spades, hoes, mattock, and soil diggers.

You can get a complete listing of the Garden Supply Company's products by calling or writing the company to request a free catalog (The company also manufactures greenhouses and provides a home greenhouse catalog free upon request). Satisfaction is guaranteed. Returns are accepted for replacement, credit, or refund. Pay by check, money order, or major credit card.

Gurney's Seed & Nursery Company
110 Capital Street Yankton, SD 57079
Phone: (605) 665-1671 (customer service)
(605) 665-1930
(orders) FAX: (605) 665-9718

Gurney's has been "helping gardeners grow for 127 years". The company specializes in garden seed, plants, and nursery stock at savings of 20% and more on some items.

A recent catalog listed an assortment of seed packets available, including cucumber, onion, corn, beans, peas, carrots, lettuce, radishes, cabbage, spinach, eggplant, cauliflower, okra, herbs and seasonings, and many others. Gurney's also has a good selection of vegetable plants including tomato, pepper, asparagus, and onion; rhubarb plants; potato sets; and strawberry plants.

Flower growers will find an ample supply of seed and spring bulbs available from Gurney's. Houseplants (African Violets, dwarf fruit trees), plant food, sprayers and dusters, Japanese beetle traps, garden hose, Bag balm, mulches, birdfeeders, shade trees, flowering trees, and fruit trees are all in stock as well.

Call or write Gurney's Supply Company to request a free catalog. Satisfaction is guaranteed. Returns are accepted for replacement, credit or refund. Pay by check, money order or major credit card. (No C.O.D. orders.)

A.M. Leonard, Inc.

6665 Spiker Road P.O. Box 816 Piqua, Ohio 45356
Phone: (513) 773-2694 (information) 800-543-8955
(orders) FAX: 800-443-0633

A.M. Leonard offers quality tools and supplies for "nurserymen, landscapers, arborists, contractors, and gardeners". You'll find affordable prices on everything for your gardening needs, from shovels to hedge shears.

A recent A.M. Leonard catalog featured a representative selection of the hundreds of products in stock, including spreaders and cultivators, wheelbarrows, planting tools (seeder/feeder, high wheel cultivator, seedling setter blade, bulb planters), spading and manure rakes, grass and weed cutting tools (shears, edgers, trimmers, scythes), and gardening tools (trowels, soil knives, hand cultivators, asparagus knives, dandelion diggers, weeders, hoes). Also available are power sprayers and lawn applicators, watering cans, hose, hose reel, sprinklers, chippers, shredders, composters, logsplitters, soil thermometers, rain gauges, and safety equipment and supplies (goggles, respirators, ear protection, etc).

A.M. Leonard's catalog is available free upon request. Quantity discounts are available. Authorized returns are accepted, but are subject to a restocking charge. A minimum order charge of $3.00 is assessed on all orders totaling less that $20.00 in merchandise. Pay by check, money order or major credit card.

Mellinger's

2382 MH Range Road North Lima, OH 44452
Phone: (216) 549-9861

Mellinger's publishes a versatile and informative "Home & Garden" catalog, which features 120 pages, listing over 4000 items including bulbs, seeds, live plants, garden equipment and tools, and reference books. The company has been in business for 67 years, and provides the catalog free upon request. Mellinger's also publishes a "Greenhouse Flyer", listing all sizes, styles, and types of greenhouses for sale. Mail-order shoppers can expect savings of 40% and more on many items.

The company's catalog lists an array of gardening products, including herb plants, vegetable seeds and plants, flower seeds and bulbs, potted trees and shrubs, fruit trees, and tropical plants. You'll also find plant fertilizers, soil additives, animal and insect repellents, pruning and grafting tools, spades, cultivators, hoes, watering systems, planters, flower boxes, and many other gardening tools and supplies. Bird lovers can choose from a selection of feeders and feed, also in stock at Mellinger's.

Call or write the company to request your free catalog. Pay by check, money order or major credit card (the company requires a minimum order of $10.00 with credit cards).

Nichols Garden Nursery
1190 North Pacific Highway Albany, OR 97321-4598
Phone: (503) 928-9280 FAX: (503) 967-8406

Nichols Garden Nursery, in Oregon's famous Willamette Valley, is a herb nursery with a retail store as well as a 68-page catalog for mail-order shoppers. The company has been in the seed and nursery business for over 40 years, offering gardeners herb, vegetable, and flower varieties at reasonable prices.

The catalog lists a good selection of garden seeds including artichokes, beans, beets, broccoli, Brussels sprouts, cabbage, cantaloupes, carrots, celery, collards, corn, gourmet baby vegetables, herbs, kale, lettuce, leeks, mustard greens, marigolds, okra, peas, squash, tomatoes, wildflower seeds, and many others. There's also a selection of plants, bulbs, roots, and tubers including comfrey, garlic, herbs, hop roots, horseradish roots, shallots, and more.

You can also order garden equipment and supplies such as pruning shears (both right- and left-handed), garden weeders, metal plant markers, diamond mesh garden netting, trowels, and hand cultivators.

Call or write the company to inquire about the catalog. Price quotes on quantity orders are also available by phone or by mail. The company guarantees that all seeds and products are of good quality. Refunds are accepted for exchange, credit, or refund. Pay by check, money order or major credit card.

Rosehill Farm
Gregg Neck Road Galena, MD 21635
Phone: (301) 648-5538

The company's free color catalog provides a thorough inspection of standard- size mini roses as well as sweetheart sizes, micro-minis, and climbers. Hanging basket type mini roses, including yellow, gold, blush, white, pink, orange, apricot, and red varieties are also in stock. The catalog also provides useful information on planting and plant care.

Rosehill Farm offers quantity discounts. Call or write to request a free catalog. Returns are accepted within 60 days for replacement (tags must accompany each item returned). Pay by check, money order or major credit card (a minimum order of $20 is required with credit cards).

Van Dyck's Flower Farms, Inc.
U.S. Reservation Center P.O. Box 430-4022
Brightwaters, NY 11718-0430

Van Dyck's offers wholesale prices on small quantities of superior Dutch bulbs. All orders are delivered directly to your door. The company's free catalog lists a huge selection of the best hand-selected Dutch bulbs direct from the growing fields in Holland. Tulips, gladiola, hyacinths, crocuses, and many other Dutch bulbs are available at wholesale prices.

Write the company and request a free catalog. Pay by check, money order or major credit card.

Van Enselen Inc.
Stillbrook Farm 313 Maple Street Litchfield, CT 06759
Phone: (203) 567-8734

Dutch bulbs at wholesale prices are available from Van Enselen. The company's free catalog features a good selection of tulips, daffodils, crocuses, lilies, hyacinths, irises, muscari, paperwhites, amaryllis, and exotic bulbs. Mammoth Darwin hybrid tulips are also available.

Write or call the company to request the free catalog and wholesale price list for fall planting. Pay by check, money order or major credit card.

Daylily Discounters
Rt. 2, Box 24, Alachua, FL 32615
Phone: (904) 462-1539

This company specializes in award winning daylily and iris plants. Since 1988, Daylily Discounters have been providing daylilies in a veritable rainbow of colors, and in a wide range of sizes. You save because you buy direct from the grower.

The Daylily catalog is available for $3.00. The catalog features over 100 color photographs as well as planting guides.Pay by check, money order or major credit card.

Flickinger's Nursery
P.O. Box 245, Sagamore, PA 16250

Phone: (412) 783-6528; (412) 397-4953

When a company has been in business for almost 50 years, it must be doing something right. Customer satisfaction has long been the strong suit of Flickinger's Nursery, providing quality seedlings at wholesale prices. In business since 1948, Flickinger's sells pine, spruce, fir, hemlock, and many other seedlings. Call or write for a free catalog and wholesale price list.

Pay by check, money order, MasterCard or VISA.

NOTES

_____

_____

_____

_____

_____

_____

XVI

Foods And Beverages

Dried fruits and nuts, fancy gourmet items, herbs, spices, coffee, and more

The firms listed in this section offer a veritable smorgasboard of culinary delights. You can shop by mail and order Caspian Beluga caviar, dried fruit, nuts, candy, deli meats, escargot, cheese, coffee and tea, winter squash, mushrooms, olives, and many other tasty and healthful foods.

While the mail-order savings vary from company to company and product to product, you can expect to save up to 80% on some items. It doesn't matter if you have a taste for gourmet and exotic foods, or if you prefer organically grown fruits and vegetables, you can get it by mail.

Mail-order shoppers should keep in mind the weather and the season when ordering foods. Avoid ordering perishable items (soft cheese, fruits, vegetables, uncured meats) during the hot summer months. Many companies will not ship certain products during warm weather, and those that do will probably advise you to have the goods shipped by an express service, and to consume them immediately.

Bates Brothers Nut Farm, Inc.
15954 Woods Valley Road

Valley Center, CA 92082
Phone: (619) 749-3333

The Bates Brothers sell nuts of all kinds, and dried fruits. You can expect savings of up to 40% on some items, compared with average prices of many firms selling comparable goods.

The specialty of this company is nuts— peanuts, cashews, walnuts, almonds, pecans, macadamias, filberts, pistachios, and pignolias. You can get nuts raw, roasted and salted, and smoked. Saltless nuts of all types are also available. The dried fruit selection includes banana chips, figs, apricots, raisins, dates, pineapple, and coconut. Trail-mix, granola, wheat germ snacks, popcorn, taffy, English toffee, nut brittle, and other taste treats are sold as well.

A price list is available by mail with a SASE. Pay by check, money order or major credit card. C.O.D. orders are accepted.

Caviarteria, Inc.
29 E. 60th St. New York, NY 10022
Phone: 800-422-8427 (212) 759-7410 (in NY)
FAX: (718) 482-8985

If you have a taste for caviar but find typical caviar prices distasteful, Caviarteria may be the company you're looking for. This family-run business offers caviar of all grades and other gourmet foods at below average prices. You can save up to 40% less than typical "caviar" prices.

The company has in stock all grades of Caspian Beluga and Sevruga caviar, as well as American sturgeon, whitefish, and salmon caviar. Caviar servers are also available at below average prices. Other gourmet selections in stock include tinned white and black Italian truffles, Norwegian gravlax, salmon steaks, Scottish salmon, and candied chestnuts.

Call or write for a free catalog. Satisfaction is guaranteed. Pay by check, money order or major credit card. Caviarteria requires a minimum order of $25 with credit cards.

A Cook's Wares

3270 37th St. Extension
Beaver Falls, PA 15010-1263
Phone: (412) 846-9490

While the catalog ($1.50) lists an impressive line of cookware and kitchen utensils at a savings of up to 60%, A Cook's Wares also offers a fine selection of vinegars and mustards as well as other foods and condiments. The company sells vinegars and mustards by Paul Corcellet, Silver Palate mustards, condiments by Blanchard & Blanchard, herbs and spices, olive spread, sun-dried tomatoes, tahini, and other foodstuffs. There are also dessert sauces, preserves, maple syrup, and chocolate by Tobler, Callebart, Ghiradelli, and Lindt (for cooking and eating).

Cookware in stock includes copper pots and pans by Mauviel and other items by Chantal, Cuisinart, Vollrath, Leyse, and Spring Copper. Bakeware, cookie cutters, mixers, coffee makers, grinders, and food processors are also sold. Send $1.50 for the catalog. Satisfaction is guaranteed. Pay by check, money order or major credit card.

Diamond Organics

Freedom, CA 95019
Phone: 800-922-2396

Diamond organics offers a healthful selection of fresh, organically grown fruits and vegetables. The company will ship these fruits and vegetables direct to your door, at competitive prices.

You can order organically grown winter squash, roots, edible flowers, apples, pears, citrus fruits, specialty greens, sprouts, and a number of vegetables. The company also has gift packs of organically grown fruits and vegetables.

Call or write the company for more information and to request a free catalog. The company has no minimum order requirement. Pay by check, money order or major credit card.

Jaffee Brothers, Inc.
P.O. Box 636 Valley Center, CA 92082-0636
Phone: (619) 749-1133 FAX: (619) 749-1282

If you're just now switching to organically grown food, Jaffee Brothers can get you started in the right direction. The company has been doing business for 45 years and can supply you with plenty of healthful, organically and naturally grown foods. You can expect savings of 30% and more on some items.

Look through the company's free catalog and choose from organically and naturally grown and produced beans, nuts, seeds, fruit, and butter. Also in stock are figs, dried peaches, raisins, dates, nuts, papaya, whole-wheat pasta, brown rice, peas, juices, olives, mushrooms, herb teas, coconut, and many other healthful and delicious foods.

Jaffe's catalog is available free upon request. Quantity discounts are available. Pay by check, money order, MasterCard or VISA.

Simpson & Vail, Inc.
38 Clinton Street Pleasantville, NY 10570-0309
Phone: (914) 747-1336

Over 60 years of supplying gourmet coffee drinkers with their favorite coffee is an impressive recommendation for Simpson & Vail. The company continues to flourish by selling its wide selection of coffees and teas at savings of up to 30%.

Coffee lovers can choose from straight coffees and blends, including American, French, Italian, and Viennese roasts; Hawaiian kuna; and Kenya AA. There's also plenty of decaffeinated coffees such as American-style roast and mocha java among the more than 40 coffees in stock. Coffee makers are also available. All coffee beans are ground to order.

If coffee isn't your cup of tea, Simpson & Vail offers over 80 types of tea. In stock are favorite teas from England and the Orient, as well as gourmet blends such as almond, chocolate and chocolate mint, which are all naturally flavored. To complement your selection of tea, the company also offers accessories such as mugs, tea cozies, canisters, tea bricks, tea towels, and kettles.

The company's catalog is free upon request. Quarterly flyers are also available to Simpson & Vail customers. Pay by check, money order or major credit card.

Sunnyland Farms, Inc.
Albany, GA 31706-8200
Phone: (912) 883-3085

Jane and Harry Wilson began selling pecans from their orchard over 40 years ago. Today, their company, Sunnyland Farms, offers mail-order shoppers plain and fancy pecans, assorted nuts roasted and raw, candies, cakes, cookies, and dried fruit. Prices are competitive and quantity discounts are available.

Pecan products include pecans in-the-shell, pecan halves, pecan pieces, and pecan meal. Jumbo cashews, peanuts, Sunnyland Royal Mix (pecans, cashews, almonds, midget brazils, hazelnuts), colossal Pistachios, Macadamias, and other "mixed delights" are also available.

For your sweet tooth, you can order pecan, peanut, and cashew brittle, pecan pralines and log rolls, coco-pecans, pistachio bark, milk chocolate pecan bark, and candied pecan halves. There's also a selection of "homemade" cakes and cookies, including rum crunch loaf cake, chocolate pecan loaf, macadamia loaf cake, oatmeal cookies, and fancy fruit cookies. Dried fruits include apricots, dates, figs, seedless raisins, pitted prunes, peaches, pears, and others. There's also a selection of specialty foods available— pure maple syrup, honey, peach jam, mayhaw jelly, sweet onion relish, and genuine wild rice.

The company's catalog is free upon request. Satisfaction is guaranteed. Pay by check, money order or major credit card.

Zabar's & Co., Inc.
2245 Broadway New York, NY 10024
Phone: 800-221-3347 (212) 787-2000 (in NY)

Zabar's is a super deli offering gourmet foods and a selection of cookware and housewares. This company has been in business for almost 60 years, and you can expect quality service and savings of up to 50% on some items.

Smoked salmon (Norwegian, Scottish, and Irish) is among the gourmet delicacies offered by Zabar's. A recent catalog also featured escargot, preserves, Brie, plum pudding, chocolates, cookies and confections, olive oil, deli meats, pates, and other gourmet specialties by Bahlsen, Lindt, Droste, Tiptree, and other top names.

You'll also find hotel-weight copper pots and pans by Mauviel, coffee makers, food processors, microwave ovens, and other cookware and houseware goods. Brand names include Cuisinart, Revere Ware, Farberware, Calphalon, Sharp, Braun, Toshiba, and Robot Coupe, among others.

Call or write (with a SASE) to request a free catalog or to get a price quote on cookware not listed in the catalog. Pay by check, money order or major credit card. The company requires a minimum order of $10.00.

XVII

General Merchandise and Buying Clubs

Great mail-order values on almost everything

Some companies sell such a wide variety of goods, it's like shopping at a "general store". The firms listed in this section fit that category, and offer everything from designer bed linens to fireplace tools. "One-stop" shopping by mail is conceivable, since these firms each feature such a wide selection of products. The goods offered are all top-quality and savings can be 60% and more.

You can also get discounts on a wide range of products and services by enrolling in a buying club. These clubs charge a yearly membership fee which entitles you to discounts on prescription-filling services, health and beauty aids, jewelry, computers, and many other products and services.

Bennet Brothers, Inc.
30 E. Adams Street Chicago, IL 60603
Phone: (312) 263-4800 FAX: (312) 621-1669

This Chicago-based company has been in business since the early 1900s and offers a selection of jewelry, appliances, electronics, sporting goods, luggage, and many other goods. Bennet's prices are competitive compared with typical retail prices on comparable goods, and in some cases you can save up to 30% and more.

Bennet's annual catalog ($5.00 refundable) lists hundreds of name brand products, ideal for personal use and/or gift-giving. There's a large selection of jewelry, including bracelets, necklaces, wedding and engagement rings, pearls, earrings, and rings. Watches by Benrus, Seiko, Timex, Armitron, Pulsar, Jules Jurgensen, Hamilton, and other manufacturers are also in stock.

Past catalogs have also shown silverware, tea sets, fine china, and kitchen appliances (toasters, blenders, can openers, etc.), microwave ovens, vacuum cleaners, sewing machines, linens, luggage, briefcases, and exercise equipment.

Bennet Brothers also sells a selection of audio, TV, and video goods including stereo systems and components, portable cassette players, and TV and video equipment. Other products in stock include telephones and answering machines, home security systems, cameras, telescopes, microscopes, calculators, typewriters,toys, sporting equipment (fishing gear, basketballs, golf clubs, volleyballs), and power and hand tools.

Send $5.00 to receive the company's current catalog. Authorized returns are accepted within 10 days for exchange or credit. Pay by check, money order or major credit card.

Consumer Thrift Club
P.O. Box 9394 Minneapolis, MN 55440
Phone: 800-562-8888 (customer service)
800-526-4848 (information)

This buying club has arrangements with many different firms to provide goods and services to its members at discount prices. Membership in the Consumer Thrift Club costs $49.95

per year. The membership entitles you to prescription-filling services at discount rates, as well as savings on home furnishings, appliances, electronics, jewelry, computers, musical instruments, and many other products and services. You can also get savings on car pricing and dealer referral services, car rentals, hotel accommodations, moving services, and real estate broker referrals with Consumer Thrift Club membership. Club membership also allows you to participate in "Coupon Exchange" for added savings on foods, cleaning products, and health and beauty needs. You'll also receive a quarterly publication which provides updates on various coupon specials.

The club does not receive commissions from the sale of any products or services— its financial benefit is derived from its memberships.

Call or write the company to request more information.

Grand Finale
P.O. Box 620049
Dallas, TX 75262-0049

Grand Finale features an assortment of clearances, closeouts, and special purchases made from manufacturers and gift houses. Mail-order shoppers can expect savings of up to 70% off list or original selling prices on some items.

The company has offered toys, designer bed linens, table linens, jewelry, teapots, pillows, leather desk sets, luggage, men's and women's apparel, cookware, and hundreds of other items. All products are of good quality.

Send $3.00 for a year's subscription to the company's catalog. Satisfaction is guaranteed. Returns are accepted for exchange, credit, or refund (except on customized or personalized goods). Pay by check, money order or major credit card.

Lillian Vernon

Virginia Beach, VA 23479-0002
Phone: (804) 430-5555 (orders) (804) 430-1500
(information, customer service) FAX: (804) 427-7900

Lillian Vernon has a 41 year tradition of offering hundreds of products at affordable prices. A recent catalog listed products and gift ideas including toys and games, jewelry, leather goods, collectible, porcelain dinnerware, fireplace tools and accessories, pet supplies, travel accessories, and many other products. Some items were priced at a savings of up to 50%.

Past catalogs have shown fine porcelain mugs and dinnerware, dessert plates, flatware, children's tea sets, punch bowl sets, decorative plates, hand- painted wood figurine collectible, and solid glass paperweights. Also available are travel accessories, including travel shirt bags, garment bags, shoe bags, travel alarm clocks, laundry bags, car organizers, compact emergency snow shovels, and car clipboards with lights.

Lillian Vernon also features fireplace tools and accessories such as shovels, pokers, brushes, log turners, hearth mats, and canvas carriers for bringing in firewood. Sporting equipment in stock includes golf accessories (drawstring golf tee pouch, golf shoe totes, and putting sets), fly wallets for fly fishing lures, and wall-mount sports racks.

Leather money clips, portfolios, safety lights, mini screwdriver sets, TV/VCR tables, bookends, watches, bath robes, toiletries, umbrellas, leather wallets, purses, earrings, and hundreds of other items for every member of the family are in stock as well. The company will personalize items at no extra charge.

Call or write the company to request a current catalog. Satisfaction is guaranteed. Returns are accepted for replacement, credit, or refund. Ask about quantity discounts. Pay by check, money order or major credit card.

Whole Earth Access
2950 7th Street Berkeley, CA 94701
Phone: (415) 845-3000

Whole Earth Access began doing business in 1969, and offers a selection of general merchandise from baby care products to inflatable. You can save 50% and more on some mail-order purchases.

The company's catalog ($7.00) features almost 500 pages of general merchandise bargains, including men's and women's clothing, overalls, boots, hand and power tools, chain saws, oil lamps, ceiling fans, and optics. Name brands available include Lee, Levis, Osh kosh, Carhartt, Frye, Homelite, Aladdin, Hunter, Celestron, and Nikon.

Appliances by Hamilton Beach, Henckels, KitchenAid, Melitta, and Cuisinart are also sold. Past catalogs have shown food processors, rototillers and other equipment for gardeners, saws and other home carpentry equipment, energy saving equipment, and more.

Send $7.00 to Whole Earth Access for the latest catalog. The catalog is also available in some bookstores, but the cover price is about $15.00. Customers in good standing receive regular flyers with product updates. Authorized returns are accepted. There is a minimum order requirement of $20. Pay by check, money order or major credit card.

Damark International, Inc.
7101 Winnetka Ave. N., Brooklyn Park, MN 55428
Phone: (800) 729-900 [order]; (612) 535-8880
[customer service]FAX: (612) 531-0281

Damark, " The Great Deal Company", has been in business since 1986 and offers hundreds of brand name items at below dealer cost. You can find everything from computers to oriental rugs at prices well below suggested retail.

Recent Damark catalogs feature Smith Corona word processors for just $299.99; Citizen, 24 pin Dot Matrix printers for $269.99; Oriental rugs, available in Kirman, Chow, and Chinese designs, in sizes 2' by 8' to 8'by 11', as low as $29.99; A PC Partner factory serviced 386SX computer with 40 mb hard drive and 14" color VGA monitor for under $700; top grain leather bomber jackets for under $90; Quicken financial management software, Ver. 5.0 for under $30; Bushnell Spectator Zoom binoculars (repackaged demonstration models) for less than $70; American Flyer 54" garmet bag and pullman suitcase $89.99, and GE 12-number memory phone with digital answering machine for $39.99.

Damark also has in stock Packard Bell computers; office furniture and electronics; TVs and accessories; camcorders; VCRs; stereo systems; speakers; cameras; automotive accessories; home fitness equipment; sports equipment; personal care products; bedding; luggage; and much more.

Damark also sells an assortment of factory serviced (reconditioned) items. The company's purchasing power enables them to buy factory serviced goods at liquidation savings, meaning you get quality products at below original wholesale.
Factory serviced values are available on everything from word processors to carpet cleaning machines.

Damark's "The Great Deal Catalog" is available free upon request. Satisfaction is guaranteed. Returns are accepted within 30 days for a refund or exchange. Drop shipping is available on some items. Pay by check, money order or major credit card. Damark also has a 4-payment installment plan.

Durham Wholesale
Box 132, Plainview, TX 789073
Phone: (806) 293-8909

Durham offers thousands of products at wholesale and below prices. The company has been in business since 1988, providing wholesale bargains on games, gift items, carpeting, household products, beepers, software, seasonal items, scanners, stereos, automotive products, security items, computers and office supplies.

The Durham Wholesale catalog is priced at $10. Call or write the company for more information.

Harriet Carter
Dept. 43, North Wales, PA 19455
Phone: (215) 361-5122; (215) 361- 5151 [orders, 24 hours-a-day, 7 days-a-week]

Harriet Carter has been offering a variety of distinctive gifts since 1958. If gift-giving has you stumped— you're not sure what to get, and you're on a limited budget—Harriet Carter can be the solution. In stock are thousands of unique and delightful gift ideas, all at the lowest possible prices. You'll find savings of at least 50% on some items.

A recent 120-page catalog listed a selection of gift ideas for people of all ages. Gift ideas for children include Barney towels (featuring America's favorite purple dinosaur), battery operated Top Gun Robot Cop (for less than $15), personalized sports wallets (boys and girls), glow-in-the-dark teddy bears, toy cars, wooden toys, giant marble raceways, and many more items. Gift ideas for grownups include T-shirts, books, videos, jewelry, bells, VCR stands, umbrellas, canvas totes, mugs, treadmills, alarm clocks, porcelain lamps, body pillows, baseball cards, caps, make-up mirrors, remote controls, Hummel stationery, andhundreds of other items.

Call or write the company to request a catalog. Returns are accepted for a refund. There's a minimum charge order of $15. Pay check, money order or major credit card.

Oriental Trading Co.
4206 S. 108th St., Omaha, NE 68137-1215
Phone: (402) 331-5511; (800) 327-9678

The Oriental Trading Co.'s wholesale catalog features over 2500 inexpensive "fun" items. The company has been offering a variety of toys, giftware, balloons, and novelties since 1950. Home shoppers can also choose from a selection of jewelry, sunglasses, notepads, plush animals, pencils, erasers, party supplies, bulk candies, stationery, traditional holiday decor, and hundreds of other items.

Oriental Trading Co.'s products are perfect for holidays, gifts, parties, and giveaways. Call or write the company to get a free catalog. Pay by check, money order or major credit card.

The Paper Wholesaler
795 N.W. 72nd St., Miami, FL 33150
Phone: (305) 836-1400; (305) 651-6900

You can get discounts of up to 30% on quantity orders of party and entertaining supplies, and other general merchandise from the Paper Wholesaler. The company has been satisfying customers since the mid-1940's.

The Paper Wholesaler can supply you with an assortment of paper plates and napkins for any occasion (birthdays, weddings, receptions, showers, etc.). Also available are plastic cutlery and cups, place mats, doilies, and tablecloths. For party decorating, the company can provide crepe paper, balloons, streamers, favors, party hats, and many other novelties. Other merchandise includes candles, cocktail napkins, gift bags, wrapping paper, guest towels, bows and ribbons, and a collection of unique and clever invitations.

Caterers and restauratuers can choose from a selection of cake pans, cake decorating supplies, ice scoops, syrup pitchers, deli and bakery containers, condiments, and snacks.

The company's catalog provides a good representation of products available, as well as tips on party planning. Satisfaction is guaranteed. Returns are accepted within 30 days for refund, exchange or credit. Pay by check, money order, MasterCard or VISA.

NOTES

_____

_____

_____

_____

_____

_____

_____

_____

_____

XVIII

Hardware, Tools, Electronics, Safety, Security, and Industrial Goods

Do-it-yourself home improvements, maintenance, and repairs require the proper tools and hardware. The listings in this section can provide mail-order savings on everything you need to get the job done right. You can find bargain prices on power and hand tools for every need. There's also supplies for loggers (chain saws, log splitters, etc.,) and repair and replacement parts for all types of machinery, including lawnmowers, snowmobiles, snow throwers, and garden tractors.

Workers, whether in a shop or home garage, should always exercise safety precautions and use safety equipment. Many of the companies in this section also sell respirators, goggles, ear protection, dust masks, and other protective gear. Don't overlook such items when ordering tools and hardware for do-it-yourself work.

The Bevers
P.O. Box 12 Wills Point, TX 75169-0012
Phone: (214) 272-8370

Since 1977, The Bevers have been supplying mail-order shoppers with quality hardware and woodworking parts. The company offers savings of up to 50% on a wide range of goods for the home handyman and hobbyist.

The Bevers' catalog ($2.00, refundable) shows a representative selection of the many products in stock for use in household repairs, do-it-yourself creations, and woodworking. The stock includes round and flathead screws, machine screws, lag screws, washers, eye bolts, screw hooks, cotter pins, clamps, picture hangers, sandpaper drums, doweling drill bits, hinges, and many other hardware items.

For those people into woodworking, The Bevers has wooden parts for repairing furniture and making toys. You'll find wooden knobs and pulls, peg boards, screw-hole buttons, toy wheels, turned finials and spindles, and wooden game pieces.

Send $2.00 for the catalog. You can also get a price quote by phone or by letter with a SASE if you are inquiring about a quantity order. Pay by check, money order or major credit card.

Leichtung Workshops
4944 Commerce Parkway Cleveland, OH 44128
Phone: 800-321-6840 (order) 800-542-4467
(product information) FAX: (216) 464-6764

Leichtung offers woodworking tools and supplies at low mail-order prices. The company invites you to check out its low prices on everything from router bits to framing clamps.

Past Leichtung catalogs have shown router accessories (bits, trimmers, letter and number templates, plug cutters, depth gauges, tables), power carving sets, jointers, table and radial-arm saws, saw blades, sharpening tools, hammers, wood bits, metal bits, drum sanders, file sets, hand tools, miniature hand drills, screwdriver sets, and many other tools and accessories. There are also patterns and hardware for building work benches, American clock kits, musical jewelry box kits, and die-cast metal 1950s style bike kits.

The company's catalog is free upon request. Satisfaction is guaranteed. Returns are accepted within 90 days for a full refund. Pay by check, money order or major credit card. No C.O.D. orders are accepted.

Manufacturer's Supply
P.O. Box 157 Dorchester, WI 54425-0157
Phone: 800-826-8563

Finding replacement parts for any type of machine can be a real hassle. You may be able to cut down on the time and expense involved by ordering replacement parts through Manufacturer's Supply. This company can get you virtually any part for any machine, and at a savings of up to 50% below list or comparable retail prices.

Manufacturer's Supply stocks replacement parts for standard and riding lawnmowers, snowmobiles, snow throwers, chain saws, motor cycles, three-wheel vehicles, rototillers, trimmers, and other machines. The parts stock includes sprockets, hubs, wheels, roller chain, bearing kits, clutches, belts, carburetor parts, air filters, starter springs, and more. Snowmobile owners can find such replacement parts as carburetors, fuel filters, cleats, tracks, pistons, gaskets, fan belts, and engines.

The company publishes a free catalog which emphasizes snowmobiles. There's also a larger catalog (400 pages) with a more comprehensive listing of the available replacement parts in stock. The larger catalog is available for $3.00. You can also get a price quote by phone or by mail with a SASE. Pay by check, money order or major credit card. The company requires a minimum order of $10.

Northern
P.O. Box 1499 Burnsville, MN 55337-0499
Phone: 800-533-5545 FAX: (612) 894-0083

Household handymen and pros alike will enjoy looking through Northern's free catalog. The company offers an outstanding selection of hydraulics, machine parts, and logging equipment— all quality products at discount prices. Save up to 50% on some items.

A recent 147-page catalog lists several pages of hydraulics, including pumps, motors and valves, cylinders, strainers, and filters. Logging gear in stock includes chain saws by Homelite and McCulloch, Oregon saw chain, hydraulic log splitters, pruners, grinders, files, and safety equipment (face shields, hearing protectors, safety helmets). Hand tools featured in the catalog include pliers, ChannelLocks, Vise-Grips, hammers, screwdriver sets, surveying equipment, wrenches, chisels, socket sets, clamps, tin snips, pipe cutters, air tools (grinders, hammers, drills, ratchets, sanders, grease guns), hacksaws, and power paint sprayers.

The catalog also lists blowers, chipper/shredders, barrel stove kits, heaters, tarps and cover repair kits, vacuums, air compressors, water heaters, propane tanks, tractors, cultivators, trimmers, tillers, sprayers and other farm and garden equipment. Safety and security equipment, machine parts, go carts, and hundreds more items are available from Northern.

The catalog is free upon request. Authorized returns are accepted within 30 days. Pay by check, money order or major credit card.

Sara Glove Company
117 Benedict Street P.O. Box 1940
Waterbury, CT 06722-   1940
Phone: (203) 574-4090

Whether you're working in a shop or in your own garage, safety is a high priority. It is essential that you have the proper tools and safety equipment. The Sara Glove Company offers both, and at a savings of up to 40%.

The stock of safety equipment includes safety glasses and goggles, ear plugs, ear muffs, respirators, fire-extinguishers, waterproof gloves, heat-resistant gloves, leather and canvas work gloves, heavy work shoes and boots, and other safety related items. There's also a good selection of tools, including routers, jointers, saws, drills, planers, hammers, and grinders, by such top- of-the-line manufacturers as Makita and Delta.

Send $1.00 for a copy of the company's catalog. Pay by check, money order, MasterCard or VISA.

The Tool Warehouse
Willow Park Center
Farmingdale, NY 11735
Phone: (516) 420-1420

Here's a company that can supply you with name-brand tools and hardware at a savings of up to 50% off comparable retail prices. The company offers everything from basic hand tools to hard-to-find items.

The Tool Warehouse catalog ($1.00) shows a full range of tools and hardware, including lathes, drill bits, saws, chisels, screws, hinges, hammers, clamps, wrenches, air compressors, calipers, vises, and much more. You can choose from name brands such as Ryobi, Campbell-Hausfeld, Hitachi, Bosch, Channelock, Speedaire, Rockwell, Stanley, Cable, Wiss, and Makita.

Send $1.00 for the company's catalog. A price quote on any item not listed in the catalog is available by phone or by letter with a SASE. Pay by check, money order, MasterCard or

VISA. There is a minimum order requirement of $20.

Trend-Lines

375 Beacham Street Chelsea, MA 02150
Phone: 800-767-9999 (order) 800-366-6966 (catalog)
(617) 884-8951
(product information) FAX: (617) 889-2072

Trend-Lines sells a full range of tools and supplies for woodworking professionals and enthusiasts. In business since 1981, Trend-Lines promises the lowest mail-order prices on power tools and accessories. Mail-order shoppers can expect to save up to 50% on some items.

A recent Trend-lines catalog shows a selection of saws (circular, jig, miter, radial-arm, scroll, band, table and chain) and accessories, routers, sanders, jointers, levels, planers, drills, wood lathes, work stations, grinders, wood bits, drill bits, clamps, bench vises, blades, carving knives, hammers, tool sets, mowers, blowers, and more. Name brands in stock include Skil, Ryobi, Makita, Reliant, Bostitch, Campbell-Hausfeld, Hitachi, DeWalt, Bosch, Delta, Oldham, Berger, and other top manufacturers. Woodworkers will also find a selection of "how-to" books and patterns.

Call the toll-free catalog number to request a free catalog. Satisfaction is guaranteed. Returns are accepted within 30 days for refund or exchange. Pay by check, money order or major credit card.

Turnkey Material Handling Company

P.O. Box 1050 Tonawanda, NY 14151
Phone: 800-828-7540

Turnkey is a mail-order firm which specializes in furnishings for both commercial and industrial use. The company has been in business for over 40 years, offering quality products at a savings of up to 50%.

In stock are work benches, office and folding chairs, stainless-steel rolling carts, lockers, files (both flat and rolling), ceiling fans, mats and runners, hand trucks, trash cans, canvas tarps, ladders, and other related goods. There's also a selection of storage units, including commercial shelving and storage bins available in sizes and styles to fit any storage need. Storage cabinets are also available, as are security gates, protective gear (goggles, glasses, etc.), pumps, hydraulic lifts, and hoists.

The company has a catalog which is free upon request. Price quotes are available by phone or by mail with a SASE. Satisfaction is guaranteed. Pay by check, money order, or major credit card. A minimum order of $25 is required.

Industrial Pipe & Steel Co.
9936 E. Rush St., So. El Monte, CA 91733
Phone: (818) 443-9467; (800) 423-4981

Industrial Pipe & Steel is the "Supermarket of industrial supplies", offering thousands of items at low industrial prices. The company's catalog contains thousands of bargains on an assortment of industrial supplies including hardware, machinery, metals, precision and cutting tools, and lots more.

Send $3.00 (refundable with first order) for the over 150-page catalog. Pay by check, money order, MasterCard or VISA.

Zip Power Parts, Inc.
P.O. Box 10308, Erie, PA 16514
Phone: (800) 824-8521

For 29 years, Zip Power Parts has been a leader in discount mail-order outdoor power equipment parts and accessories. Prices are competitive with other firms selling comparable goods.

A recent Zip Power Parts catalog shows an ample assortment of chainsaw parts and accessories including sprockets, chain and bar combo sets, chain joining links, safety footwear (chainsaw footwear priced as low as $54.95— compare at $69.95), carbide chain loops, chain grinders, air filters, hard hats, fuel lines, hose clamps, NGK sparkplugs, and many other chainsaw items. There's also a selection of service manuals available.

Zip Power parts also has a sizable inventory of lawnmower parts (replacement mufflers, tires, tubes, blades) and snowblower parts (mufflers, disc drives, idler pulleys, gasket sets, piston rings, connecting rods, Tecumseh oil seals, roller chains, and belts).

Call or write the company to request a free catalog. Satisfaction is guaranteed. Returns are accepted for refund or exchange. Pay by check, money order, or major credit card. Volume buyers are also welcome.

For other listings of companies which sell related goods, see the following sections in this catalog:

"Audio, etc."

Crutchfield— offers home security systems, including the Dicon 900 and the X- 10 DS-7000, with standard features such as door/window sensors and external siren. You can also add a smoke detector, pet-compatible infrared motion detector, freezer and flooding sensors, and other security options. Dual floodlights with motion detectors and personal assistance systems, remote controls to operate all your house lights from as far away as your driveway, and other home security devices are also available. Car security systems are also sold.

S & S Sound City— sells security and surveillance equipment by Magnavox, Monitech, GBC, Ikegami, and Sharp.

"Farm & Garden"

A.M. Leonard, Inc.— sells safety equipment, including hard hats, goggles, safety glasses, respirators, ear protection (anti-noise muffs and plugs), masks, first-aid kits and refills, reflective safety vests, plastic safety fence, and protective clothing (rainwear, disposable coveralls, work gloves and boots).

NOTES

_____

_____

_____

_____

_____

_____

_____

_____

XIX

Health Care:

Medicine, prescription drugs, contact lenses, prescription glasses, vitamins, and more

Mail-order pharmacies offer brand-name prescriptions and over-the-counter (OTC) drugs at prices that are often well below those you would pay at the local drugstore. Generics, which have the same active ingredients as brand- name versions, are also often less expensive when ordered from mail-order pharmacies. Being able to buy prescription drugs and OTC products through the mail and have them delivered right to your door is also a great convenience, especially for those people who may not be well enough to leave their homes.

While mail-order firms can not fill prescriptions as quickly as your local pharmacy (delivery often takes up to 2 weeks), they can supply maintenance medications for long-term conditions such as high blood pressure, diabetes, and heart disease.

Most mail-order pharmacies require you to send them your prescription form and/or your doctor's authorization. Some firms sell prescription drugs only, while others carry a variety of OTC medication and other health-care products as well. In some cases, before you can buy from a mail order pharmacy, you are required to belong to a membership group. Such membership may be available through your employer, union, or health insurance plan. You can also join an association which offers a mail-order pharmacy plan, such as the National Council of Senior Citizens (800-631-7780) or the American Association of Retired Persons (see listing this section). Other mail-order pharmacies serve the public, and several of those are listed in this section.

In general, you can expect to save 35% and more on some prescription drugs, over-the-counter medicines, contact lenses, prescription eyeglasses, vitamins, and other health-related products listed in this section. However, before you order a product through a mail-order pharmacy, you should consult your doctor. This is especially important if the mail-order product is different from your usual prescription. If you are buying contact lenses, avoid those mail-order firms which do not require an actual prescription. You should also consult your doctor before you order products such as vitamins or dietary supplements to augment your diet.

Action Mail Order Drug Company

P.O. Box 787 Waterville, Maine 04903-0787
Phone: 800-452-1976 FAX: (207) 872-6130

Action Mail Order Drug Company is a division of the family-owned LaVerdiere's Super Drug Stores. The mail-order company was founded in 1975, and offers mail-order savings on prescription drugs, over-the-counter medicines, diabetic supplies (a list is available upon request), vitamin and mineral products, skin care products, foot care products, first aid products, dental care products, and other related items.

Most prescription drug orders are shipped within 12 hours of the company's receiving them. If possible, Action will substitute a less expensive, quality generic for your prescription unless you request a brand-name. Due to fluctuations in drug costs, and varying quantities ordered, Action does not publish its prescription prices. You can, however, call the toll-free number and request written quotes on prescription items guaranteed for 30 days.

Action has an information catalog which is free upon request. The catalog contains a list of OTC medicines, including allergy medications, analgesics, antacids, arthritis pain medications, children's cough and cold medications and eye and ear medications. The catalog also lists a good selection of vitamin and mineral products, including vitamin A, B-complex vitamins, and Vitamins C and E, for adults and children. Other health-related products as well as information on ordering and the company's prescription drug service can also be found in the catalog. Call or write for a free catalog.

Action invites you to compare its products and prices with comparable name- brands. All products sold by Action Mail-Order Drug Company are fully guaranteed. Inquire about the company's return policy. Pay by check, or major credit card.

AARP Pharmacy Service
144 Freeman's Bridge Road P.O. Box 2211
Schenectady, NY 12309
Phone: 800-456-2279 800-456-2226 (price quotes)

Ordering from the AARP Pharmacy Service is a benefit of being a member of the American Association of Retired Persons (AARP). To qualify for an AARP membership, you must be 50 years or older and pay a $5.00 annual fee. The AARP pharmacy-by-mail service is administered by The Retired Person's Services, Inc.

For AARP members, the pharmacy-by-mail service offers a "drugstore at your door" with a complete range of prescription drugs— both brand name and money- saving generics. Savings can be from 10% to 90% on generic equivalents. If your prescription is covered by a "third party" prescription insurance plan, the AARP Pharmacy Service will bill you for your "co-payment" only. The pharmacy will bill your insurance company for the balance. The pharmacy-by- mail service currently participates in PCS, PAID, INSURX, NPA, MEDIMET, RxNET, AETNA, APS, PDI, PHS, and others.

The AARP Pharmacy Service has a free, color catalog which lists 1500 popular items, including pain remedies, vitamins and minerals (special formulas, C vitamins, B vitamins, E vitamins, multi-vitamins, iron, calcium), antacids, diabetic products (blood glucose monitoring kit, Glucometer 3 diabetes care system, artificial sweetener), toiletries, first aid supplies (bandages, gauze pads, sterile cotton, adhesive tape), foot care products, dental care products, and much more. Call or write to request the free catalog. No payment in advance is necessary. The pharmacy will send you an invoice payable upon receipt.

Prescription price quotes are available by calling the toll-free number, or by mail. Satisfaction is guaranteed. Any non-prescription items can be sent back for a full refund (state laws prohibit the return of prescription medicines). Call for price quote. Over-the-counter catalog free upon request.

America's Pharmacy
P.O. Box 10490 Des Moines, IA 50306-0490
Phone: (515) 287-6872

Savings of up to 60% on prescription-filling services by mail are offered by America's Pharmacy. The services include generic equivalents of name-brand drugs. Also available by mail are vitamins, dietary supplements, OTC remedies (analgesics, antacids), beauty aids and other drug store products.

Send for a free catalog. The firm guarantees satisfaction, and accepts returns within 30 days. A minimum order of $15 is required. Pay by check, money order or major credit card.

Bruce Medical Supply
411 Waverly Oaks Road P.O. Box 9166
Waltham, MA   02254
Phone: 800-225-8446 FAX: (617) 894-9519

The free Bruce Medical Supply catalog offers a comprehensive range of medical supplies at savings of up to 60%. Products listed in the catalog include antiseptics, bandages and dressings, diabetic supplies, eyeglasses, heating pads, nurses supplies, electronic pill timers, skin care items, walkers and accessories, pureed foods, and disinfectants. Brand names available include 3M, Hollister, Ace, All Kare, United, Convatec/Squibb, and Johnson & Johnson. Reference books on various health-related topics are also available.

Call or write Bruce Medical Supply to request a catalog. The company guarantees satisfaction. Returns are accepted within 60 days for a full merchandise refund, credit or exchange (You pay only shipping and handling). All orders are delivered within 2 days. Orders placed by 2.p.m. E.T. are shipped the same day. C.O.D. orders are accepted. Pay by check, money order or major credit card.

Contact Lens Replacement Service
P.O. Box 1489 Melville, NY 11747
Phone: (516) 491-7763

This mail-order firm sells all types of replacement lenses at savings of up to 70%. Hard, soft, extended-wear and gas permeable replacement lenses are available. The lenses are from major manufacturers such as Bausch & Lomb, American Optical, Boston, American Hydron, Ciba Vision, Cooper Vision, Wesley- Jessen, and Hydrocurve. You can also order standard hard lenses.

To order replacement lenses from Contact Lens Replacement, you must supply a prescription. A price quote is available by phone or by mail with a SASE. C.O.D orders are accepted. Pay by check, money order, or certified check.

The Eye Solution, Inc.
P.O. Box 262-H Galion, OH 44833
Phone: (419) 683-1608

Contact wearers can save up to 70% on lens-care products when shopping by mail at the Eye Solution. The firm specializes in cleaning, disinfecting, and lubricating preparations and equipment.

The Eye Solution stocks brands by leading manufacturers such as Alcon, Allergan, Barnes-Hind, Bausch & Lomb, Ciba Vision, Boston, and others. A catalog is available free upon request. Get the Eye Solution catalog, then compare products and prices at your local drug store.

A minimum order of $20 with credit cards is required. Payment can be made by check, money order or major credit card.

General Lens Corporation (GLC)
34 Northwest 168th Street, Suite 200 North Miami, Beach, FL. 33169
Phone: 800-333-LENS (5367) FAX: 800-285-LENS (5367)

GLC Offers savings of 25% to 75% on name brand contact lenses. You can get the same brand lenses your doctor prescribed. Choose from brand names such as Bausch & Lomb, Barnes-Hind, Acuvue, DuraSoft, NewVues, Wessley-Jessen, SeeQuence, Ciba Vision, and Johnson & Johnson.

Ordering through GLC is fast and easy with the company's fully computerized order system and qualified staff. Lenses are delivered directly to your door. Your prescription is kept on computer for instant access whenever you need replacement lenses. Special order lenses are no problem. Hard, Gas Permeable and Toric lenses are also available.

A free cleaning kit and UV sunglasses are available when you become a GLC member. Membership is $15 for a full two years and entitles you to additional discounts and other benefits. GLC will send you a free brochure upon request. Price quotes and general information are available by phone.

Satisfaction is guaranteed. All contact lenses are factory fresh and shipped in the manufacturer's sealed, sterile vials. Returns are accepted for a full refund or merchandise credit within 30 days (depending on condition of return) 24 hour delivery service is available. Pay by check, money order or major credit card.

Harvest Of Values AV
178 U.S. HWY. 51 North Woodruff, WI 54568
Phone: 800-535-7742

Vitamins, minerals, and other nutritional supplements are offered at "factory- direct" prices by Harvest Of Values. The firm's parent company, the Hillestad Corp., makes the products which are sold at a savings of up to 40%.

The Harvest Of Values free catalog lists a good selection of multivitamin and mineral formulations for adults, chewable versions for children, vitamins A, B-complex, C, and E; personal care products (anti-perspirant, liquid soapless soap, shampoo, body lotion), over-the-counter medicines (antacid, anti-pain cream, cold tablets, herbal diuretics), home care products (dishwashing compound, laundry compound), skin care items (vitamin E creme, Vitamin E oil), and more. The catalog also provides label information for most of the products, as well as ordering instructions and policies. Call or write the company to request a free catalog and price list.

Satisfaction is guaranteed. Returns are accepted within 30 days of receipt on any product discovered to have a defect in quality of manufacturing. Returns are also accepted on products ordered in error, but are subject to a 10% restocking charge on the catalog price of the product. Pay by check, money order or MasterCard or VISA.

Hidalgo
P.O. Box 1390
Wimberly, TX 78676
Phone: (512) 847-5571 FAX: (512) 847-2393

Mail-order shoppers can save up to 50% on prescription eyeglasses and sunglasses when ordering from Hidalgo. The company has been in operation for over 25 years.

Hidalgo's free catalog lists many of its products, including lenses, frames, and special coatings. The catalog also features informative guides to choosing bifocal and trifocal lenses, and sunglasses. The lens choices available from Hidalgo's include glass, polycarbonate, and other materials, coatings, colors, and ultra violet protection. Bausch & Lomb, Ray-Ban, and Vaurnet sunglasses are also in stock.

Call or write to request the free catalog. Returns in new, unused condition are accepted within 30 days for exchange, refund or credit. Pay by check, money order or major credit card.

Dr. Leonard's Health Care Catalog
74-20th Street Brooklyn, NY 11232
Phone: (718) 768-0010

Dr. Leonard's catalog is full of health-care items at savings of up to 60% on some products. The catalog lists everything from hand-held blood pressure monitors to rotary nose clippers.

Among the wide assortment of health-care items listed in Dr. Leonard's catalog are therapeutic facial compresses, easy slip-on bandages, body pillows for sleeping comfort and support, bath tub safety rails, wheelchairs, canes, stair-climbing machines, massagers, therapeutic slippers, cosmetics and skin care products, breast forms, Sunblockers sunglasses for protection from ultraviolet rays, and manicure kits. The catalog also lists several health- related books, such as "Gray's Anatomy" at low prices. There's also a selection of women's and men's undergarments and footwear.

Women will find savings on a selection of fine fashion wigs. The wigs are natural looking, of fine quality, and are designed for fashion and comfort.

Call or write the company to request a catalog. The company promises a "money- back" guarantee on every product in its catalog. Pay by check, money order or major credit card. (no C.O.D. orders).

Lens Express, Inc.

2780 Gateway Drive Pompano Beach, FL 33069
Phone: 800-666-5367 (information and ordering)
800-866-1004 (customer service)

Convenience and affordability are important factors when buying contact lens replacements. Lens Express, the nation's largest contact lens replacement service, guarantees both. You can order the exact same brand-name prescribed by your doctor at "direct-to-you" savings of up to 50%. The company has over 40,000 laboratory sealed lenses in stock.

Lens Express has an easy one-step process for ordering. Just call the company and give them your doctor's name and phone number or your contact lens prescription. The company's professional staff will take your order over the telephone and guarantee prompt service. Your replacement lenses will be shipped directly to your home or office by

Federal Express.

Brand names available include Barnes Hind, Bausch & Lomb, Ciba Vision Care, Cooper Vision, Vistakon/Johnson & Johnson, Wesley-Jessen, Metro Optics, and many other leading manufacturers. You'll save on daily and extended wear, visibility tints, fashion tints, torics, and bifocals, as well as on Lens Express saline solution and lens lubricant.

Call or write for more information and/or to request a free brochure. Ask about the discount club membership.Satisfaction is guaranteed. Returns (in unopened manufacturers' packages) are accepted within 30 days for a full refund. Pay by check, money order, or major credit card.

Mausen Company

P.O. Box 901 Tonawanda, NY 14151
Phone: 800-831-0894 FAX: 800-222-1934

If you are looking to replenish your medicine cabinet, Mausen Company can provide medical supplies and first-aid kits at savings of up to 30% with quantity discounts. The company's free catalog lists many items for the medicine chest as well as a selection of first aid kits. Also listed in the catalog are resuscitators, thermometers, adhesive bandages and dressings, swabs, splints, braces, soaps, protective clothing, and gloves.

Mausen offers a wide assortment of items to fill your medicine chest, including antiseptics (Hydrogen Peroxide, Povidone-Iodine solution, Bactine, Johnson & Johnson antiseptic wipes), skin care products (Vitamin A & D ointment, Petroleum Jelly, Unguentine Plus, Ivarest Medicated lotion, Cutter Insect repellent, antibacterial soap), adhesive bandages, sterile cotton rolls, gauze, dressings, adhesive tape, cleansers and disinfectants, analgesics, antacids, and cough suppressants. The company also sells a complete line of first aid kits from the small, portable "Guardian First Aid Kit" to the "Master First Aid Kit", which can handle most first aid emergencies for up to 60 people.

Call or write (with SASE) to request a price quote and/or the free catalog. Quantity discounts are available. Satisfaction is guaranteed. Returns are accepted for a full refund, replacement or credit. Pay by check, money order, major credit card, or open an account.

Medi-Mail
P.O. Box 98520
Las Vegas, NV 89193-8520
Phone: 800-331-1458

Medi-Mail is a national "deep-discount" pharmacy that has been used by HMO's, insurance companies, unions, and employer trusts and affinity groups since 1987. The services and low prices are now available to individual mail-order customers as well. This shop-at-home discount pharmacy offers prescription medications, over-the-counter remedies, and home care products at discount prices. You'll discover savings on national brands, and super discount savings of 50% and more on generics. Get the company's free catalog, and compare products, and prices with those offered by other companies selling comparable products.

Medi-Mail's free 47-page catalog lists a full selection of health care products and supplies. The items include brand name and generic cold and allergy products (decongestant tablets, cough syrup, nasal spray, allergy tablets), aspirin and other pain relievers, dental care products (mouthwash/breath spray, toothpaste, toothbrushes, dental floss), diabetes products, footcare products, heating pads, ice packs, laxatives, eye and ear care products, prescription medications, toiletries (shampoo, skin cleansers, body lotion, bath/shower gel), men's and women's colognes, vitamins and minerals, hearing aid batteries, vaporizers, hosiery, and much more.

Call or write the company to request the free catalog. Call

for a price quote on prescription medications. You must supply your doctor's written prescription when ordering prescription medication. If that isn't possible, Medi-Mail will verify your prescriptions with your physician. Inquire about Medi-Mail's guarantee of "the lowest prescription prices". Satisfaction is guaranteed. Returns (except prescription medications) are accepted. Pay by check, money order or major credit card.

The Ultimate Contact
721 N. Beers St. Holmdel, NJ 07733
Phone: 800-432-5367 FAX: (908)-264-5068

The Ultimate Contact is a replacement contact lens service that is under the supervision of an ophthalmologist. The company promises to sell you the same prescription lenses you purchased from an eyecare professional and, in some cases, at a savings of up to 70%.

Your replacement contact lens order will be filled to your exact prescription under the supervision of the company's ophthalmologist. All replacement lenses sold are FDA-approved and shipped in the original manufacturer's sealed vial. All orders will arrive within 7 days— in some cases overnight. The company has lenses available by American Hydron, American Optical, Barnes-Hind, Ciba Vision Care, Cooper Vision, Syntex, Wesley-Jessen, Vistakon, Bausch & Lomb, Acuvue, and others.

Call or write for information and a free price list. When ordering, you must furnish your prescription and doctor's phone number. Satisfaction is guaranteed. Returns are accepted for full money-back refund or full merchandise credit within 30 days. Pay by check, money order or major credit card.

Creative Health Products, Inc.
5148 Saddle Ridge Road, Plymouth, MI 48170
Phone: (313) 996-5900; (800) 742-4478
FAX: (313) 996-4650

Since 1976, Creative Health Products has been a leading supplier of health, fitness and exercise products. The company takes pride in offering quality brand-name products at the "lowest prices anywhere". In fact, Creative Health products guarantees to"either match or beat" any lower prices you find on the same products, anywhere.

Fitness-minded people can choose from an assortment of exercise equipment, as well as fitness and health testing and measuring products. In stock are heart rate monitors, stethoscopes, digital blood pressure testers, stop watches, underwater weight systems, exercise bicycles, rowing machines, treadmills, fitness books and software, lung capacity testers, and many other health and fitness products.

A recent discount price catalog lists many quality products at discount savings. A Marshall Medical Digital Blood Pressure unit, with a suggested retail price of $78 was discount-priced at $62. Other products listed at discount savings include skinfold calipers, a 22-page book, "How To Measure Your % of Bodyfat"; Tunturi Air Bikes and Rowers, and many more items.

Call or write the company to find out about the availability of its most recent discount price list. While prices are typically discounted on most items, further quantity discounts are available on some items. Returns are accepted within 30 days for a refund or exchange. Pay by check, money order major credit card.

Lens First
400 Galleria #400, Southfield, MI 48034
Phone: (800) 388-2400

Lens First is "Your first source for contact lens replacement". The company offers every major brand of contact lens including Bausch & Lomb, Ciba Vision, Barnes-Hind, and Johnson & Johnson. Savings range up to 70% off typical retail prices. You can order your replacement lens by phone if you have your prescription available when you phone.

Lenses are shipped in factory sealed vials to guarantee their quality. Orders are shipped with 24 hours. Satisfaction is guaranteed. A free color catalog is available upon request. Instant price quotes are also available by calling the toll-free number listed above. Pay by check, money order or major credit card.

Precision Optical
300 N. 6th St., Rochelle, IL 61068
Phone: (815) 562-2174

Precision Optical offers over-the-counter reading glasses at low prices. The company's catalog features a selection of non-prescription reading glasses to correct blurred and close up vision. The catalog also includes a guide to assist you in choosing the correct strength. Precision's prices begin as low as $7.00.

A color catalog is available free upon request. Pay by check, money order, MasterCard or VISA.

Star Pharmaceutical, Inc.
1500 New Horizons Blvd., Amityville, NY 11701-1130
Phone: (800) 274-6400

Star Pharmaceutical has been offering discount prices on vitamins since 1954. Star's catalog features a large selection of natural vitamins, minerals, health supplements, natural cosmetics, andweight control products. Savings are also available on many generic health products which are similar to national brands, but at a fraction of the cost.

Call or write the company to request a free catalog. Pay bycheck, money order, MasterCard or VISA.

XX

Home Furnishings, Decor, Bedding, And Accessories:

Indoor and outdoor furniture, floor coverings, wall and window treatments, bedding and accessories

This section lists firms that sell all types of household furnishings and bedding, redecorating and remodeling goods, decorative accessories, and services at an average savings of up to 50%. The furnishings and accessories available are all well-known, name-brand goods, which if purchased in department and retail furniture stores would be subject to exorbitant markups. By ordering from mail-order discounters, you effectively "cut-out" the middleman, eliminating those markups.

Most of the mail-order discounters listed in this section can supply quality goods from literally hundreds of reputable manufacturers. Many of the firms also have available catalogs, brochures, flyers, swatches, sample kits, videos, and other information. Some are staffed to provide decorating advice over the phone.

It's worth noting again that whether you are shopping for a new bedroom grouping or window blinds, you should compare 4 to 5 sources before making your final decision. You may find a substantial price spread from store to store, as well as considerable differences in quality and service. Take your time in evaluating merchandise, price, and services. It is advisable that you take advantage of in-home-delivery service whenever offered by a company. This type of delivery assures that your furniture order will be uncrated in your home, in the room and location of your choice. You will also be able to see any flaws or damages right away. You can then contact the company (while the shipper is still in your home) and find out what to do about the problem. This makes returning damaged goods less of a hassle.

You can get some good advice and tips on buying furniture, floor coverings, bedding, and so on, in "The Better Business Bureau A to Z Buying Guide", (Henry Holt, 1990).

American Blind & Wallpaper Factory

28237 Orchard Lake Road
Farmington Hills, MI 48334
Phone: 800-735-5300 FAX: (313) 553-6262

Savings of up to 80% off average retail prices on mini blinds and verticals are promised by the American Blind & Wallpaper Factory. Top manufacturers such as Levolor, Delmar, Bali, Graber, Profile, Hunter Douglas, Louver Drape, Joanna, Kirsh, Veresol, and M & B are available. American brand mini blinds can be shipped in 3 working days. The company also offers savings of over 75% on all national brands of wallpaper.

You can get information about American Blind & Wallpaper Factory products by calling the toll-free number or by letter with a SASE. Price quotes are also available by phone or by mail. If you are interested in wallpaper, shop in your own neighborhood, write down the book name and pattern number, then call American for a price quote. Pay by check, money order or major credit card.

Around The Window

326 N. Stonestreet Ave. Suite 204

Rockville, MD 20850
Phone: 800-642-9899 Ext. 9

Around The Window offers factory direct mini and vertical blinds at savings of up to 75% off suggested retail prices. The company also features treatments for special shapes, such as arches, skylights, incline, and many others. Name brand manufacturers such as Bali, Levolor, Artistica, Duette, and Joanna are available.

Call the toll-free number and request a designer sample kit. The kit includes actual fabric, aluminum, wood, and vinyl samples. Around The Window's products are shipped in 5 working days. One day service is also available. Pay by check, money order or by MasterCard or VISA.

Cherry Hill Furniture, Carpet, & Interiors
P.O. Box 7405 Furnitureland Station
High Point, NC 27264
Phone: 800-328-0933, 800-888-0933,

For 60 years Cherry Hill has been in the business of selling a wide range of quality home furnishings, accessories, and floorcoverings. Prices range up to 45% off average list prices. The company supplies name brand home and office furniture and floor coverings from over 500 top manufacturers.

A video catalog, representing many of the company's most popular products and brands is available. Call the toll-free number and ask for information. You can also get a listing of brands carried and ordering information in a free brochure.

To get a price quote or information, call or write with a SASE. Shipment of orders is made by van line or common carrier. Pay by check or money order.

Crawford's Old House Store
550 Elizabeth Room 253
Waukesha, WI 53186

Phone: 800-556-7878

Crawford's provides a successful alternative to plastic corner protectors. The company's cornerbeads are among hundreds of hard-to-find "old-style" items sold at savings of up to 30%. Products include wall coverings, cast moldings, Victorian style light fixtures, bath fixtures and plumbing hardware, and many more.

Call or write to get Crawford's free literature (brochures and flyers). Quantity discounts are available. Pay by check, money order or major credit card.

Direct Wallpaper Express

374 Hall St. Phoenixville, PA 19460
Phone: 800-366-9255

Mail-order shoppers can expect top brands of wallpaper at 40% to 70% off retail prices (with orders of 12 rolls or more) when ordering from Direct Wallpaper Express. The company provides a pattern identification service, enabling customers to shop at home and compare prices. Call the company with the book name and pattern number and it can supply the wallpaper at factory direct prices.

Call the toll-free number for more information about products and services available. Pay by check, money order or major credit card.

Factory Direct Table Pad Co.

959 N. Holmes Ave. Indianapolis, IN 46222
Phone: 800- 428-4567

Custom-made table pads at savings of up to 70% are available from Factory Direct. Much of the savings comes from cutting out the fee paid to the person who measures the table. You can write to the company and request information and a guide which shows you how to measure your own table. Factory Direct will use your measurements to custom-make your table pad. The pads come with a guarantee good for up to 20 years.

Send $1.00 for information, price list, and samples. You can also get a price quote by phone. Authorized returns are accepted within 15 days. Pay by check, money order or major credit card.

The Furniture Barn
1190 HWY. 74 Bypass Spindale, NC 28160
Phone: (704) 287-7106 FAX: (704) 287-8785

Furniture, bedding, and decorative accessories at savings of up to 50% are available to mail-order shoppers from The Furniture Barn. In business for over 20 years, this company provides the best-known name brand furnishings, prompt attention to orders, and excellent delivery service.

A free brochure, featuring a list of products and brands sold, and ordering information is available upon request. Phone or send a letter with a SASE. Shipments are made by a "professional delivery service" and a deposit is required. Payment can be made by check, money order or major credit card.

Interior Furnishings, LTD.
P.O. Box 1644 Hickory, NC 28603
Phone: (704) 328-5683

Interior Furnishings specializes in quality home furnishings and accessories at savings of up to 50%. Bedding, lamps, mirrors, table pads, home furnishings, and accessories by well-known manufacturers are available. The company sells first-quality goods only.

Call or send a letter with a SASE for a price quote. Delivery is made by common carrier and van line. Pay by check, money order or certified check.

Nationwide Wholesaler
P.O. Box 40 Hackensack, NJ 07602
Phone: 800-488-9255

Wallcovering, fabrics, and blinds at savings of 50% to 75% are the specialty of Nationwide Wholesaler. The company offers wallcovering from every book and pattern. Also available are quality fabrics by Waverly, Gear, Clarence House, Robert Allen, Jay Yang, Kravet, and Mario Buatta.

If it's blinds you need, Nationwide Wholesaler has a selection of vertical, mini and micros by Louver Drape, Graber, Hunter Douglas, and other manufacturers.
Call the toll-free number for information and price quotes. Pay by check, money order or major credit card.

Post Wallcovering Distributors, Inc.
P.O. Box 7026 Bloomington Hills, MI 48013
Phone: 800-521-0650 FAX: (313) 338-7943

In business for over 15 years, Post Wallcovering offers homeowners and decorators up to 80% off on wallcoverings and window blinds. The firm promises it can supply customers "any wallpaper in any wallpaper book" at substantial savings. Instant price quotes are available if you furnish the pattern number and book name.

Post Wallcovering also sells all major brands of window blinds, in all styles- - verticals, pleated shades, horizontals, roller shades, mini-micro, real wood, and mini blinds. Save up to 80% off average retail prices.

Call for a price quote and/or information. C.O.D. orders are accepted. Pay by check, money order, or major credit card.

Renovator's Supply Old Mill
Dept. 9123 Millers Falls, MA 01349

Phone: (413) 659-2211

It has been 15 years since Renovator's Supply began selling reproduction hardware and fixtures. Over the years, the company has become well known for its fine selection of items to enhance and improve the beauty of any home. Renovator's has over 1,800 products, including brass lighting fixtures, china sinks, brass and chrome faucets, solid brass door and cabinet hardware, wallplates, and more. From classic traditional to contemporary styles, Renovator's has it in stock.

Send for Renovator's Supply's free catalog. Customers are guaranteed satisfaction on every order. Returns are accepted within 30 days. Pay by check, money order, or major credit card.

S & S Mills
2650 Lakeland Road Dalton, GA 30720
Phone: 800-848-8114 Ext. 176

Quality carpeting at savings of up to 50% off retail prices is available direct from the factory of S & S Mills in Dalton, Georgia. The company makes quality carpeting using Scotchgard by 3M and Dupont Stainmaster carpet protectors. A wide selection of colors and styles is available. The company guarantees its service, selection and quality. Call or write for a free color brochure. Pay by check, money order or major credit card.

Shaw Furniture Galleries, Inc.
P.O. Box 576
Randlemann, NC 27317
Phone: 800-334-6799

Shaw Furniture provides a free brochure which lists many of the more than 300 brand name home furnishings it sells. The company has been in operation for over 50 years and offers savings of up to 45%. With a large inventory of top quality home furnishings, Shaw Furniture is likely to have what you're looking for.

Call or write with a SASE to get a price quote and/or the brochure. You can also ask about a manufacturer you've priced and whi is not listed in the brochure. All shipments are made by common carrier or van line. Payment can be made by check, money order or MasterCard or VISA.

All States Decorating Network
810 Main St., Toms River, NJ 08753
Phone: (800) 334-8590

In business for over 20 years, All States Decorating Network offers savings of over 80% on blinds for every window. The company promises to "beat anyone's prices down to our cost".

You can choose from mini-blinds, micros, wood blinds, and verticals, by such famous manufacturers as Symphony; Toppers; Bali; Levolor; Delmar; Graber; Versol; Hunter Douglas; Joanna; and Louver Drape. Call with any window size, brand name, pattern, and color.

Call or write the company for more information. Pay by check, money order or major credit card.

Bearden Bros. Carpet Corp.
3200A Duggap Rd., Dept. BG, Dalton, GA 30720
Phone: (800) 433-0074,

If it's carpeting you're looking for, Bearden Bros. offers savings of up to 80% on national brand-name carpeting from over 80 major mills, as well as their own premium Showcase label. In business for almost 30 years, all of Bearden's carpeting is first quality and comes with wear and stain warranties. You can also get padding at considerable savings off typical retail prices. Call the company with the brand name, style and color carpeting you are interested in, and the odds are very good that the Bearden Brothers can save you from 50% to 80% off the average retail price.

The company also offers savings on Orientals, border and braidedrugs, vinyl, bath sets, stair rods, and Hoover vacuum cleaners.

A color catalog is free upon request. You can also call for price quotes and samples. Payment may be made by check, money order or major credit card.

$5 Wallpaper & Blind Company
Phone: (800)-5-Dollar [536-5527]

Five dollars may not go very far most places these days but, as the name suggests, $5 Wallpaper & Blind Company offers some unique savings. Brand-name, top books wallpaper, which retails in most stores for $17 to $25 is only $5 at $5 Wallpaper. The company features all brands of wallpaper, in any pattern, fromany book. Call the toll-free number for an instant price quote.

You can also choose custom blinds by Hunter Douglas, Graber and other famous manufacturers. Ready-made 23 x 64 Horizontal blinds are priced as low as $5. Other recent savings at the $5 Wallpaper & Blind Company have included these prices on ready-made verticals for sliding glass doors:

5 Ft. 66 x 84 for $54.99
6 Ft. 78 x 84 for $59.99
7 Ft. 84 x 84 for $64.99
8 Ft. 102 x 84 for $79.00

Call or write the company for more information and/or for a price quote. The company offers free, same day shipping. Pay by check, money order, or major credit card.

Star Blind Co.
Phone: (800) 782-7800

Established in the early 1930's, the Star Blind Co. has been offering top-quality blinds for over 60 years. You can save up to 85% off regular retail prices when you buy from Star Blind Co.

Star Blind features some of the best values you'll find on mini-blinds, pleated shades, wood blinds, and more. Brand names available include Levolor, Duettes, Hunter Douglas, Bali, Delmar, and Joanna. A free designer sample kit is available.

The company offers factory direct, free U.P.S shipping. Pay by check, money order or major credit card.

Style Wallcovering
P.O. Box 865, Southfield, MI 48037
Phone: (800) 627-0400

The folks at Style Wallcovering in Michigan offer savings of up to 50% on every wallpaper pattern in every book. The amount of savings depends upon the volume of your purchase. The more you buy,the more you save. Call the toll-free phone number and provide the pattern number and book name, and Style Wallcovering promises to equal or beat any other price you may have found. They can also decode altered pattern numbers.

Only first-quality wallcoverings are sold, and there are no extra processing fees. Style Wallcovering also provides a no-hassle return policy. Pay by major credit card. Call or write the company for more information.

Wells Interiors

7171 Amador Plaza Road, Dublin, CA 94568
Phone: (800) 547-8982

With a guarantee to beat any other dealer's prices "down to our costs", Wells Interiors offers savings on first-quality blinds by famous manufacturers. The company features such brand names as Levolor, Hunter Douglas, Kirsch, DelMar, and Louver Drape. You can choose from mini blinds, verticals, wood blinds, pleated shades, and Duettes.

Call the toll-free number for a price quote. Pay by check, money order or major credit card.

Worldwide Wallcoverings and Blinds, Inc.

333 Skokie Blvd., Northbrook, IL 60062
Phone; (800) 322-5400

Worldwide Wallcoverings promises that you will never have to pay retail prices again if you take advantage of their savings on blinds and wallcoverings. Save as much as 80% off typical retail prices on first-quality verticals, horizontals, duettes, pleated shades, and wooden blinds. Brand names include Levolor, Hunter Douglas, DelMar, and other famous manufacturers. You can also save up to 75% off regular retail prices on all brands of first-quality wallpaper.

Worldwide offers special case discounts on wallcoverings. Check with your local retailer and write down the book number, manufacturer's name, style, color, and quantity. Then call Worldwide and give them that information and get an instant price quote. You can also get a free ordering kit for blinds. The kit has measuring guides and color selectors.

Returns are accepted for a refund. The company offers free shipping within 2 days on wallcoverings, and within 3 days on blinds. Pay by major credit card.

XXI

Jewelry and Watches:

Bargains on fashion and costume jewelry, rings, chains, and gems

This section of the Wholesale Bargains & Free Stuff Guide lists firms that sell both fine and costume jewelry and accessories, gemstones, and watches. All the goods listed in this section make elegant personal purchases and investments. The listings feature firms which sell everything from $10.00 digital timepieces in plastic cases to necklaces selling for thousands of dollars. As always—and especially important when purchasing expensive jewelry, stones, watches, etc.—you should know as much as you can about what you intend to buy before you make a purchase.

All too often jewelry is purchased based on sentiment, whim, or a desire to be fashionable. The best way to get the best merchandise for your money is to know as much as you can about jewelry and gems before you buy. This advice may sound redundant, but if you want to get quality goods at the lowest possible prices, you must be a smart and informed shopper. You can get valuable information about jewelry and stones in reading material available at your local library. The Federal Trade Commission (FTC) also has several pamphlets for consumers, which can be very helpful when it comes time to make a purchase. The pamphlets include such titles as "Bargain Jewelry", and "Guidelines for the Jewelry Industry". Write to the Federal Trade Commission, Public Reference Office, Washington, D.C. 20580 to request the phamplets. Also, before you buy, you should contact the Better Business Bureau for a reliability report. You can also get valuable information from the Jewelers' Vigilance Committee, which monitors the jewelry trade industry. Write to the Jewelers' Vigilance Committee, 1180 Avenue of the Americas, 8th floor, New York, NY 10036.

If you're contemplating buying investment-grade stones (which are normally sold on an approval basis), be sure to get at least two professional appraisals. Make arrangements to have the appraisals completed before you buy the stone(s).

When buying a new watch, follow these guidelines from Jewelers of America, Inc., and The American Watchmakers Institute:

1) Make sure you buy from a reliable source.

2) Avoid buying watches with unknown brand names. Those with familiar brand names and trademarks are usually well-known because of their reputations for performance.

3) Be careful of special promotions which offer "drastic reductions" on so- called "designer" or "famous name" timepieces.

4) Find out about the availability of replacement parts, before buying.

5) Ask about the warranty before you buy. You should know what parts of the watch are covered and for how long. You should also find out who will perform the repairs.

Eloxite Corporation
806 Tenth Street, Dept. 4 Wheatland, WY 82201
Phone: (307) 322-3050

For more than 35 years, Eloxite has been offering an outstanding selection of jewelry findings and other lapidary supplies. The company's prices can provide a savings of up to 75% compared with those of other sources selling comparable products.

Among the jewelry findings featured in past catalogs are belt buckles and inserts, slide medallions, and bola ties. Coin jewelry has also been offered. The company also has a selection of rings, earrings, lockets, pendants, tie tacks, and pins, which can be set with cut stones or carbochons. Loose stones, including black onyx, garnet, agate, opal, jasper, and malachite are sold as well. You'll also find an assortment of jewelers' tools and supplies.

Call or write the company to inquire about its current catalog. Quantity discounts are available on most of the goods sold. Returns of undamaged goods are accepted within 15 days for exchange or refund. Some returns may be subject to a minimal restocking fee. Pay by check, money order or major credit card. C.O.D. orders are also accepted.

Good `n' Lucky Promotions
P.O. Box 1185
Chino Valley, AZ 86323
Phone: 800-658-9193 (602)636-0350

Good `n' Lucky was established in 1971 and is an established closeout specialist and swapmeet supplier. The company purchases closeouts, overruns, bankrupt stock, etc. in huge lots and is able to pass on savings to customers who buy in smaller quantities. The minimum order is only $30.00.

Past catalogs have shown a selection of costume jewelry

pieces sold by the dozen, including pins, clip on earrings, black enamel metal earrings, silver chain necklaces, hand-knotted natural color pearls, handset crystal stone earrings, double heart bracelets, rings, and birth stone pendants.

Send $3.00 for the latest wholesale merchandise catalog. Call or write the company for more information. Most items are sold by the dozen. Minimum order is $30.00. Pay by check, money order or certified check. C.O.D. orders are accepted with a 25% deposit.

House of Onyx
The Aaron Building 120 N. Main St. Greenville, KY 42345
Phone: 800-844-3100 FAX: (502) 338-9605

The House of Onyx was founded in 1967 and began offering fine jewelry and investment grade stones at reasonable prices. The company continues that tradition today and is nationally known for its quality merchandise, services, and competitive prices. There is no single comprehensive catalog, but rather a series of tabloids featuring "articles and merchandise of interest".

Recent tabloids have featured rainbow jewelry (bracelets, pendants, rings, earrings, necklaces, broaches) which is composed of a variety of colorful, hand-cut genuine gemstones. The company has also offered emerald jewelry, coral jewelry, diamond earrings and pendants, precious bead necklaces, and cultured pearls. Jewelry bags are also available.

The House of Onyx also offers carvings of fluorite, agate, Chinese turquoise, soapstone, Mexican onyx, verdite, and lapis lazuli, among others. There are watches by Seiko, designer beads and pearl necklaces, Intarsia, and a wide range of gemstones (smoky quartz, rubies, topaz, emeralds, etc.) available.

The monthly tabloids are free upon request. Satisfaction is guaranteed. Pay by check, money order or major credit card. No C.O.D. orders are accepted. There is a minimum order of $25.

The Jewelry Warehouse
28 N. Michigan Ave. Chicago, IL 60602
Phone: (312) 670-0817

If your taste runs to fashion jewelry, but your budget has a hard time keeping pace, The Jewelry Warehouse may be the solution. The company offers beautiful, stylish fashion jewelry at some of the lowest prices available. You can expect savings of up to 50% less than typical retail prices on some items.

Fashionable earrings, necklaces, and pins are among the many pieces offered at down-to-earth prices. A recent catalog shows kiln-fired post earrings, multi- strand necklaces with clasps, and many other pieces, representing the latest looks and fashions. The company sells many of its items by the dozen. Quantity discounts are also available.

Send $3.00 (refundable) with a SASE for the catalog. A price quote is also available by mail with a SASE or by phone. Pay by check, money order, MasterCard or VISA.

Marcus & Company
815 Connecticut Ave. N.W. Washington, D.C. 20006
Phone: (202) 331-0671 800-654-7184

Marcus & Co. is one of "America's largest" fine watch and jewelry discounters. The company has an established reputation for quality products and low prices. You can expect savings of up to 50% on many select pieces of fine jewelry and watches by famous manufacturers.

Past Marcus' catalogs have listed a selection of fine jewelry, including earrings, bracelets, necklaces, pins, rings, pendants, pearls, diamonds, and other beautiful pieces. All types of watches, with all the latest features, by such makers as Rolex, Audemars, Patek, Breitting, Baume & Mercier, Cartier, and other top manufacturers are also available.

Call or write the company to request a copy of its free shop-at-home catalog. Pay by check, money order or major credit card.

Bucks County Classic
73 Coventry Ln., Langhorne, PA 19047
Phone: (215) 757-8185; (800) 942-4367 [orders]

Bulk prices and no minimum— that's what you get when you purchase semi-precious beads, metals, and supplies from Bucks County Classic. The company has been in operation since 1987 and offers gemstones, porcelain, Thai silver, cloisonne, metal, stone donuts, and many other items. Findings and tools are also available at bulk prices.

You can get the Bucks County Classic catalog for $2.00. Call or write the company. Pay by check, money order, MasterCard or VISA.

Diamond Essence Co.
6 Sample Rd., Cedar Knolls, NJ 07927-9990
Phone: (201) 267-8597 [in NJ]; (800) 642-4367

The best alternative to mined diamonds is jewelry made of Diamond Essence Jewels. Diamond Essence offer exceptional simulated diamonds, set in 14K solid gold. The prices are so low you can build your own collection of distinctive jewelry in no time. This is an excellent, low-cost way to purchase beautiful jewelry.

Send for the Diamond Essence catalog ($5.00). Pay by check, money order or major credit card.

Vanity Fair Diamonds
S.A. Peck & Co.
55 E. Washington St., Chicago, IL 60602
Phone: (312) 977-0300; (800) 992-0090

For over 70 years S.A. Peck has offered a comprehensive collection of diamonds, fine jewelry, and watches at savings of up to 50% off typical retail prices. Since 1921, the company has been committed to quality design and value. Customer satisfaction is guaranteed.

S.A. Peck's "Vanity Fair" catalog is free upon request. Pay by check, money order or major credit card.

Williamson International, Inc.
Box 6778, Reno, NV 89513
Phone: (702) 972-1105

Williamson International has been in business since 1968. The company offers a selection of jewelry and parts at below wholesale prices. Call or write for a catalog ($1.00). Pay by check, money order or major credit card.

Windsor Collection
P.O. Box 94549, Cleveland, OH 44101-4549
Phone: (800) 800-0500; (800) 800-0200

The Windsor Collection is a truly unique assortment of fashion jewelry, watches and fine gems. The collection is available in all popular styles, from classical to contemporary. The company's purchasing power brings beautiful fashion jewelry and other items direct to you at some of the lowest prices around.

Contact the company to request a free catalog. Pay by check, money order or major credit card.

For other listings of companies that offer jewelry and related products, see the following sections in this catalog:

"Art, Antiques, etc."

Albert S. Smyth Co.— sells a wide range of fine jewelry and watches, including colored stone jewelry, pearls, strands of semiprecious beads, and diamonds, as well as watches by Citizen, Pulsar, and Seiko.

"General Merchandise and Buying Clubs"

Bennet Brothers, Inc.— offers a large selection of jewelry, including charms, lockets, medallions, wedding and engagement bands, pearls, bracelets, necklaces, anniversary jewelry, religious jewelry, and other pieces featuring precious and semi-precious gems. Also in stock are watches by many leading manufacturers. Prices range from moderate to expensive.

XXII

Linens And Fabrics:

Bath, bed, and table linens and accessories, and decorator fabrics

Shopping by mail for all your linen needs can result in average savings of 35%. Some discounters offer savings of as much as 60% on towels, sheets, pillows, and table linens.

The listings in this section represent companies which sell a combination of first-quality and irregular linens as well as those firms which sell first- quality goods only. If your interest is in buying first-quality goods only, you should not place an order until you are certain of what are getting. Some of the firms also feature waterbed sheets and sheets for oddly shaped mattresses, and "custom services".

Also in this section are listings for quality, brand-name decorator fabrics at savings of up to 50%. From drapery to upholstery fabrics, these firms offer some special values for discriminating mail-order shoppers.

American Discount Wallcoverings
1411 Fifth Ave. Pittsburgh, PA 15219
Phone: 800-777-2737

This company has been in business for over 80 years selling quality wall coverings and window treatments. It also features an excellent line of decorator fabrics. American Discount Wallcoverings first-quality decorator fabrics are typically priced at 10% to 30% below regular retail. Brands sold include Greeff, Schumacher, David & Dash, Scalamandre, and others.

American Discount Wallcoverings will provide a price quote by phone or by mail with a SASE. Order forms are available upon request. While most returns are accepted within 20 days, a restocking fee of 25% is required. Methods of payment include check, money order or major credit card.

Coming Home
1 Lands' End Lane Dodgeville, WI 53595
Phone: 800-345-3696

Coming Home is a division of Land's End, Inc. (see "Clothing" section in this catalog) and is relatively new in the "bed and bath" business. However, you get the same Land's End quality, service, and affordable prices on bed, bath and table linens.

The Coming Home catalog (free upon request) shows a wide selection of quality sheets that fit, made with a 12-inch deep pocket, and elastic all around to make sure they stay on your bed. Sheets that fit are available in 100% cotton, easy-care blends, flannel, and all natural fabrics. There's also a selection of shams, dust ruffles, comforters and covers.

Also in stock are cotton bath towel sets, shower curtains, bath rugs, tablecloths, dish towels, napkins, placemats, decorative pillows and pillow covers, beach towels, window treatments (drapes, valances), mattress pads, quilts, and other related items.

Call or write to request your free Coming Home catalog.

Satisfaction is guaranteed. Returns are accepted for refund. Pay by check, money order or major credit card. No C.O.D. orders.

Ezra Cohen Corp.
307 Grand St. New York, NY 10002
Phone: (212) 925-78000

The Cohen Corp. has in stock a full line of quality bed and bath linens at savings of up to 60%. This firm also carries a good selection of accessories, and provides custom services.

Among the major mill products sold by Cohen are bed linens by Cannon, Martex, Dan River, and Springmaid. Designer lines such as Bill Blass, Christian Dior, and Perry Ellis are also offered. Bath linens sold include those from major mills such as Avanti, Martex, and Fieldcraft. Comforters and bedspreads are also in stock. If you have a nonstandard mattress, ask about Cohen's custom services.

No catalog is available. To get a price quote, phone or send a SASE. Pay by check, money order or major credit card.

Domestications Unique Merchandise Mart
Hanover, PA 177333-0040
Phone: (717) 633-3313

Domestications, from Hanover House Industries, offers fine and fashionable linens for bed, bath, or table. All of the goods listed in the Domestication catalog are first-quality, and at a savings of up to 35%. From timeless classics to floral prints, this shop-at-home source features products from major mills, such as Bibb, Cannon, Martex, Dan River, J.P. Stevens, Wamsutta, and others.

The Domestications 95-page catalog is priced at $2, and features a selection of lamps, curtains, rugs, and other decorative accents. Satisfaction on all orders is guaranteed and returns are accepted. Methods of payment include check, money order or major credit card (A minimum order of $20 is required with credit cards).

Eldridge Textile Co.
277 Grand St. New York, NY 10002
Phone: (212) 925-1523

Bed, bath, and table linens from major mills are provided by Eldridge Textile at savings of up to 40%. The company has been in business for over 50 years and stocks fine linen by Laura Ashley, Beau Ideal, Cameo, Cannon, Croscill, Faribo, Jackson, Martex, Dan River, and others. There's a great selection of sheet and towel sets, bath towels and wash cloths, bath rugs, bedspreads, curtains, comforters, and table linens.

Eldridge publishes a brochure which is priced at $3. The brochure lists many values on quality sheets and towels. When requesting the brochure, be sure to include a check or money order.To get a price quote, phone or send a letter with a SASE. The return of unused purchases is accepted for refund or credit. Pay by check, money order or major credit card.

The Fabric Center Inc.
485 Electric Ave. Fitchburg, MA 01420
Phone: (508) 343-4402

Since the early 1930's, The Fabric Center has been selling the finest decorator fabrics at savings of up to 50%. The firm's 164 page catalog costs $2.00, and is a comprehensive guide to thousands of beautiful fabrics for home decorators.

The Fabric Center stocks decorator fabrics by Robert Allen, American Textile, Waverly, John Wolf, and many other top manufacturers. A price list, representing some of the products in stock, is available free upon request— phone or send a letter with a SASE. Pay by check, money order, or master card.

Fabrics By Design
3100 S. Congress, #7 Boynton Beach, FL 33435
Phone: (407) 738-6600

Mail-order shoppers who send $7.50 for Fabrics By Design's catalog will receive an impressive swatch book representing the company's collection of country prints and solids. Besides its own collection of decorator fabrics, this company also features selected lines from name-brand manufacturers. Designer fabrics by Robert Allen, Anju, Covington, Cyrus Clark, Spectrum, and others are also available. All in all, mail-order shoppers can expect an average savings of 30% when ordering from Fabrics By Design.

Satisfaction on each order is guaranteed. Returns on goods over 5 yards in length, and which have not been worn or washed, are accepted within two weeks. There is a minimum order of 1 yard.

For a price quote, send a letter with a SASE or phone. Pay by check, money order or major credit card.

Fabrics By Phone
P.O. Box 309 Walnut Bottom, PA 17266
Phone: 800-233-7012

Fabrics By Phone, in business since 1937, offers decorator fabrics from major manufacturers at average savings of up to 50%. Name-brand fabrics in stock include those by Robert Allen, Design Craft, Kinney, Schumacher, Warner, Westgate, and others. If you are also in need of draperies and accessories, Fabrics By Phone will make them to your specifications.

You can get the company's brochure, price list and sample swatches for $3.00 (check or money order). Price quotes are available by phone or by mail with a SASE. There is a minimum order of 1 yard on fabrics not in stock. Pay by check, money order or major credit card.

Harris Levy, Inc.
278 Grand St. New York, NY 10002 800-221-7750
Phone: (212) 266-3120 in NY FAX: (212) 334-9360

In 1894, Harris Levy began selling top-quality bed, bath, and table linens at wholesale savings. The firm is still at it today, offering the finest linens at savings of up to 50%. Levy does not sell seconds or discontinued goods.

Mail-order shoppers can choose from one-of-a-kind imported items, such as Egyptian percale and linen sheets, Irish damask tablecloths, and Belgian crash towels. Also in stock are bed and bath linens by Cannon, Fieldcrest, Martex, Dan River, J.P. Stevens, and other major mills. Levy's custom services include sheets in special sizes and shapes, monogramming, tablecloths, pillow cases and more.

No catalog is available. To get a price quote, phone or send a letter with a SASE. Phone orders are accepted Monday through Friday from 10 a.m. to 4 p.m. only. A minimum order of $15 is required with credit cards. Pay by check, money order or major credit card.

Home Fabric Mills
882 South Main St. P.O. Box 888 Cheshire, CT 06410
Phone: (203) 272-3529

Decorator fabrics and custom services have been the specialty of Home Fabric Mills for 25 years. This company features top-quality upholstery and drapery materials at average savings of up to 50%. Home decorators can choose from an abundant stock of first-quality goods from Robert Allen, Covington, Kaufmann, Waverly, Wolf, and other top manufacturers.

In stock is an abundant supply of drapery and upholstery materials, workroom supplies, trim, linings, and other related goods.

Home Fabric Mills has a brochure which is free upon request. You can get a price quote by phone or by mail with a SASE. Method of payment is check, money order or MasterCard and VISA (the company accepts credit cards on out-of-state mail orders only).

The Linen Source
5401 Hangar Court P.O. Box 31151
Tampa, FL 33631-3151
Phone: 800-431-2620 FAX: (813) 882-4605

The Linen Source features savings of up to 50% on sheet sets by Bill Blass, Waverly, Liberty of London, and Croscill as well as great savings on table linens and accessories. There's also a selection of handcrafted rugs and other home decorator goods.

The company provides a free catalog which is available upon request. Request the catalog by phone or mail. Orders are usually shipped within two days of receipt (depending on availability). The Linen Source will not ship freight outside the continental U.S.. When your total purchase exceeds $100, The Linen Source has an installment plan available (applies to credit card payments only). Pay by check, money order, or major credit card.

Mother Hart's Natural Products, Inc.
P.O. Box 4229 Boynton Beach, FL 33424-4229
Phone: (407) 738-5866 (407) 734-5942

Mail-order shoppers who are looking for "natural" bargains will be delighted to discover Mother Hart. Featuring natural-fiber bed and bath linens and clothing, Mother Hart offers savings of up to 70%.

This company stocks a good selection of flannel sheets and sheet blankets to fit any size bed. Flannel sheets for waterbeds are also available. Also in stock are box spring covers and pads, wool mattress pads, cotton covers, and pillows made of down, feathers and wool.

Mother Hart's catalog is free upon request and features clothing and other products as well as linens. This is a small company and some items in the catalog may be available in limited quantities only.

Satisfaction is guaranteed on each purchase, with unused goods accepted as returns within 30 days. Pay by check, money order or major credit card.

Rubin & Green, Inc.
290 Grand St. New York, NY 10002
Phone: (212) 266-0313 (212) 226-5015

Mail-order shoppers can choose from decorator and upholstery fabrics from famous manufacturers such as David & Dash, Schumacher, Jay Yang, Robert Allen, and others. Rubin & Green also offers custom service, creating custom-made bedspreads, draperies, and other accessories for home decorators.

Call for a price quote and/or information about goods and services or send a letter with a SASE. Pay by check, money order, or major credit card.

XXIII

Photographic and Processing Equipment:

Cameras, photographic and darkroom equipment, optics, film, and services

Both amateurs and professionals can take advantage of mail-order discount prices on cameras and photographic equipment and accessories. Whether you are shopping for just the basics— cameras, bulbs, film; film-processing services; or lenses; filters; darkroom equipment, splicers, camcorders, and slide projectors, you can save 40% and more on many mail-order purchases.

Amateur photographers should consult more knowledgeable friends, colleagues, or professionals before purchasing a camera and/or equipment, to make sure they get exactly what they need. Here are a couple of general buying tips:

1) Beware of grey-market goods (see "How To Shop By Mail" section of this catalog). While such goods are usually offered at "good" prices, they may not be covered by valid U.S. warranties. You can contact the manufacturer of the product(s) you're interested and find out if the mail-order firm you're

considering is an authorized distributor of its products. You should also ask the mail-order company if the warranty is honored by the manufacturer's U.S. service centers.

2) Make sure the mail-order firm hasn't "repackaged" a manufacturer's camera package by removing extra lenses, lens covers and other accessories from the original package. Some camera sellers have been known to replace such original packaging with inferior goods, and then offer the camera outfit at a greatly reduced price. The manufacturer's original lens covers, extra lenses, and other accessories may then be sold as "extras". If you buy those "extras" (which were intended by the manufacturer to be included in the original outfit), you could end up paying close to the actual list price, negating any savings.

For more buying tips and information, contact your local Better Business Bureau and inquire about receiving a copy of its booklet, "Buying Photographic Equipment By Mail".

Astronomical/Christophers, LTD.
2401 Tee Circle, Suite 106-W Norman, OK 73069
Phone: 800-422-7876

For over 20 years Astronomical/Christophers (formerly Ad-Libs Astronomics) has been selling some of the finest quality telescopes and astronomical equipment on the market. Prices are up to 50% below typical list prices.

The company's catalog ($2.00, refundable) shows a good selection of optics (telescopes, binoculars) and accessories by Celestron, Bushnell, Astromedia, Edmund, Bausch & Lomb, Meade, Mirador, Day Star, Swarovski, TeleVue, Kowa, Motofocus, and Questar, among others. Astronomical equipment including reflector and refractor telescopes, eyepieces, lenses, mirrors, photo adapters, filters, equatorial mounts and wedges, tripods, and spotting scopes are all in stock. There's also a selection of maps, atlases, manuals, books, star charts, and slides to help novice astronomers, as well as buying guidelines.

Send $2.00 for the catalog. A price list is available for a long SASE. Get a price quote by phone or by mail. Pay by check, money order or major credit card. The company requires a minimum order of $25.00.

Camera World of Oregon
500 S.W. 5th Avenue Portland, OR 97204
Phone: (503) 227-6088 (information, customer service)
800-222-1557 (orders) FAX: (503) 222-7070

Established in 1977, Camera World of Oregon is one of the nation's largest photo and video camcorder mail-order dealers. The company offers a huge selection of name-brand cameras and accessories and camcorders. Camera World's prices are competitive with those of other firms selling comparable goods.

You'll find cameras, lenses, binoculars, flashes, tripods, meters, camcorders, video recorders, slide projectors, video lights, and other related goods. Name brands available include Olympus, Pentax, Minolta, Nikon, Canon, Panasonic, RCA, JVC, Sony, Hitachi, Quasar, Kodak, Sigma, and others. The company also guarantees full USA warranties on all its major products.

Call the company for more information. Authorized returns are accepted within 14 days. Non-defective merchandise returned is subject to a minimal restocking fee. Pay by check, money order or major credit card.

Freestyle
5120 Sunset BLVD. Los Angeles, CA 90027
Phone: 800-292-6137 (orders) (213) 660-3460
(information) FAX: (213) 660-4885

Freestyle has been a reliable "photo source" for over 40 years, providing quality goods at affordable prices. The company has in stock a good selection of color film, black-and-white film and paper, color and black-and-white papers, and accessories.

The company's free 48-page catalog lists name brand products such as color film by Kodak, color and black and white papers by Mitsubishi and Arista; black and white film and paper by Ilford, Ultra, Kodak, Fuji, and Arista, and accessories, including tanks and reels, darkroom accessories (grain focusers, thermometers, enlarging easels), deluxe mount boards, optical glass filters, reloadable 35mm cartridges, and much more.

Call the company for more information and to request a free catalog. Pay by check or money order (minimum order $20.00) or by major credit card (minimum order $35.00).

Orion Telescope Center

2450 17th Avenue P.O. Box 1158
Santa Cruz, CA 95061-1158
Phone: 800-447-1001 800-443-1001 (in CA)
FAX: (408) 464-0446

Stargazers can find a huge selection of telescopes, binoculars and accessories listed in Orion's discount catalog. The company has been in business since the mid-1970s, and offers savings of up to 40% on everything from eyepieces to astronomy videos.

A recent 75-page catalog lists deep space, lunar and planetary reflector telescopes for beginning and advanced observers, equatorial refractors, and spotting scopes by Orion and Celestron. Filters, eyepieces and barlows, components (diagonal mirrors, focusers and mounts), camera adapters, tripods, telescope covers, equipment cases, astronomy videos, star charts and atlases, books, computer software (for DOS and Windows— "The Sky", "Voyager II", "Dance of the Planets"), and other accessories. The catalog provides information on choosing a telescope.

Binoculars are also in stock at Orion. You'll find astronomy and deep sky binoculars by Orion, Celestron Pro binoculars, and Alderblick binoculars for birding and casual astronomy. Binocular accessories, such as dew caps, lens caps, tripod adapters, and straps, are also available.

Orion's catalog is free upon request. Satisfaction is guaranteed. Returns are accepted within 30 days for a refund. Pay by check, money order or major credit card.

Peach State Photo
1706 Chantilly Drive Atlanta, GA 30324
Phone: (404) 633-2699 (information, customer service)
800-766-9653 (orders) FAX: (404) 321-6316

Peach State Photo is a division of Wolf Camera & Video, one of the nation's leading photographic and video dealers. In business for over 15 years, Peach State Photo offers competitive mail-order prices that are below typical retail prices on comparable goods. Save up to 25% on some items.

Camera buffs can choose from a selection of cameras by manufacturers such as Nikon, Minolta, Canon, Olympus, Fuji, Pentax, and others. Lenses by Nikon, Sigma, and Tamron; flashes; camera and video bags; and binoculars by Minolta and Nikon are also in stock. You can also order film by Kodak, Polaroid, and Ilford, as well as the most popular types of filters.

Peach State also sells video equipment and accessories. Video recorders by Nikon, Panasonic, Sony, Canon, and other manufacturers; Sony VCR's; tripods; video tape; video lights; and video batteries are also available. All items are new and covered by USA warranties. The company does not sell grey market goods.

Call the company for more information and to inquire about the availability of product literature. Authorized returns are accepted within 15 days (A minimal restocking fee may be applied to some returns). Pay by check, money order or major credit card. No C.O.D. orders are accepted.

Pro Photo Labs
P.O. Box 2000 West Caldwell, NJ 07007

Pro Photo offers film-processing services at some of the lowest prices available. The company specializes in film developing and enlargements, and provides friendly, efficient service to new and repeat customers alike. You can get your 35mm, 110, 126, and Disc film developed by Pro Photo. The company will also make prints from your 35mm slides and negatives. Custom services such as enlargements, and black and white proof sheets are also offered.

Film mailers are available free upon request. Pay by check, money order or major credit card (there is a minimum order of $5.00 with credit cards).

Solar Cine Products
4247 South Kedzie Avenue Chicago, IL 60632
Phone: (312) 254-8310

Since 1937, both amateur and professional photographers have been taking advantage of Solar Cine's great buys on photographic equipment and supplies. Past catalogs have shown an outstanding selection of still and movie equipment, including video. You'll find cameras by Minolta, Pentax, Fuji, Kodak, Polaroid, Canon, and other manufacturers, as well as lenses, tripods, darkroom equipment, studio lights, books, and many other supplies and accessories. Electronic and processing services are also available.

A price quote is available by phone or by mail with a SASE. The company's catalog is free upon request. Pay by check, money order or major credit card. There is a minimum order of $10.00 required.

World of 35mm
P.O. Box 2845 Clifton, NJ 07015.

Film-processing services at affordable prices are available from World of 35mm. The company can save you up to 50% on film-developing and other services. You can have World of 35mm develop and print 35mm negatives and slides, duplicate slides, and make enlargements. Other custom services are also available. The company uses Kodak papers.

Film mailers are available free upon request. The company will replace lost or damaged film with an equal amount of unexposed film. Pay by check or money order.

XXIV

Smoking Needs:

Pipes and accessories, tobacco, and cigars

Even though there is no longer any disputing the fact that smoking is a health hazard, many people still enjoy pipe smoking and/or fine cigars. While smokers do so at their own "health-risk", and are finding it increasingly difficult to smoke in public places, there are still many established tobacconists who sell smoking needs at discounts of 50% and more.

The companies listed in this section have all been in business for many years and offer cigars, pipes, pipe tobacco, and smoking accessories, often at well below retail prices.

Famous Smoke Shop, Inc.
55 W. 39th St. New York, NY 10018
Phone: 800-672-5544 (212) 221-1408 (in NY)

Name-brand and generic cigars and tobacco at savings of up to 40% are available from the Famous Smoke Shop. The firm has been in business for over 50 years offering smokers a great selection of the finest hand-rolled cigars available. Imported brands include Arturo Fuente, Canaria, Cuesta-Rey,

Dom Domingo, Don Diego, Flor Palmera, Macanudo, Primo Del Rey, Punch, Temple Hall, Troya, and many others.

Famous also carries an assortment of fine, unbranded house cigars at great savings. Pipe tobaccos by Dunhill, MacBarens, James Russell, and others are also in stock. Call or write to request the Famous Smoke Shop free catalog.

Satisfaction with every order is guaranteed. Returns are accepted. C.O.D. orders are accepted. Pay by check, money order or major credit card.

Wally Frank LTD.
63-25 69th St. Middle Village, NY 11379
Phone: (718) 326-2233

In business for over 60 years, Wally Frank offers a selection of cigars, pipes, and tobaccos. Mail-order shoppers can expect savings of up to 50% on some brand name cigars and tobacco.

The company's free catalog lists many of its fine cigars, including brands such as Don Diego, Lancer, Martinez, Te-Amo, H. Upmann, and others. Also available are privately produced "smoke-alikes" and some closeout specials. Briar, corncob and meerschaum pipes, pipe tobacco, pipe-cleaning tools, racks, lighters, humidors, and other smoking needs are also sold. Call or write Wally Frank to request your free catalog. Payment may be made by check, money order or major credit card.

Holt's Tobacconist
N.W. Corner 16th & Sansom Sts. Philadelphia, PA 19102
Phone: (800) 523-1641 FAX: (215) 563-2751

Since 1898, Holt's has been supplying smokers with fine cigars, tobacco, pipes and accessories. Holt's prices are often well below average retail prices, with savings of 25% and more on comparable goods.

Holt's offers a good selection of handmade imported cigars, including brands such as Ashton, Julia Marlowe, Davidoff, Cortesia, Arturo Fuente, Montesino, Macanudo, Montecruz, Partagas, Primo Del Rey, Royal Jamica, Don Diego, Bohemia, and many others. Also available are Italian pipes and an outstanding selection of fine pipe tobaccos. Imported tobaccos include Ashton, Balkan Sobrannie, Condor, Davidoff, Dunhill, Erinmore, MacBaren, McClelland, St. Bruno, Three Nuns, Troost, Wessex, Capstan, Four Square, and Harry A. Tint & Sons. Holt's custom blends are also available.

The company also carries lighters, Swiss Army knives and watches, and a complete line of writing instruments, including pens by Mont Blanc, Waterman, Parker, and others.

Call for prices and information. Ask about Holt's catalog. All merchandise is guaranteed. Returns are accepted for full refund, credit or replacement. All orders are shipped within 24 hours. Minimum order is $10. Pay by check, money order or major credit card.

Thompson Cigar Company
5401 Hanger CT. Tampa, FL 33634
Phone: (813) 884-6344

Thompson Cigar's free catalog shows both national-brand and private-label cigars at savings of up to 30%. The company, in operation since 1915, also features pipe tobacco, pipes, and accessories.

Cigars in stock include those by Hoya de Monterrey, Macanudo, Montecruz, Partagas, Royal Jamaica, and many others. Thompson's also has its own line of cigars available. Also in stock are an assortment of pipe tobacco blends, handmade pipes, ashtrays, humidors, and other smoking accessories and gift ideas.

Call or write to request your free catalog. Satisfaction is guaranteed. Pay by check, money order or major credit card.

XXV

Sporting Goods And Recreation Equipment:

Fishing and hunting gear, camping equipment, sports equipment

All work and no play is no fun at all. Everyone needs at least a little recreation in their lives. Some people forgo a favorite sport or recreation because retail prices on quality equipment and supplies is beyond their budgets. The listings in this section can help solve that problem. The companies listed offer average mail-order savings of up to 30% on everything from squash racquets to golf tees. Fishermen, hunters, bicyclists, water- skiers, runners, campers, hikers, tennis players, golfers, and archers can all save on quality gear by shopping by mail.

The Austad Company
P.O. Box 1428 Sioux Falls, SD 57196-1428
Phone: (605) 336-3135

While Austad sells a variety of sporting goods and equipment, it is best known for offering a full range of golfing equipment and supplies. Savings average from 15% to 40% and even more on some overstocked and closeout goods.

The company features a large selection of golf clubs by Pinnacle, Ram, Hogan, and other top manufacturers. The clubs are available in sets or as singles, for men, women, and young golfers. All other golfing needs are also in stock— golf balls (Top Flite, Hogan, Titleist, Pinnacle, and other brands), tees, gloves, bags, carts, club head covers, umbrellas, score-card holders, golf shoes, and golf apparel. There's also a selection of "how-to" videos and practice equipment.

Austad's catalog is free upon request. Call or write the company to get on its mailing list. Returns are accepted within 30 days for exchange, credit, or refund. Pay by check, money order, or major credit card.

Bart's Water Ski Center, Inc.
P.O. Box 294 North Webster, IN 46555
Phone: 800-348-5016 800-552-2336 (in IN)
FAX: (219) 834-4246

Water skiers can browse through Bart's free catalog and discover some super bargains on water-skiing gear and supplies. The company has been in business for over 20 years, offering quality goods at prices up to 40% below typical list prices.

The novice or the pro can find water skis at Bart's by such manufacturers as Kidder, EP Skis, Connelly, Jobe, and O'Brien. Also available are floats, tubes, kneeboards, ski vests, wet suits and accessories, swimwear, sunglasses, tow lines, instructive water-skiing videotapes and manuals, and other related items.

Bart's catalog is free upon request. Satisfaction is guaranteed. Returns are accepted within 60 days. Quantity discounts are available. Pay by check, money order or major credit card.

Bowhunters Warehouse, Inc.
1045 Ziegler Road, Box 158 Wellsville, PA 17365
Phone: (717) 432-8611

This company has been supplying bowhunters with quality equipment and supplies since 1978. Everything needed for bow fishing, hunting, and archery is available, with savings of up to 40% on some items.

The Bowhunters Warehouse carries a full range of bows and arrows, quivers, points, bow sights, rests, targets, game calls, feathers, and optics. Name brands include Browning, Bear, Anderson, Jennings, Bushnell, Euston, PSE, Darton, Martin, and other respected manufacturers. You'll also find rifles and assorted shooting equipment, camping gear, outdoor clothing, and other related goods.

The company's catalog is free upon request. Authorized returns are accepted (some returns may be subject to a minimal restocking charge). A minimum order of $10 is required. Pay by check, money order, MasterCard or VISA.

Cabela's, Inc.
812 13th Avenue Sidney, NE 69160
Phone: (308) 254-5505

Cabela's has established a solid reputation for supplying quality fishing and hunting gear at savings of up to 40%. The company's catalog ($2.00) shows one of the nation's finest selections of name brand goods for sportsmen.

For fishermen, Cabela's offers a complete selection of fishing gear by top manufacturers. There are rods and reels (individually and combos) by Daiwa, Garcia, Mitchell, Shakespeare, Shimano, Fenwick, and other manufacturers. A full range of tackle (fishing line, lures, hooks, etc.), tackle boxes, nets, and other fishing equipment is also in stock. Boating accessories such as electric boat motors by Minn Kota, boat covers, seats, winches, marine batteries, dinghies, trailer parts, and downriggers are also sold at affordable prices. Hunters will also find a similar wide selection of gear and supplies, from spotting scopes and ammo pouches to camouflage wear.

Cabela's catalog is available for $2.00. Satisfaction is guaranteed. Returns are accepted for exchange, credit, or refund. Pay by check, money order or major credit card.

Campmor
P.O. Box 997 Paramus, NJ 07653-0997
Phone: (201) 445-5000

Campers can save up to 50% (off list prices) on a fine selection of camping gear and supplies when ordering from Campmor. For over 45 years, Campmor has been offering quality camping gear and outdoor clothing at affordable prices.

Past catalogs have featured cooking equipment by Coleman, tents, sleeping bags, knives, compasses, backpacks, camping and survival books and manuals, and other related goods. Clothing by Borglite Pile, Woolrich, Thinsulate, and Poly-Pro; Timberland boots; and other outdoor wear is also available.

Campmor's catalog is free upon request. Returns are accepted for exchange, credit, or refund. Pay by check, money order or major credit card. There is a minimum order of $20 required when you order by phone.

Custom Golf Clubs, Inc.
10206 N. International HWY. 35 Austin, TX 78753
Phone: (512) 837-4810

Savings of up to 50% on golf equipment and supplies is possible when you order from Custom Golf Clubs. The savings is based on typical prices of comparable name-brand products. You can get clubs made to order, along with a full range of golf accessories and repair equipment.

The company features its own line of custom made clubs ("Goldsmith"), including irons and woods (men's and women's, right-and left-handed) in several degrees of flexibility. The custom department can also supply any length, weight, color, or grip size you specify. Accessories in stock include bags, golf clubs (singles and sets), balls, carts, bags, club covers, gloves, golf shoes, clothing, and many other related items.

If repairs are in order, the company offers replacement parts including club heads and grips, as well as tools, refinishing supplies, and "how-to" guides.

Custom Golf Clubs publishes two catalogs, "Accessories", and "Repairs". The catalogs are available for $1.00 each. Specify which catalog you want. Pay by check, money order or major credit card.

Gander Mountain, Inc.

Box 248, HWY W Wilmont, WI 53192
Phone: 800-558-9410 (order) 800-426-3371
(customer service) FAX: 800-533-2828

Gander Mountain has been "outfitting sportsmen for generations" with quality hunting and fishing gear and apparel. Sportsmen can expect savings of 30% and more on some items.

A recent 207-page catalog lists a full line of rods and reels for fishermen. The selection includes baitcast and spinning reels, rods, and combos by Abu Garcia, Shimano, Quantum, Daiwa, Mitchell, Zebco, Shakespeare, Penn, Berkley, and Silstar. Fishing line by Stren and Dupont; lures by Rapala, Bagley, Storm, Mepps, Rebel, and others; nets, tackle boxes, fishing gloves, rod cases, and other equipment and supplies are also in stock.

Hunters can choose from muzzleloading black powder rifles, replacement parts for shotguns, gun cases, holsters, practice equipment, shell boxes, rifle rests, and other related items. Compound bows, hunting videos, spotting scopes, Pentax binoculars, and sights are also sold.

Marine electronics, trolling motors, boating accessories (bilge pumps, winches, safety vests, flotation jackets, boat seats), outdoor clothing (western shirts, rainwear, field trousers, jackets, work shirts, bib overalls, camo uniforms), and footwear (hiking boots, general terrain shoes, walking shoes, boat shoes), are also available.

The catalog is free upon request. Satisfaction is guaranteed. Returns are accepted for exchange or refund. Pay by check, money order or major credit card.

Holabird Sports Discounters
9008 Yellow Brick Road Baltimore, MD 21237
Phone: (301) 687- 6400 FAX: (301) 687-7311

Whatever your "racquet" may be, Holabird can supply you with the necessary equipment and supplies. You can save up to 40% compared with typical list prices on comparable goods for all types of racquet sports (tennis, squash, racquetball). You'll also get free stringing on all racquets.

In stock are tennis racquets by such top manufacturers as Wilson, Spalding, Dunlop, Wimbledon, Yamaha, Pro-Kennex, Puma, Fox, Fin, Bard, Prince, and many others. Balls by Penn, Dunlop, and Wilson; ball machines; and footwear by Converse, Adidas, Keds, Nike, Reebok, Puma, and other makers are also available.

Racquetball equipment includes Wilson, Pro-Kennex, Voit,

Ektelon, and Leach racquets. Squash players can choose a racquet by Dunlop, Ektelon, Bancroft, Unsquashable, Spalding, or Wilson.

Call or write the company to request a copy of its free catalog. You can get a price quote by phone or by mail with a SASE. Pay by check, money order or major credit card.

Road Runner Sports
6310 Nancy Ridge Road, Suite 101
San Diego, CA 92121-3209
Phone: 800-551-5558

Road Runner Sports offers name-brand running shoes and apparel at savings of up to 35% below typical list prices. The company has over 30 years of experience in outfitting runners.

The company's free catalog lists running shoes by Converse, Avia, Adidas, Nike, Reebok, New Balance, Frank Shorter, Brooks, Etonic, Footjoy, and other top manufacturers. Also in stock are running suits, shorts, T-shirts, socks, and other related items.

Call or write the company to request a free catalog. You can also get a price quote by phone or by mail with a SASE. Pay by check, money order or major credit card.

Stuyvesant Bicycle, Inc.
349 W. 14th Street New York, NY 10014
Phone: (212) 254-5200 (212) 675-2160

Stuyvesant has over 50 years experience selling bicycles and cycling equipment. Mail-order shoppers can expect a savings of up to 30% on some items.

The company carries bicycles for everyone—children to pros—including touring bikes, tandems, city bikes, used bikes, and some closeouts. Stuyvesant also sells professional quality track and racing bikes. Accessories include helmets, jerseys, shoes, pumps, locks, water bottles, and a good selection of parts. Name brands available include Huffy, BMX, Suntour, Ross, Atala, and other manufacturers.

A price quote is available by phone or by mail with a SASE. Pay by check, money order or certified check.

For listings of other sources, selling related goods, see the following sections in this catalog:

Golf Day
375 Beacham Street, Chelsea, MA 02150
Phone: (800) 669-8600
[order hot-line]; (800) 472-4653 [customer
service, catalog request] FAX: (617) 889-2072

Duffers can have a field day browsing through a catalog of Golf Day's bargains. The company sells a wide assortment of golf equipment and accessories at discount prices. In fact, Golf Day offers to "beat any nationally advertised retail mail-order
price" on identical brand-name products (The offer does not apply to volume purchases or lower prices resulting from misprints, closeouts, or going out of business sales). You can expect savings of 40% and more when purchasing from Golf Day.

A past Golf Day catalog features a selection of golf bags by Spalding, MacGregor, and Sun Mountain. Some of the bags were priced as low as $30 under the suggested retail prices. Golfballs by Pro Staff, Titleist, Spalding, Maxfli, Dunlop, and Wilson are also available at low prices. Also in stock are golfclubs by Wilson, Spalding, MacGregor, Trends, Yamaha, and other quality manufacturers. You can purchase entire sets, or individual clubs.

Golf Day also has available gloves, grips, headcovers, hats, rainwear, shoes, cart accessories (seatcovers, windshields, all weather covers), clothing, teaching aids, and videos and books.

Call or write the company and request a free catalog subscription. Satisfaction is guaranteed. Return of unused merchandise is accepted within 30 days for a refund or exchange (returned items must be in new condition and in original boxes). Pay by check, money order or major credit card.

"Army Surplus"

Massachusetts Army & Navy Store— sells a selection of camping and survival gear, including knapsacks, sleeping bags, back packs, air mattresses, mess kits, and other camping equipment.

The Surplus Store— offers sleeping bags, hunting knives, camp stoves, cookwear, and outdoor wear.

"Auto, Marine, etc."

Bass Pro Shops— sells a full range of fishing gear (rods, reels, tackle), boats for fishing, cruising, and skiing; boat accessories; inflatable; water skis; kneeboards; diving fins and snorkles; and outdoor clothing.

"Hardware, Tools, etc."

Northern— sells boating accessories, including bilge pumps, inflators, inflatable, ski tubes, tow-behind tubes, binoculars, BB/pellet rifles, and go-karts.

XXVI

Surplus And Used Goods

Army Surplus

argain hunters can find an interesting assortment of merchandise available when dealing with firms which stock surplus and used goods. The word surplus does not mean inferior quality or useless merchandise. In many cases, surplus goods are military overstock, and obsolete (but still useful) electronics, tools, hardware, and industrial goods.

Most surplus dealers publish catalogs with representative listings of their available stock of goods. You can find smoke detectors, socket wrenches, power tools, computers, camping equipment, clothing, and other bargains in a surplus catalog, and save a considerable amount of money by buying by mail.

H & R Corporation
401 E. Erie Ave. Philadelphia, PA 19134-1187
Phone: (215) 426-1708 FAX: (215) 425-8870

The H & R catalog lists a wide assortment of surplus electronics and computer components at bargain prices. The company has been in business for almost 60 years, and features savings of up to 60% on some items.

Most of the goods listed in the catalog are electronics and computer components, but other items are featured as well. There are oscillators, adapters, capacitors, transformers, keyboards, monitors, circuit breakers, disk drives, video and audio cables, printers, modems, and joysticks. Other surplus goods available include tool cases, binoculars, flashlights, magnets, surge suppressors, telephones, security devices, thermometers, and compasses.

You can get a comprehensive listing of the surplus goods sold by H & R Corporation by requesting the company's free catalog. A price quote is available by phone or by mail. Satisfaction is guaranteed. Returns are accepted within 30 days. Pay by check, money order or major credit card. There is a minimum order of $15.00.

Massachusetts Army & Navy Store
15 Fordham Road Boston, MA 02134
Phone: (617) 783-1250

This company specializes in government surplus apparel and accessories. You can save up to 40% on many items listed in the Massachusetts Army & Navy Store's free catalog.

Don't expect to find formal wear in this catalog. Instead, the listings include an assortment of camouflage clothing, pith helmets, French Foreign Legion caps, U.S. Air Force sunglasses, Vietnam jungle boots, leather pilots' caps, Canadian battle pants, and other related items. There's also a selection of knapsacks, backpacks, sleeping bags, air mattresses, duffel bags, camping gear, mess kits, jeans, bomber jackets, pea coats, and casual footwear.

The catalog is free upon request. Pay by check, money order or major credit card.

Ruvel & Company, Inc.
4128-30 W. Belmont Ave. Chicago, IL 60641
Phone: (312) 286-9494

Campers can find an outstanding selection of government-surplus camping and field goods on display in Ruvel's catalog. Savings average up to 70% off typical retail prices for comparable goods.

The company offers U.S. Army & Navy surplus goods such as leather flying jackets, high-powered binoculars, duffel bags, mosquito netting, and U.S. Army technical manuals. Also available are electric lamps, mess kits, snowshoes, camp stoves, parade gloves, and similar goods.

Ruvel's catalog is available for $2.00. You can get a price quote by phone or by letter with a SASE. Pay by check, money order or major credit card.

Surplus Center P.O.
Box 82209 Lincoln, NE 68501-9973
Phone: 800-488-3407 Fax: 474-5198

Surplus Center has over 60 years experience selling surplus tools, hardware, and other goods at low prices. The company offers name brand merchandise in 33 different categories. You can expect savings of 25% to 80% on over 2000 items, from hydraulics to electrical and home security to hand tools. The company purchases large quantities of manufacturer's surplus or excess stock, and over 80% of the products it sells are brand new, never used.

Surplus Center is a warehouse distributor for many top equipment manufacturers, including Gresen Hydraulics, Hydro Pumps, Prince Hydraulics, and David White surveying instruments. All these items are brand new, direct from the factory, and covered by full warranty. Items in stock include submersible pumps, hydraulic powered pressure washers, chemical pumps, hydraulic cylinders, fittings, motors, pumps, and valves; sighting levels; hand levels; aluminum tripods; hoists; air compressors, welders; winches, generators, gearboxes, and motors.

There's also a selection of automotive equipment such as alternators, military surplus 55 gallon fuel tanks, steering assembly, headlamp assembly, combination turn signal, high beam, horn switch; oil pressure gauge kits; emergency jumper cables; and Fram oil filters. Home and vehicle security systems (see "Hardware" section), propane heaters, tools (air drills, hammers, sanders, steel marking stamp sets, soldering irons, calipers), transformers, battery chargers, heating elements, immersion heaters, ac and dc blowers, sprayers and spraying outfits, gas engines, and hundreds more items are also in stock. You can select from brand names such as G.E., Cessna, Briggs& Stratton, Kawasaki, and many others.

Surplus Center publishes a comprehensive 147-page catalog, which is free upon request. Returns are accepted. Some returns are subject to a minimal restocking charge. Pay by check, money order or major credit card.

The Surplus Store
P.O. Box 2727 Culver City, CA 90231-2727
Phone: (213) 870-4687

If you're looking for genuine and/or reproduction government surplus, this company can supply your needs. The Surplus Store is a division of the Airborne Sales Company, and offers a typical savings of up to 50% off average retail prices on camping gear and other surplus goods.

The company specializes in camping gear, and paramilitary and survival gear. Among the goods available are genuine G.I. uniforms, caps and hats, jungle boots and oxfords, hunting knives, sleeping bags, folding shovels, knapsacks, first-aid kits, campstoves, and inflatable dinghies.

The Surplus Store catalog is free upon request. Returns are accepted within 30 days. Pay by check, money order or major credit card. The minimum order is $15.

American Science & Surplus Co.
3605 Howard St., Skokie, IL 60076
Phone: (708) 982-0870

American Science & Surplus specializes in industrial and military surplus items of a scientific and/or mechanical nature. In business since 1937, AS & S offers savings on thousands of surplus items, including tools, motors, books, lenses, lasers, blowers, speakers, mechanical devices, electronic components, electronic equipment, and an assortment of novelties and gadgets. There are also supplies for the office and lab, and for crafting and hobbies.

Send $1.00 to the above address for the AS & S 64-page catalog. Pay by check, money order or major credit card.

Duke's Army Surplus, Inc.
1015-124 Atlantic Blvd., Atlantic Beach, FL 32233
Phone: (904) 390-6531

Duke's Army Surplus offers a selection of uniforms, boots, hats, T-shirts, and many other surplus items at genuine savings. Send $1.00 for Duke's complete surplus catalog. Pay by check, money order, MasterCard or VISA.

Ruvel & Company, Inc.
4128-30 W. Belmont Ave., Chicago, IL 60641
Phone: (312) 286-9494; (312) 286-9323

Since 1965, Ruvel & Co. has been a leading source for government camping and field surplus. Savings range up to 70% on some items.

A recent Ruvel & Co. catalog features USMC shooting jackets, field jackets, G.I. duffel bags, leather flying jackets, high-powered binoculars, mosquito netting, U.S. Army technical manuals, rations, and many other surplus items. Ruvel's has also offered carbide and electric lamps by Justrite, dinghies, messkits, snow shoes, parade gloves, and night sticks.

Send $2.00 for a catalog of available surplus items. Since this is the type of merchandise that sells quickly, you should order as soon as you find something in the catalog that you want. Pay by check, money order or major credit card.

XXVII

Toys And Games:

Fantastic savings on fun for children and adults

M any unique toys and games for kids and grown ups can be purchased at a savings by mail-order. The companies listed in this section offer a selection of wooden toys, educational toys (puzzles, maps, card games), kites, party supplies, games, dolls, and other fun items at a savings of 20% and more.

When buying toys for children, you should consider items that are suitable to his or her physical capabilities, as well as mental and social development. Safety and durable construction should also be determining factors.

Cherry Tree Toys, Inc.
P.O. Box 369-140 Belmont, OH 43718
Phone: (614) 484-4363 FAX: (614) 484-4388

Since the early 1980s, Cherry Tree Toys has been selling a collection of unique wooden toy kits and parts. The company offers savings of up to 50% below typical retail prices for similar toy kits and parts.

A recent catalog ($1.00) featured a host of kits for pull

toys, doll houses, wooden wagons, sleds, whirligigs, nursery character clocks, vintage cars, and many other kits. Wooden parts such as wheels, spindles, smokestacks, knobs, pulls, beads, and pegs are also available. You'll also find music boxes, plans and patterns, "how-to" books, and other items.

Send $1.00 for the company's catalog. Satisfaction is guaranteed. Returns are accepted for exchange, refund, or credit. Pay by check, money order, MasterCard or VISA. C.O.D. orders are accepted.

Educational Toys, Inc.
Box 630685 Miami, FLA 33163
Phone: 800-554-5414 (ext. 109)

Educational Toys features an extensive line of products that are unique, educational, and entertaining. Each product is tested carefully for safety and accuracy. The company's toys are designed for ages 3 to adult, and are reasonably priced.

You'll find authentic dinosaur replicas, vanishing wild replicas, educational card games, microscopes, posters, and other toys listed in Educational Toys' free catalog. Call or write the company to request a copy of the full-color catalog. Pay by check, money order or major credit card.

Into the Wind
1408 Pearl Street Boulder, CO 80302
Phone: 800-541-0314

The next time you're told to "go fly a kite", don't take it as an insult, take it as an opportunity to check out the fantastic selection of kites available from Into the Wind. For 13 years, Into the Wind has been carrying some of the most amazing flying kites available anywhere, and at affordable prices.

Even if you're a beginner, you'll find something in the

company's free catalog to get you into the kite-flying mood. The kites listed include Stunt kites, which are flown on two strings (one for each hand). These kites are capable of moving at 60 mph or more in strong winds. Beginners, intermediate, ultralight, speed fliers, radical fliers, and stunt kite lines are available.

The catalog also lists box, delta, diamond, dragon, airfoil and sled, and fighter kites. The company also stocks mylar and nylon tails and accessories such as kite cases, kite packs, field repair kits, wind meters, kite lights, gloves, and an assortment of line and reels. Boomerangs, german gliders, flying discs, yoyos, and assorted flying toys are also sold.

Into the Wind's catalog provides a guide to rate its kites for ease of flying and wind range. The guide is especially helpful to beginners. There's also a section which lists kites available for under $13.00.

Call or write the company to request a free catalog. Satisfaction is guaranteed. Returns are accepted for a refund or exchange. Pay by check, money order or major credit card.

Paradise Products, Inc.
P.O. Box 568 El Cerrito, CA 94530
Phone: (415) 524-8300

Paradise Products can help you be the life of the party by offering materials and supplies for over 120 different kinds of theme events. The company has 40 years of experience and can save you up to 50% compared with prices charged by typical retail party-supply outlets.

If you are planning a theme event, you should take a look at Paradise Products' catalog ($2.00). The company has materials and supplies for many different theme parties, including Hawaiian luaus, Super bowl parties, St. Patrick's Day, July Fourth Parties, pirate parties, Oktoberfest, and other themes. You can also get what you need if the party's theme centers around a specific era, such as the Roaring 20s, or the 1950s. Accessories such as balloons, streamers, bells, party hats, crepe paper by the roll, glassware, garlands, and tissue balls are also available.

Send $2.00 for the company's catalog. Satisfaction is guaranteed. Pay by check, money order or major credit card.

"Hardware, Tools, etc."

Leichtung Workshops— sells die-cast metal kits for building "back-to-the- fifties Bikes", die-cast metal and brass WWII Spitfire kits, patterns for creative wooden construction toys (earth-moving equipment, highway trucks, steam shovels), plans for small-scale Christmas elves, Santa sleigh and reindeer.

"General Merchandise"

Lillian Vernon— offers a selection of toys and games, including marbles, Chinese checkers, magic boxes, die-cast metal sports cars, play mats, stencil kits, stacking blocks, solid wood rocking horses, dolls and accessories, tops, educational toys (clocks, calendars, magnetic puzzles), coin collection kits, stickers and sticker albums, mosaic art kits, and many other fun and educational products for children.

Bennet Brothers, Inc.— offers a group of toys by Playskool, Hasbro, and Fisher Price. Also in stock are board games, play cards, radio-controlled cars and planes, and collector's trains.

XXVIII

Travel: Business and Pleasure Travel Savings

Travelling can be one of life's most enjoyable and rewarding experiences, but it can also be one of life's most expensive experiences as well. Whatever your reason for travelling, whatever your destination, there are ways to do it more economically. If you are planning a vacation, trip, cruise, etc., you should investigate every savings possibility before making a financial commitment.

There are actually several ways you can save an average of 20% to 30% on travel. As is the case with shopping in general, the more you know about the goods or services you need, the better your chances of getting them at a savings.

Buying and Travel Clubs

Buying clubs (see "General Merchandise" section in this catalog) establish working relationships with different firms to provide a wide range of good and services (at discount prices) to its members. Many buying clubs have such arrangements with travel agencies. A club member can save on travel booked through his or her buying club's travel agency. Some buying club members can also get lower rates on hotel accommodations.

Some clubs are "travel only" clubs, such as "cruise-only agencies". These agencies operate as private clubs and usually charge $25 to $50 a year for club membership. Members receive newsletters, gifts (flight bags, etc.), the best cabin selection, and in many cases, discount prices on various cruises. Travel clubs can save you a considerable amount if you do a lot of travelling. Here are two well-respected travel clubs:

Worldwide Discount Travel Club

1674 Meridian Ave. Miami Beach, FL 33139
Phone: (305) 534-2082

Annual membership rate is $50. Call or write the company for more information.

MVP Cruise Club

917 N. Broadway North Massapequa, NY
Phone: 800-252-4242 (516) 541-7782 (in NY)

Annual membership fee is $30. Call the toll-free number for information.

"Cruise Travel Magazine" (a major cruise publication), is a good source if you're looking for agencies or clubs that handle cruises.

Standby Travelling

Travelling on a standby or "last-minute booking" basis can result in discounts that range from 25% to more than 60% on cruises and air travel. You have to be flexible in order to travel this way— in some cases, you should be prepared to leave on as little as 24 hours notice. Cancelled flights, cruises, unsold cabins, etc., can bring travel prices well below typical rates for anyone who is flexible enough to take advantage of such last-minute opportunities.

Airhitch is one such company which deals in standby travel. This company conducts most of its business by mail, but you must first phone for information. Call Airhitch at 800-372-1234, or (212) 864-2000.

Consolidators

Another way to save on travel expenses is to book your trip through a consolidator. A consolidator purchases airplane tickets, cruise slots, and blocks of rooms from various airlines, charter cruise agents, and hotels. The consolidator then sells the airplane seats and rooms for a good deal less than individual tickets and accommodations would have cost if you bought them directly from the airline or other supplier. Here are two such consolidators:

Council Charter New York, NY 10001 800-223-7402 (212) 661-0311

In business for over 40 years, Council Charter invites you to call its toll-free number for more information, and to find out what is currently available.

Unitravel Corporation
St. Louis, MO 63155
800-325-2222

Unitravel is one of the nation's most respected travel consolidators. The company books flights in the U.S. and Europe and sells directly to individual travellers. Call the toll-free number for more information.

Travel Agents

In many cases, booking with a full-service travel agent can save you both time and money. The agent can make all your travel arrangements, dealing directly with cruise companies, airlines, hotels, resorts, and car-rental agencies. You won't be charged a service fee because agents make money on commissions from the travel supplier (cruise lines, airlines, etc.). You'll also avoid long distance calls and postage.

A good way to find a qualified travel agent is to look through the Yellow Pages. Look for agents identified as members of the American Society of Travel Agents (ASTA) or Cruise Lines International Association (CLIA).

Cruise-Only Travel Agents

Most competent travel agents can get you a good price on a cruise, but cruise-only agents are likely to do much better. By booking your cruise through a cruise-only travel agency, you can save as much as 25% to 35% on out-of-season sailings and discount fares. Here are several of the largest cruise-only travel agencies;

Cruises of Distinction
Montclair, NJ
Phone: (800) 327-3021

This cruise-only agency offers an assortment of discounted cruises. A catalog is also available. Call the toll-free number listed above.

The Cruise Line
Miami, FL
Phone: (800) 327-3021

For the past decade, this Miami-based cruise-only agency has been a clearinghouse for discount cruises.

Spur of the Moment Cruises
Phone: (800) 343-1991

Last-minute bargains on exotic cruises is the specialty of this cruise-only agency. A last-minute booking is one made three months or less before sailing. Discounts increase the closer you get to the sailing date, sometimes reaching as much as 60%.

Landry & Kling
Coral Gables, FL
Phone: (800) 448-9002

Based in Coral Gables, Fl since 1982, this agency is the one to contact for special-interest cruises.

World Wide Cruises
Fort Lauderdale, FL
Phone: (800) 882-900o

This cruise-only agency has been in operation for seven years and is a volume discounter.

For a complete list of other cruise-only agencies in your area, send a SASE to:

National Association of Cruise
P.O. Box 7209,
Freeport, NY 11520.

For other listings of companies which also sell toys and games see the following sections in this catalog:

XXIX

Secret Sources For Buying Almost Anything For As Low As $.10 On The Dollar

Most of the wholesale (and below) sources in this edition of The Wholesale Bargains & Free Stuff Guide have catalogs and price lists available for wholesale bargain hunters. Some of these sources also advertise in various monthly publications. There are, however, many other relatively "secret" sources for buying quality brand-name merchandise which do not have catalogs and seldom advertise. If taken advantage of, these "secret" wholesale sources-can save you thousands of dollars every year. You can save on practically everything imaginable, including cars, boats, home furnishings, entertainment systems, tools, lawn and garden equipment, expensive jewelry, carpet, scrap metal, motorcycles, stereos, auto parts, computers, building supplies, cleaning supplies, land, or even a home! Many of these items are sold for well below wholesale— some as low as $.10 on the dollar!

It may surprise you to find out that many of these "secret" sources for exceptional bargains are a part of the U.S. Government. That's right! You can save thousands of dollars by buying practically everything you need at government auctions. This chapter will tell you who to contact, and how to take advantage of the fantastic bargains offered by the government.

Government-Seized, And Surplus Property At Almost Give-Away Prices

The federal and state governments are excellent sources for bargains on virtually any type of merchandise imaginable. You can save thousands of dollars by purchasing surplus government property and property seized by various government agencies. The government sells its surplus and confiscated property by conducting regular auctions around the country. The InternalRevenue Service auctions off an assortment of property which has been seized from delinquent taxpayers. The U.S. Customs Service auctions seized property which has been brought in illegally from another country. The U.S. Marshals Service sells property seized from convicted drug dealers, and other crime related cases.

Homes, which have been repossessed on government foreclosures, are auctioned off by The U.S. Department of Housing.

As a matter of fact, anything you are looking for, from a camera to an entire working business, can be bought—often at unbelievably low prices—at government auctions. You can buy individual items for your own personal use, or you can buy a large inventory for resale at a huge profit.

Here are some actual sales from past auctions: Nikon 35mm camera for $10; 3 bedroom home for $100; Winnebago motor home for $13,000; like-new Corvette for $2,000; a 1987 motorhome for $300; a 1989 Honda motorcycle for $75; a 1965 Mustang for $50; a 1989 Mercedes for $200; a 1K diamond ring for $10; a giant screen TV for $575; and a $143,000 apartment building sold for $38,500.

Since the federal government does not advertise, the circumstances (date, time, location) and inventory of these auctions are virtually a secret to most people. That's good news for you, because it means less competition in bidding on merchandise.

Listed below are several federal government auctions and the offices you can contact for more information and to get on auction mailing lists.

Buying Property From The Federal Government

The federal government offers a remarkable amount and assortment of property and merchandise through auctions conducted by a number of different governmental agencies. The auctions are open to anyone who wants to bid. Sales are conducted through public auctions, as well as sealed and open bids.

IRS Auctions

Believe it or not, you can get great bargains from the Internal Revenue Service (IRS)! The IRS auctions off a wide assortment of property which has been seized from delinquent taxpayers. You can bid on all sorts of merchandise, including real estate, automobiles (and other vehicles), office and industrial equipment and hundreds of other items seized from delinquent taxpayers. The property is sold by both sealed bid and public auctions (see chapter 10).

There are some super bargains to be found at IRS auctions. Abidder at a past auction purchased a 2-story house for $350. A Valentino fur sold for $550. One bidder purchased over $2,500 worth of computer equipment including monitors, keyboard, disk drives, and printers, for $310. Other IRS auctions have yielded VCRs for as low as $20, and computers for

$100 to $500.

Successful bidders may pay for merchandise with cash, certified or cashier's check, or money order. Full payment may be required at the time of the sale or a downpayment of 20% or $200 (whichever is greater) may be required to hold the property until the balance is paid. In the latter case, the balance due must be paid by a specified date within one month of the date of the sale.

It should be noted that land, which has been seized from delinquent taxpayers, may be redeemed by the original owners up to 180 days after the property has been sold at auction. That means the purchaser of such land will not be issued a legal deed to the property until the time period for redeeming it has passed.

If you've been taking a beating from the IRS every year at tax time, here's your chance to even things out. You can actually save thousands of dollars every year by buying IRS-seized property. You'll need to contact a local office to find out how you can get on a "bidders list" for IRS auctions in your area. You can call the INTERNAL REVENUE SERVICE NATIONAL INFORMATION HOTLINE: (800) 829-1040, and find out which local office you should contact.

U.S. Customs Service Auctions

The U.S. Customs Service auctions an amazing selection of merchandise which has been forfeited and confiscated after being brought in from another country. Property which has been brought into the country illegally (contraband) and/or property for which the owner can not pay the duty is seized and subsequently auctioned to the general public.

You can bid on real estate, clothing, jewelry, furniture, computers, tools, boats (both pleasure and commercial), automobiles, and hundreds of other items. At one auction, a

$2,200, 2 carat diamond ring sold for under $200! Another ring, worth $35,000, sold for $8000. One bidder bought $2,000 worth of auto parts for $700, and another purchased a Mercedes Benz for $600. A Waterfordcrystal candelabrum, valued at $300, sold for $40, and $50 ski vests have sold for $8.00.

Of course, such remarkable bargains won't be available at every auction. In some cases, you might even have to pay close-to-market prices for certain merchandise. However, below wholesale bargains are possible every time you bid on U.S.Customs-seized property. Sales are conducted by public auctions, as well as sealed and open bids. The items are sold by lot at these auctions. There may be oneitem in a lot or several items, and bidders must bid on the entire lot.

A recent public auction (in Ohio) of merchandise purchased at a U.S. Customs Auction featured mahogany furniture (Davenport, Chippendale glass cabinet, Drop front bureau desk, Chippendale wine table, Dutch carved leather chairs, Regency table); Handmade Oriental carpets in all sizes from Kashmir, Turkey, China, and Pakistan; Oriental Art (porcelain fishbowls and vases, Cloisonne Clock, Mother of Pearl Screens and Cabinets, and carvings); Tiffany style lamps; and bronze sculptures.

Before you can "cash in' on U.S. Customs seized inventory, you must get on a mailing list. For $25 per year, you can subscribe to a mailing list of items to be auctioned in one specific region of the U.S. You can subscribe to a nationwide mailing list for
$50 per year. There are five regions: General, Northeast sales, Southeast sales, Northwest sales, and Southwest sales. Either a $25 or $50 subscription will bring you fliers which provide descriptions of merchandise to be sold at future auctions. The
first flier usually takes a month to a month-and-a-half to arrive following your subscription. Thereafter, you will receive

fliers three weeks before an auction's scheduled viewing peri-od. The fliers will provide you with information on where and when you can inspect the merchandise as well as specific auc-tion procedures.

To get on a mailing list, you must call the number listed below, or send your name, address, telephone number, and a money order (for $25 or $50, depending upon which mailing list you prefer) to the following address:

E.G. & Dynatrend
2300 Clarendon Blvd., Suite 705
Arlington, VA 22201
Phone: (703) 351-7880
703) 351-7887 [this is the U.S. Customs Public Auction Line. You can call this number to subscribe to the mailing list and to get more information about U.S. Customs auctions].

E.G. & Dynatrend is under contract with the U.S. Customs Service to conduct auctions of seized property. The proceeds of the auctions are forwarded to the Department of Treasury of which the Customs Service is a branch.

U.S Marshals Service Auctions

Each year, the U.S. Marshals Service auctions off millions of dollars worth of property which has been confiscated by the Drug Enforcement Agency (DEA) in drug-related and other criminal cases. The property is auctioned to the public through more than 90 U.S. Marshal Service offices across the United States. Past auctions
have featured houses, automobiles (A like-new Mercedes 450SL, recently sold for under $3,000!), jewelry (A $10,000 Rolex watch, seized from a convicted drug dealer, sold for under $900!), businesses, rare coin collections, stamp collec-tions, and hundreds of other items of varying value.

Listed below are some recent DEA property seizures. The

list is from the "USA Today" newspaper, and provides a sample of the variety of items you might be able to bid on at a U.S. Marshals Service auction.

Vehicles

1987 Nissan Maxima; 1989 Lincoln Continental; 1987 Jeep Wrangler; 1980 Mercedes Benz; 1992 Honda Prelude; 1989 Ford Mustang GT; 1991 Toyota Land Cruiser; 1990 Chevrolet 1500 truck; 1975 Corvette; 1969 Mercedes Benz; 1984 Mercedes Benz 190E; 1983Mercedes Benz 380; 1969 Chevrolet Camaro; 1986 Mercedes Benz 190E; 1992 Corvette; 1993 Mazda M-X 6 Sports Coupe; 1992 Mercedes Benz 300SE; 1972 Winnebago; 1987 Cadillac Coup De Ville; 1987 Ford Bronco; 1980 Kenworth tractor.

Jewelry

5 diamonds valued at $31,400; assorted jewelry valued at $35,640; assorted jewelry valued at $25,223; assorted jewelry valued at $3,950; assorted jewelry valued at $29,740; assorted jewelry valued at $5,000; diamond cocktail ring valued at $13,000; 10K gold chain and pendant, valued at $1,400; assorted jewelry, valued at $14,700.

Miscellaneous

Kubota L2550 Tractor; 1989 Harley Davidson motorcycle; Motorola cellular phone with battery; Packard Bell personal computer with monitor and CD Rom; Oki cellular telephone; Ivan-Earle LimitedEdition Print, "Gardners Ranch"; 1990 Bayliner 1800 Capri Bowrider Boat; assorted electronic equipment valued at $9,915; assorted clothing valued at $7992.99; Panasonic Telephone answering system/fax/copier; Motorola telephone pager; Panasonic Ag-800 Video floppy recorder; Mitsubishi color video printer; satellite system valued at $2,000; Sony Handycam 8MM video camera; Sony cordless telephone answering system; man's Rolex watch valued at

$4,400; Magnavox TV with Memorex VCR; Women's Rolex watch valued at $4,250; electronic equipment valued at $2,000; Sony video camera recorder, valued at $800; 1980 Trailmobile flat bed trailer.

The U.S. Marshals Service does not hold auctions on a regular basis. Auctions are scheduled when an individual office has an accumulation of confiscated property. The Marshals Service may conduct these auctions or they may be conducted by privateauctioneers. Payment at U.S. Marshal Service auctions is usually by cash or certified check.

There is no mailing list associated with these auctions. If you wish to bid on items auctioned by the U.S. Marshals Service you can check the appropriate section of your local newspaper for auction notices. You can also contact the U.S. Marshals office in your area. For more information, contact:

U.S. Marshals Service
Seized Assets Division
Department of Justice
Constitution Ave. & 10th St., N.W.
Washington, DC 20530

U.S. Postal Service Auctions

You can bid on unclaimed merchandise which is auctioned by the U.S. Postal Service. The bargains found in Postal Service auctions can include jewelry, books, clothing, toys, electronic equipment, tools— any type of merchandise that goes unclaimed at the post office. Auctions featuring the most valuable items are usually conducted by private auctioneers. All other sales are conducted through several dead letter branches of the U.S. Postal Service.

The Postal Service also conducts vehicle auctions through

a number of Vehicle Maintenance Facilities in various parts of the country.Past vehicle auctions have featured jeeps—in fair to good condition—for under $2,000. One bidder purchased several jeeps for under $200 each. The used Postal Service vehicles are all generally in good condition and can be exceptional bargains.

While the prices for unclaimed and damaged goods (auctioned through the dead letter branches) depends on the specific merchandise and the number of people bidding, you can almost always find some outstanding bargains at Postal Service auctions. The best approach is to get on a mailing list which will enable you to get advance notice of future auctions. The mailing list will also provide you with a list of items which will be available for inspection before the auction. Payment is usually accepted in cash only. In some auctions there may be a minimum bid required.

You can get more information about the auction of surplus property and used vehicles in your area by contacting your local Postmaster.

General Services Administration Auctions

The General Services Administration (GSA) sells millions of dollars worth of surplus civilian merchandise, equipment, and nonforeclosed government real estate each year. The surplus property available at GSA auctions comes from most all other agencies of the government including, The F.B.I., Federal Communications Commission, The I.R.S., Department of Energy, Bureau of Land Management, and the Department of the Interior.

The GSA disposes of an assortment of surplus equipment, supplies and furnishings, used in government offices. The GSA also sells a veritable "fleet" of used government vehicles including automobiles (typically American-made models such as Ford, Chevy, and Plymouth), trucks, jeeps, and tractors.

The GSA also occasionally sells seized and confiscated property. However, it may be best to contact the seizing agency, such as the I.R.S, or U.S. Customs Service, to get information about the sale of such property.

The GSA takes possession of usable property which is discarded by government agencies. If no other government agencies are interested in purchasing the property, it is then offered for sale to the general public. It's not unusual to find office furniture (a businessman bought over $13,000 worth of office furniture for under $800 at past GSA auctions!), automobiles, trucks, vans, boats, computers, telephone answering machines, desks, calculators, cameras, clothing, jewelry, and hundreds of other items for sale at GSA auctions.

You can expect to save a bundle at GSA auctions. Many items are sold for well below typical wholesale prices. In order to get such bargains, you must get your name on the GSA's mailing list. You can do that by writing to the GSA Customer Service Bureaus which conduct sales in your area (see regional offices list below).

Request an application for a surplus property mailing list, and any information available concerning the sale of surplus property. Once you're on the mailing list, you will receive advance notice of auctions. You'll also get a catalog describing some of the merchandise to be sold. Some regional offices have no mailing lists and will, instead, give you a telephone number to call for a recording of information about upcoming auctions.

GSA sales are conducted as regular auctions, by sealed bid (entered on a form and mailed in), and as spot auctions (bids are submitted in writing, at the auction). If the auction is conducted by sealed bid, you'll be allowed one week (before submitting your bid) to view and inspect the property. For regular auctions and spot bids, you'll have two days. Before you can bid at a GSA sale, you'll need to register at the auction site and get a bidder number.

Payment may be by cash, cashier's check, money order, or by other arrangements. In most cases, payment in full must be made by the day after the sale. Successful bidders are also responsible forremoving all property purchased— so make sure you bring a truck!

There are 11 GSA regional offices across the country. You can write to the office(s) in your area to get on a mailing list and to get specific information about GSA auctions of Federal Government surplus personal property in your area. Write to: Surplus Sales, Customer Service Bureau, U.S. General Services Administration

U.S. General Services Administration
7th and D Sts., SW
Washington, DC 20407

The GSA also sells real estate to the general public. You can call (800) GSA-1313 for a national listing of real estate for sale. Once you have that listing, you can contact the local GSA office for the area in which you wish to purchase property.

Your can also get information on the sale of real estate by the GSA, by writing to:

General Services Administration
Office of Real Property
Federal Property Resources Services
18th and F Streets, NW
Washington, DC 20405

Department of Defense Auctions

Like the GSA and other government agencies, The Department of Defense (DoD) sells an impressive selection of surplus items to the general public. The goods may include any item used on a military base (except activated items which have military applications). Past DoD sales have featured office equipment, tents, recyclable scrap metals, vehicles, farming equipment, cameras, electronic components and supplies, tools, clothing, industrial equipment, and hundreds of other items.

The first thing you should do is write to the following address (or phone) and request a free booklet titled, "How To Buy Surplus Personal Property", and a Surplus Property Bidders Application:

The Defense Reutilization Marketing Service
National Sales Office
P.O. Box 5275 DDRC
2163 Airways Blvd.
Memphis, TN 38114-52210
Phone: (901) 775-4974

The National Sales Office listed above is the consolidated sales office which handles all DoD national auctions of surplus property. This office prepares sales catalogs which describe the property, sale location, property location, and inspection and sale dates. The catalogs are mailed several weeks in advance of a sale date to allow prospective bidders ample time to inspect the property.

National sales methods include sealed bids and national auctions.Sealed bid sales are typically used to sell large quantities of surplus property to buyers on a regional or national marketinglevel. Both recyclable and scrap materials are normally sold by this method. Bids are submitted by mail on forms provided in sale catalogs, which aresent free to everyone on a mailing list. A deposit is also required to be sent along with the sealed bid. National auctions are held to dispose of a large quantity or variety of merchandise which is of wide commercial interest.

You can get notices of DoD Sealed Property sales in the "CommerceBusiness Daily" which is available from the Superintendent of Documents, Government Printing Office, Washington DC 20402-9325; PHONE: (202) 783-3238. You may also be able to view a copy at your local library.

The National Sales Office in Memphis keeps a National Bidders List. If your name is on the list you will automatically receive national sales catalogs. To get your name on the list, write to the National Sales Office in Memphis at the address listed aboveor phone: (800) 222-DRMS [3767].

Local DoD sales of surplus property are handled through several regional Defense Reutilization and Marketing Offices (DRMO) across the country. You can get information from the DRMO in your area by writing to the appropriate address listed below.

Local sales are conducted by cash and carry (retail sales), spot bids, and local auctions. The cash and carry method is used by most DRMO's to offer small quantities of individual items at fixed prices. The prices are based on current market value. Local auctions are typically held when there are a variety of items in small quantities which are in demand in the local market. When spot bids are used as the method of sale, bidders must submit bids on forms which are provided by the DRMO.

You can find some of the best bargains at DoD auctions. Vehicles, tools, electronic equipment, appliances, office equipment, and many other items are typically sold at well below wholesale at these auctions. Here's a sample of some of the bargains bidders have cashed in on at past auctions:

Canon copier...$20
Dodge Sports Van...$150
Litton Fax Machine...$25
Microwave oven...$35
2 Johnson Outboard Motors...$235
Toyota Celica...$60
Color TV...$35
1971 Chrysler New Yorker...$10

For more information about local sales in your geographical area contact the appropriate regional Defense Reutilization and Marketing sales office listed below.

DRMR- Columbus: Includes Ohio, Minnesota, Wisconsin, Michigan, Iowa, Nebraska, Kansas, Missouri, Illinois, Indiana, West Virginia, Virginia, Delaware, New Jersey, Pennsylvania, Maryland, Connecticut, New York, Rhode Island, Maine, Massachusetts, Vermont, New Hampshire, and Washington DC.

DRMR- Columbus
P.O. Box 500
Blacklick, OH 43004-0500
(614) 238-2114

DRMR- Memphis: Includes Texas, Oklahoma, Arkansas, Mississippi, Louisiana, Alabama, Kentucky, Tennessee, Georgia, Florida, and North and South Carolina.

DRMR- Memphis
2163 Airways Blvd.
Memphis, TN 38114-0716
(901) 775-6417

DRMR- Ogden: Includes Alaska, Washington, California, Oregon, Colorado, Idaho, North and South Dakota, Wyoming, and Utah.

DRMR- Ogden
P.O. Box 53
Defense Depot Ogden
Ogden, UT 84407-5001
(801) 399-7257

Small Business Administration Auctions

The primary purpose of the Small Business Administration (SBA) is to provide financial assistance to small businesses. When a small business defaults on its loan obligations in a SBA-sponsored program, the SBA forecloses and then "liquidates" any property owned by the business. That's the only way the SBA can recover the balance due on the loan. The property sold by the SBA can include working businesses, office furniture and equipment, computers, buildings, tools, and many other valuable items. SBA liquidation auctions provide excellent opportunities for some really great bargains.

The SBA has 10 Regional Offices throughout the United States. You can contact the office which serves your region to find out more about SBA auctions and what merchandise is available in your area. If you specify what type of merchandise you are interested in, you can get your name on a mailing list for future SBA auctions of that specific merchandise.

Here are the 10 SBA Regional offices:

Region 1: Includes Maine, Massachusetts, Connecticut, Vermont, New Hampshire, and Rhode Island.

Small Business Administration
155 Federal Street, 9th Floor
Boston, MA 02110

Region 2: Includes New York, New Jersey, Puerto Rico,

and the Virgin Islands.

Small Business Administration
26 Federal Plaza, Room 31-08
New York, NY 10278

Region 3: Includes Pennsylvania, Washington DC, Maryland, Delaware, West Virginia, and Virginia.

Small Business Administration
475 Allendale Rd., Suite 201
King of Prussia, PA 19406

Region 4: Includes Florida, Georgia, Alabama, North and South Carolina, Mississippi, Tennessee, and Kentucky.

Small Business Administration
1375 Peachtree St., N.E. 5th Floor
Atlanta, GA 30367-8102

Region 5: Includes Ohio, Indiana, Michigan, Illinois, Wisconsin, and Minnesota.
Small Business Administration
Federal Building
230 Dearborn St., Room 510
Chicago, IL 60604-1593

Region 6: Includes Texas, Oklahoma, Arkansas, and New Mexico.

Small Business Administration
8625 King George Drive
Dallas, TX 75235-3391

Region 7: Includes Kansas, Missouri, Iowa, and Nebraska.

Small Business Administration
911 Walnut St., 13th Floor
Kansas City, MO 64106

Region 8: Includes Colorado, Montana, Wyoming, North and South Dakota, and Utah.

Small Business Administration
999 18th St. Ste. 701
Denver, CO 80202

Region 9: Includes California, Nevada, Arizona, and Hawaii.

Small Business Administration
450 Golden Gate Ave.
San Francisco, CA 94102
(415) 556-7487

Region 10: Includes Washington, Oregon, Idaho, and Alaska.

Small Business Administration
2615 4th Ave. , Room 440
Seattle, WA 98121
(206) 442-5676

Department of Housing and Urban Development (HUD) Real Estate Auctions

HUD real estate auctions occur when homeowners default on FHA-insured home mortgages. The homes become the property of HUD when the department pays the balance on the defaulted mortgages. Qualified buyers can purchase a HUD home with as little as a 3%to 5% down payment. In many cases, the down payment may be as low as $100. HUD may also pay your closing costs. Your local newspaper may carry HUD foreclosure listings, or you can contact your regional HUD office (see addresses below). If you prefer, you may also contact a HUD-approved real estate broker.

Besides homes, HUD properties up for auction may also include apartments andcondominiums. All HUD properties are sold "as is". In some cases, "as is" means "need lots of work". If you are willing to take on such work (repairs, etc), you can get yourself a real bargain. In general, the condition of HUD properties is fair to good. In all cases, the buyer is responsible for repairs and improvements.

In order to buy a HUD property, you must place a bid through a private real estate broker who is "HUD-approved". You may contact the participating broker of your choice and request to view the property. The broker will show you the property, and help you complete an application to bid on the property. The services of a HUD-approved broker are free to prospective buyers.

Your bid, submitted through a broker, must be accompanied by an earnest money deposit. The amount of earnest money you submit varies from region to region, and generally runs from $500 to $2000. In the case of all HUD properties, bidders must furnish their own financing.

How much will you pay for a HUD home? Prices will vary, and depend on the condition of the property. Some HUD properties are sold at market value, but there are many instances of such properties being offered at 10% to 40% below market value.

If you have heard stories about people buying homes for $1.00through HUD's Urban Homesteading Program, you may have high hopes. While it is true that such homes have sold for $1.00 through a lottery-like program, The Urban Homesteading Program has been replaced by the Hope 3 Program. The Hope 3 Program is designed to provide low income families and individuals a means of becoming homeowners. In order to qualify for the Hope 3 Program, your income must be 80% below the median income in your area, and you must be a first-time home buyer. You can get information on the Hope 3 Programs available in your area and exact qualifications from the Community and Development Office at the field or regional HUD office nearest you (see below).

You can get a brochure, "A Home of Your Own", which is a comprehensive guide to purchasing HUD-auctioned homes, by calling the HUD Homeline at (800) 767-4483.

You can also get a 119-page booklet which provides information on the over 100 housing programs offered by HUD. Call, (202) 708- 1420 and ask for the booklet, "Programs of HUD". You can also get the booklet by writing to: Department of Housing and Urban Development, Washington, DC 20410-4000.

Here is a listing of regional HUD offices:

Region I (Boston)

Boston Regional Office
Thomas P. O'Neill Federal Building
10 Causeway St., Room 375, Boston, MA 02222-1092
Phone: (617) 565-5234

Field offices in this region are in Bangor, ME;
Burlington, VT;
Hartford, CT; Manchester, NH; and Providence, RI.

Region II (New York)

New York Regional Office
26 Federal Plaza, New York, NY 10278-0068
Phone: (212) 264-8068

Field offices in Region II are in Albany, NY; Buffalo, NY; Camden, NJ; Newark, NJ; and Hato Rey, PR.

Region III (Philadelphia)

Philadelphia Regional Office
Liberty Square Building
105 South Seventh St., Philadelphia, PA 19106-3392
Phone: (215) 597-2560

Field offices are in Baltimore, MD; Charleston, WV; Pittsburg, PA; Richmond, VA; Washington D.C.; and Wilmington, DE.

Region IV (Atlanta)

Atlanta Regional Office
Richard B. Russell Building, 75 Spring St., S.W.,
Atlanta, GA
30303-3388
Phone: (404) 331-5136

Field offices are in Birmingham, AL; Columbia, SC; Coral Gables, FL; Greensboro, NC; Jackson, MS; Jacksonville, FL; Knoxville, TN; Louisville, KY; Memphis, TN; Nashville, TN; and Orlando and Tampa, FL.

Region V (Chicago)

Chicago Regional Office
626 West Jackson Blvd., Chicago, IL 60606-6765
Phone: (312) 353-5680

Field offices are in Cincinnati, Cleveland and Columbus, OH; Detroit, Flint and Grand Rapids, MI; Indianapolis, IN; Milwaukee, WI; Minneapolis/St. Paul, MN; and Springfield, IL.

Region VI (Fort Worth)

Forth Worth Regional Office

1600 Throckmorton, P.O. Box 2905, Fort Worth,
TX 76113-2905
Phone: (817) 885-5401

Field offices are in Albuquerque, NM; Dallas, TX; Houston,
TX; Little Rock, AR; Lubbock, TX; New Orleans, LA; Oklahoma
City, OK; San Antonio, TX; Shreveport, LA; and Tulsa, OK.

Region VII (Kansas City)

Kansas City Regional Office
Professional Building, 1101 Grand Ave., Kansas City,
 MO 64106-2496
Phone: (816) 374-6432

Field offices are in Des Moines, IA; Omaha, NE;
St. Louis, MO; and Topeka, KS.

Region VIII (Denver)

Denver Regional Office
Executive Tower Building, 1405 Curtis St.,
Denver, CO 80202-2349
Phone: (303) 844-4513

Field offices are in Casper, WY; Fargo, ND;
Helena, MT; Salt Lake City, UT; and Sioux Falls, SD.

Region IX (San Francisco)

San Francisco Regional Office
Phillip Burton Federal Building and U.S. Courthouse,
450 Golden
Gate Ave., P.O. Box 36003,
San Francisco, CA 94102-3448
Phone: (415) 556-4752

Field offices are in Fresno, CA; Honolulu, HI; Las Vegas,

NV; Los Angeles, CA; Phoenix, AZ; Reno, NV; Sacramento, CA; San Diego, CA; Santa Ana, CA; and Tucson, AZ.

Region X (Seattle)

Seattle Regional Office
Arcade Plaza Building, 1321 Second Ave.,
Seattle, WA 98101-2054
Phone: (206) 442-5414

Regional offices are in Anchorage, AK;
Boise, ID; Portland, OR; and Spokane, WA.

State and Local Government Auctions

The sources listed above are all federal government sources of surplus and seized property. You can also find some great bargains on such property at the state and local govern-menlevel. Agencies at these levels typically sell at auction surplus
and used office equipment, furniture, real estate, and unclaimed (or abandoned) items such as automobiles (and trucks), and bicycles.

In many cases, state and local auctions of surplus and seized property are advertised in local newspapers. The ads are normally in the legal or classified sections. At the local level, the police department and sheriff's department may have periodic
sales of stolen or unclaimed property. Bicycles are a common item st such sales, and it's possible to purchase brand name merchandise such as an unclaimed Schwinn bicycle for $50 or less. You can contact these agencies and others to find out the specifics (date and location) of any surplus property auctions in your area.

State government offices also hold auctions of surplus

property on a regular basis. While you won't always find the vast assortment of goods which is available at most federal auctions, there are still plenty of bargains offered at state auctions. You can contact the appropriate state government office (see state-by-state list below) to find out about surplus property to be auctioned by your state.

State-By-State Government Offices and Auctions

Alabama

The state of Alabama sells surplus goods such as office equipment and furniture. Also sold at auction are cars, trucks, tractors, and boats. These state auctions are held about once every 4 months, and are usually advertised in local newspapers. To get more information, and to get your name on a mailing list, write to: Alabama Surplus Property, P.O.Box 210487, Montgomery, AL 36121; Phone: (205) 277-5866

Alaska

It's not too cold in Alaska for some "hot" bargains on surplus office equipment and furniture. Such surplus items are auctioned every week by the Division of General Services and Supply. Vehicles are sold by the state about twice a year. A mailing list is available. Write to: Office of Surplus Property, 2400 Viking Drive, Anchorage, AK 99501.

Arizona

Arizona offers some great bargains about every three months through auctions of surplus property. Past sales have featured computers, office furniture and equipment, and a variety of vehicles. For more information, write to: Office of Surplus Property, 1537 W. Jackson St., Phoenix, AZ 85007; Phone (602) 542- 5701

Arkansas

President Clinton's home state conducts regular auctions of surplus property. Past auctions have featured medical equipment, vehicles, automotive supplies, mobile homes, and office equipment. A mailing list is available. Write to: State Marketing and Redistribution Office, 6620 Young Rd., Little Rock, AR 72201;Phone: (501) 565-8645

California

The General Services Department of California conducts auctions of surplus automobiles every month. Most of the vehicles are American-made, and include a selection of cars, vans, and pickups. A mailing list is available. Contact the State of California, Office of Fleet Administration, 1416 10th St., Sacramento, CA 95814.

The California Highway Patrol auctions off a large selection of used vehicles. These auctions are by sealed bid and in the past have featured every make and model from Mustangs to 4 x 4's. For more information, contact the California Highway Patrol, Vehicle Sales Office, 2812 Meadowview Rd., Sacramento, CA 95814; Phone (916) 421-0285.

Colorado

Throughout the year, the state of Colorado auctions off an assortment of surplus property. The auctions include a variety of items such as office equipment and furniture, computers, typewriters, and file cabinets. Motor vehicles are not included in these auctions as they are not sold to the general public. The auctions are held whenever enough surplus items have accumulated. It should be noted that first choice of Colorado's surplus merchandise goes to non-profit organizations. For more information, write to: Department of Correctional Inductries, State Surplus Agency, 4200 Garfield Street, Denver, CO 80216; Phone: (303) 428-5972.

Connecticut

Connecticut conducts daily auctions of surplus property, including office equipment and furniture. Vehicles are auctioned off at different times and locations and typically include most American-made models such as Ford, Chevrolet, and Plymouth. Write to: 60 State St. Rear, Old Wethersfield, CT 06109; Phone: (203) 566-7018.

Delaware

At state auctions of surplus and used property in Delaware, you can bid on an assortment of vehicles, such as cars, pick-ups, trucks, and vans. Past auctions have also featured school buses and boats. Office furniture and equipment are sold at these auctions which are held several times a year. A mailing list is available. Write to: Division of Purchasing, P.O. Box 299, Delaware City, DE 19706; Phone: (302) 834-4550.

Florida

About twelve times a year, a variety of surplus items are auctioned off at various locations in Florida. Past auctions have featured industrial and heavy equipment, pleasure and fishing boats, automobiles, and other items. Used and confiscated cars, trucks, vans, and other vehicles are also auctioned several times a year. These auctions are normally advertised in newspapers across the state. For more information, write to: Department of General Services, Division of Motor Pool Bureau of Motor Vehicles, 813 B Lake Bradford Rd., Tallahassee, FL 32304; Phone: (904) 488-2041.

Georgia

Automobiles (sedans and station wagons), pick-up trucks, vans, audio-visual equipment, air conditioners, office equipment, computers, cameras, and shop equipment are just some of the items featured at past auctions of surplus and used property in Georgia. The auctions are held several times a year and are usually advertised in local newspapers. A mailing list is available. Write to: State of Georgia, Department of Administrative Services, Purchasing Division, Surplus Property Services, 1050 Murphy Ave. S.W., Atlanta, GA 30310; Phone: (404) 756-4800

Hawaii

There are no state level auctions of surplus property in Hawaii.

Idaho

The Bureau of Supplies in Idaho offers a variety of surplus goods for auction. Bids may be made on automobiles, televisions, office equipment, desks, and other items. A mailing list is available. Write to: Bureau of Supplies, 5565 Kendall St., Boise, ID 83706; Phone: (208) 334-2468.

Illinois

Below market, and wholesale prices are available on some items auctioned off by the state of Illinois. Past auctions have included major appliances (refrigerators, etc.), office equipment, filing cabinets, desks, and a variety of vehicles. A mailing list is available. Contact the Office of Property Control, 3550 Great Northern Ave., Springfield, IL 62707; Phone: (217) 793-1813.

Indiana

The state of Indiana auctions surplus and confiscated property such as computers, office equipment, real estate, farming equipment, scrap metal, appliances (stoves, refrigerators), bicycles, VCR's, and many other items. The auctions are usually conducted by sealed bids. The bids are opened each month and the goods sold to the highest bidders. You can get your name placed on a mailing list for specific items of interest. You'll be required to specify, in writing, what type of merchandise is of interest to you. To get on the mailing list, write to State Surplus Property Section, 545 W. McCarty St., Indianapolis, IN 46225-1239.

Iowa

Iowa's Department of Natural Resources conducts an auction each year, featuring fishing and hunting equipment. This auction could be a sportsman's dream with bargains on fishing boats, rods and reels, tackle boxes, and other items. The auction is advertised in local newspapers. For more information, write to: Department of Natural Resources, Wallace State Office Building, Des Moines, IA 50319;PHONE (515) 281-5145.

Kansas

The state of Kansas Surplus Property Office disposes of a wide assortment of surplus, used, and confiscated property. Other state agencies are given first choice of buying the property, with the remainder being offered for sale to the general public. Past sales have included automobiles (some cars seized in drug raids), office equipment, snowplows, and bulldozers. For moreinformation, contact: Kansas State Surplus Property, P.O. Box 19226, Topeka, KS 66619-0226; Phone: (913) 296-2334.

Kentucky

The Kentucky Office of Surplus Property conducts several auctions each year. Bids may be made on a number of items, including electronic equipment, vehicles, and office equipment and furniture. A mailing list is available. Contact the Kentucky Office of Surplus Property, 514 Barret Ave., Frankfort, KY 40601;Phone; (502) 564-4836.

Louisiana

Monthly auctions in Louisiana offer potential buyers a large selection of items from which to choose. Items sold at past auctions include boats, bicycles, automobiles, television sets, medical equipment, office equipment, and furniture. For more information, write to: Division of Administration, Louisiana Property Assistance Agency, 1059 Brickyard Lane, Baton Rouge, LA 70804; Phone: (504) 342-6849.

Maine

The state of Maine auctions off a good selection of vehicles to the general public. Office equipment and other items are also featured in most auctions. The selection of vehicles is impressive. Past auctions have featured a variety of makes and models of mostly American-made automobiles, pick-up trucks, snowmobiles, graders, backhoes, and more. You must register before you can bid. Once you are registered, you will receive advance notification of future auctions. For more information, contact: Office of Surplus Property, Station 95, Augusta, ME O4333; Phone 9207) 289-5750.

Maryland

The state of Maryland sells surplus property to state agencies and non-profitorganizations. No sales are made directly to the general public.

Massachusetts

Motor vehicles comprise the bulk of the surplus property sold by the state of Massachusetts. Past sales have included automobiles, vans, and pick-up trucks ranging in condition from good to "needs work". For information, write to: Massachusetts State Purchasing Agency, 1 Ashburton Place, Boston, MA 02108.

Michigan

Good buys on office furniture and equipment can be found at state auctions in Michigan. Other items include vehicles (cars, trucks, buses), boats, household goods, and tools. Contact the State of Michigan, Department of Management and Budget, State Surplus Property, 3353 N. Logan, Lansing, MI 48913; Phone: (517) 335-8444.

Minnesota

An abundance of surplus and confiscated property is auctioned throughout the year by the state of Minnesota. Past auctions have featured an assortment of furniture, tools, jewelry, computers, electronic equipment, office equipment, cars, trucks, vans, snowmobiles, and boats. Successful bidders have purchased many items at these auctions for a good deal less than market prices. A mailing list is available. Write to: Minnesota Surplus Operations Office, 5420 Highway 8, New Brighton, MN 55112.

Mississippi

The Department of Public Safety in Mississippi holds sporadic auctions of motor vehicles. The auctions are held when there is an accumulation of working vehicles. Past sales have featuredAmerican-made patrol cars with a good bit of mileage on them. A mailing list is available for these auctions. Write to: Department of Public Safety, P.O. Box 958, Jackson, MS

39205.

The state of Mississippi also auctions off surplus machinery, textiles, and other items. These auctions are held once a year. Contact the Bureau of Surplus Property, P.O. Box 5778, Whitfield Rd., Jackson, MS 39208.

Missouri

A selection of surplus office equipment and vehicles can be found at state auctions in Missouri. The auctions are held about every six months. A mailing list is available. Write to: State of Missouri, Surplus Property Office, 117 N. Riverside Drive, Jefferson City, MO 65102; Phone: (314) 751-3415.

Montana

Each month, the state of Montana auctions off an assortment of surplus goods. Bids may be made on such items as computers, tables, chairs, and office supplies and equipment. Vehicles, including patrol cars, are also offered for sale. For more information, write to: Property and Supply Bureau, 930 LyndaleAve., Helena, MT 59620; Phone:(406) 444-4514.

Nebraska

In Nebraska, auctions are held about every four months. Surplus goods may include office furniture and equipment, chairs, tables, and other items. Motor vehicles and heavy equipment are also auctioned off about 4 times a year. A mailing list is available, Write to: Office of Administrative Services, Material Division, Surplus Property, P.O. Box 94901, Lincoln, NE 68509: Phone:(402) 479-4890.

Nevada

Motorcycles, automobiles, pick-up trucks and other vehicles have been offered at past state auctions in Nevada. The vehicles are auctioned separately from other surplus property (scrap metal, tables, chairs, desks, file cabinets), which is offered for sale once a year. You may request that your name be placed on a mailing list if you are interested in bidding on merchandise. Contact the State Purchasing Division, KinkeadBldg., Room 400, Capitol Complex, Carson City, NV 89710; Phone: (702) 885-4070.

New Hampshire

Twice a year, New Hampshire auctions off surplus property which may include vehicles, office furniture and equipment, appliances (refrigerators, freezers, etc.), and other items. A mailing list is available, Write to: Office of Surplus Property, 78 Regional Drive, Building 3 , Concord, NH O3331; Phone: (603) 271-2126.

New Jersey

New Jersey offers a selection of used state vehicles at auction several times a year. Past auctions have featured Chevy and Dodge cars and vans, as well as otherAmerican-made vehicles. You can get your name on a mailing list by writing to the following address: Purchase and Property Distribution Center, 1620 Stuyvestant Ave., Trenton, NJ 08628; Phone: (609) 530-3300.

New Mexico

State auctions in New Mexico are held once a year and typically feature pick-up trucks, vans, cars, snowplows, tractors, and a selection of office equipment and supplies. Get more information and your name on a mailing list by making such a request to the Highway and Transportation Department, SB-2, P.O. Box 1149, Santa Fe, NM 87504-1149; Phone: (505) 827-5580.

New York

New York is a good state for auctions of surplus and used property. Auctions are held weekly in various locations throughout the state and provide some real bargains on a number of items. Past auctions have featured photographic equipment, scrap metal, chain saws, and office equipment and supplies. The state also auctions a selection of motor vehicles including pick-up trucks, buses, tractors, mowers, and cars. To get your name placed on a mailing list, write to: Office of General Service, Bureau of Surplus Property, Building 18, W.A. Harriman State Office Building Campus, Albany, NY 12226; Phone: (518) 457-6335.

North Carolina

Sealed bid is the typical method used to dispose of surplus property in North Carolina. Surplus items offered in past auctions have included desks, chairs, office equipment, automobiles, vans, and much more. For more information, write to: State Surplus Property, P.O. Box 33900, Raleigh, NC 27636-3900; Phone: (919) 733-3889.

North Dakota

North Dakota auctions surplus property, including office furniture and equipment and motor vehicles, about once a year. For information, contact the Surplus Property Office, P.O. Box7293, Bismarck, ND 58502; Phone: (701) 224-2273.

Ohio

Public Auctions and Sealed Bids are the methods used by the state of Ohio to sell its surplus property. Merchandise offered at auction may include cars, trucks, vans, boats, furniture, office equipment, mowers, tractors, and other items. For information, write to: Office of State and Federal Surplus Property, 226 N. 5th St., Columbus, OH 43215; (614) 466-

5052.

Oklahoma

The state of Oklahoma auctions off used motor vehicles as they accumulate. The vehicles may range in condition from good to poor. You may request more information, and that your name be placed on a mailing list, by writing to: Central Purchasing,State Capitol, Oklahoma City, OK 73105.

Oregon

Oregon auctions off surplus property about every four months. Past auctions have featured vehicles and general merchandise, such as computers; computer equipment; and office furniture. You can get more information and your name on a mailing list by writing to the following address (include a SASE): Department of Surplus Property, 1655 Salem Industrial Drive, N.E., Salem, OR 97310.

Pennsylvania

Pennsylvania is a good state in which to get a bargain on used motor vehicles. The state's Department of General Services conducts auctions every month, and offers a good selection of mostly American-made vehicles— Ford, Chevy, Dodge, etc.). A mailing list is available. Write to: General Services Department, Bureau of Vehicle Management, 221 Forster St., Harrisburg, PA 17105; Phone: (717) 783-3132.

Rhode Island

An assortment of surplus and confiscated items are auctioned off on a regular basis by the Division of Purchase in Rhode Island. Surplus items offered for sale may include office equipment, automobiles, food products, electronic equipment, computers, office supplies and more. To request more information and an application to bid, write to: Department of

Administration, Division of Purchase, 1 Capitol Hill, Providence, RI 02908; Phone: (401) 277-2375.

South Carolina

Several times a year, the Department of Public Transportation in South Carolina auctions off surplus and used cars, pick-up trucks, patrol cars, and other vehicles. A mailing list is available. Write to: Public Transportation Department, P.O. Box 191, Columbia, SC 29202.

South Dakota

South Dakota's Department of Transportation auctions off surplus property and used vehicles twice a year. Past auctions have featured office supplies and equipment, cars, and pick-up trucks. Most of the vehicles have a lot of mileage (over 100,000) on them, but sell for bargain prices. You can get more information by writing to: Bureau of Administration, State Property Management, 701 East Sioux Ave., Pierre,SD57501; Phone: (605) 773-4935.

Tennessee

Tennessee auctions off its surplus property, including vehicles, office equipment, tools, and machinery, several times a year. Past auctions have featured everything from dump trucks to welders. These auctions are advertised in local newspapers. You may request more information from the Department of General Services, Property Utilization, 6500 Centennial Blvd., Nashville, TN 37243-0543; PHONE: (615) 741-1711.

Texas

Six times a year, the state of Texas puts up for auction surplus and used property. Items may include office furniture and equipment, vehicles and other equipment. A mailing list is available. Write to: State Purchasing and General Services

Commission, 1711 San Jacinto, P.O. Box 13047, Capitol Station, Austin, TX 78711-3047; Phone: (512) 463-3445.

Utah

Surplus and used property, such as office equipment and furniture, vehicles, and some heavy equipment, is sold at auction by the state of Utah. Items are sold by public auction and by sealed bid. You may request more information, and that your name be placed on a mailing list by writing to the following address: State Surplus Office, 522 South 700 West, Salt Lake City, UT 84104; Phone: (801) 533-5883.

Vermont

In Vermont, the state sells its surplus property—office furniture and equipment—on a daily basis. Past sales have included computers, chairs, desks, file cabinets, and other items. Vehicles are sold by public auction every six months. A mailing list is available. Contact the Vermont Central Surplus Property Agency, RD #2, Box 520, Montpelier, VT 05602; Phone: (802) 828-3394.

Virginia

Bids may be made on a variety of property, from car batteries to bulldozers,atauctions conducted by the state of Virginia. Scrap metal, tires, cars, pick-up trucks, vans, computers, and office furniture have all been sold at past auctions. Auctions are held almost every week at various sites across the state. A mailing list is available for bothpublic auctions and sealed bids. Write to: State Surplus Property, P.O. Box 1199, Richmond, VA 23209; Phone: (804) 786-3876.

Washington

The state of Washington auctions used state vehicles about four times a year. Most of the vehicles (passenger cars, patrol cars, pick-up trucks) have over 100,000 miles on them. Bids are submitted in writing at auctions held every month for the sale of surplus goods such as office furniture and equipment. Some auctions are conducted by sealed bids. Write to the Office of Commodity Redistribution, 2805 C St., S.W., Building 5, Door 49, Auburn, WA 98001; Phone: (206) 931-3931.

West Virginia

West Virginia hold auctions every month, offering an assortment of surplus property for sale. Past sales have included such items as telephones, computers, desks, miscellaneous office equipment, and vehicles. While not a monthly occurence, past vehicle auctions have featured a Mercedes or two. For more information, write to: West Virginia State Agency Surplus Property, 2700 Charles Ave.,Dunbar, WV 25064; Phone: (304) 348-3456.

Wisconsin

Wisconsin's Department of Administration conducts monthly auctions of passenger vehicles, trucks, and other vehicles. These auctions are advertised in local newspapers, and you can also have your name placed on a mailing list. Write to: Department of Administration, P.O. Box 7880, Madison, WI 53707; Phone: (608) 266-8024.

Wyoming

Surplus vehicles constitute the bulk of the property auctioned off by the state of Wyoming. The vehicles sold may include jeeps, sedans, vans, and pick-up trucks. A mailing list is available. Write to: State Motor Pool, 723 West 19th, Cheyenne, WY 82002; Phone: (307) 777-7247.

District of Columbia

Once every four months the DC Office of Property Control sells at auction a variety of items. Past sales have featured such goods as refrigerators and other appliances, tools, clothing, office equipment, and file cabinets. For more information, contact The District of Columbia Property Division at (202) 767-7586.

XXX

Make Money

Buy Wholesale And Sell Retail For Huge Porfits

Buying products for personal use at wholesale prices can add up to a savings of hundreds, even thousands of dollars every year. Many people are content to be "buyers", keeping their wholesale bargains for their own enjoyment. There's certainly nothing wrong with that approach. In this day and age, saving money is a priority for most people, and buying everything wholesale is a sure-fire way to do that. However, more and more people are beginning to discover a "bonus" which comes from buying merchandise at wholesale prices. Not only can you save thousands of dollars on wholesale bargains but, as a bonus, you can make thousands of dollars by re-selling your wholesale purchases at retail prices!

Here's how it works— you buy name brand products at prices as much as 90% below typical retail prices, mark them up for at least twice what you paid, and then resell for huge profits. Instead of buying one piece of jewelry at a low wholesale price, you can buy in quantity, keep one piece (or more) for yourself and resell the rest. Or, buy one expensive product at a wholesale price and resell it for thousands of dollars in

---

profit. For example, one man bought a 4-carat diamond ring valued at $7,500 for just $1000 and resold it to a friend for $5,645. That's a profit of $4,645! The friend saved money too, since the ring was actually worth $7,500. Just one sale like that and you can make enough money in one day to bring you peace of mind and financial security for the rest of the year! One sale of a house, boat or a luxury car can earn you more money in one week than many people make in a year!

Here are several examples of the potential profits you can make reselling wholesale bargains:

1) A home bought for $25,000...resold for $150,000 = profit of $125,000.

2) A speed boat bought for $8,000...resold for $37,500 = profit of $29,500.

3) A Mercedes Benz bought for $3,000...resold for $34,000 = profit of $31,000.

4) A motorhome bought for $6,000...resold for $21,100 = profit of $15,100.

Of course, you may not find such fantastic bargains as those listed above right away. It takes time, experience, and sometimes a little luck (being in the right place at the right time) to cash in on the most expensive merchandise. You'll probably want to start by selling a small inventory of wholesale bargains until your profits have built up enough to enable you to expand from part-time sales to full-time. You can also begin by selling directly from a wholesale supplier's catalog, without having an actual inventory on hand.

Some people make huge profits reselling bargains they have purchased at government auctions (see chapter 31). Others buy products at wholesale prices from one or more suppliers and then resell to their own customers and/or retail outlets. In this chapter, you will learn how to do both— resell government auction bargains and resell products purchased at wholesale directly from suppliers. You will learn how to make money part-time or full-time by starting your own business. This chapter also features a list of wholesale sources that supply general merchandise to independent dealers and businesses for resale.

While no one can guarantee that you will make a fortune reselling wholesale bargains, it is possible to make over $100,000 a year. You have to work at it. The wholesale bargains are there. It's up to you to find them and then decide whether to be a buyer only or to resell them for substantial profits. In either case, you'll end up ahead of the game.

XXXI

How To Resell Government Auction Bargains For A Profit

Government auctions can be the source of some outstanding bargains. As seen in the previous chapter (chapter 31), various government agencies, at both the state and federal levels, auction off a wide assortment of surplus, used and confiscated property. In fact, virtually any product you can find in retail outlets can also be found at government auctions and, more often than not, at much lower prices. Successful bidders can walk away with some truly amazing bargains for their own personal use, or they can turn those bargains into substantial profits by reselling them to other people.

If you plan to buy merchandise at low prices at government auctions and resell for a profit, you'll need to do some marketing. That's because buying a product at wholesale or below wholesale is just the first step. It is not an automaticguarantee that you can make a huge profit. Obviously you will need customers, and that takes marketing.

The extent of your marketing campaign depends on your total investment in merchandise. For example, if you bought a used car at a state auction and plan to sell it locally, your marketing campaign may simply entail running an ad in the local newspaper for a few days. On the other hand, the purchase of a large quantity of merchandise would most likely require a more complicated marketing strategy. The key is in letting as many potential customers as possible know that you have government-auctioned merchandise for sale at low prices.

How To Resell A Car Bought At A Government Auction

You don't have to purchase thousands of dollars worth of merchandise at government auctions in order to make a big profit. Small purchases can also be very profitable when resold. If you are "mechanically inclined" you may be able to buy a car at auction, fix it up and resell it for two or three times the money you have invested. For example, you buy a used car at a state auction for $100 and invest an additional $200 in fixing it up. You then advertise the car in your local newspaper and resell it for $1000. That's a profit of $700— more than twice your investment of $300.

The important thing to remember is to restore the car so that it looks good and is in good running condition. Don't try to sell an obvious clunker for a huge profit. You are much more likely to make money on the car by offering potential buyers a genuine bargain. That doesn't mean you have to restore the car to mint condition— just fix it up so it's good enough for resale. Have all the mechanical problems and body work taken care of, and clean the car thoroughly, inside and out. A good appearance will make a good initial impression on a potential buyer and increase your chances of making a sale.

How much you sell the car for depends on your investment, both in money and labor. You can check at your local library for reference material concerning the car's current market value. Use that information as a guideline for pricing the car. As a general rule, you should get at least twice the amount you paid for the car plus any additional investment for fixing it up for resale as well as consideration for the labor involved.

Besides the local newspaper, you may also take advantage of another effective means of marketing your merchandise which is absolutely free. Most supermarkets, libraries, and public buildings have bulletin boards with free space available to the general public. You can post your ad on as many of these local bulletin boards as you can find around town. You'll reach a lot of potential buyers without having to pay for ad space.

The above suggestions for selling a car bought at government auction also hold true for any other type of small purchases. Whether you are trying to resell a computer you bought at a government auction, a few pieces of jewelry, a desk, or a stereo system, you'll need to make the item(s) as presentable for resale as possible and then market them so you reach as many potential buyers as possible.

How To Become A Dealer Of Government Auction Bargains

Experienced dealers of government surplus always follow this basic rule, "find buyers before acquiring a large inventory". It seems straightforward enough, but all too often the temptation of a huge profit overshadows sound business judgement. Some first time dealers spend several thousands of dollars on bulk purchases and then begin trying to find buyers. That approach might work if you have adequate storage space for your inventory, and you are in no hurry to recoup your investment and make a profit. Otherwise, your inventory will probably gather dust while cluttering your basement and/or garage. You can avoid that risk by lining up buyers before you purchase a large inventory.

Finding buyers before you have an inventory is not as difficult as it may appear. The truth is, there are buyers everywhere who are looking for the kinds of bargains you can supply them with government surplus, confiscated and used merchandise. Not many of these buyers attend auctions, preferring instead to purchase large inventories from people like you— if the price is right.

So, how do you find these eager and willing buyers? There are actually several methods of establishing a dependable and profitable network of buyers. One not-so-obvious method is to contact liquidators. Most Sunday newspapers feature numerous ads by liquidators. Your best bet is to review large newspapers such as "The Washington Post", "New York Times", "Chicago Tribune", and so on. Your local library should have most of these newspapers, and from their classified sections you can find several liquidators. Make a list and then contact each liquidator. You are almost certain to find at least one or two potential buyers.

You can also find buyers by doing some advertising of your own. Ads in publications such as "The Wall Street Journal", "The Journal of Commerce", and even "USA Today" can help you reach buyers who trade within the U.S. and/or export. Your local library may also have these publications available for your review. You can also contact these publications for advertising and subscription information.

"The Wall Street Journal"

Write to: Advertising Services Department, Dow Jones & Co. Inc., 420 Lexington Ave., New York, NY 10170.

Phone: (800) 366-3975 [Advertising]; (800) 841-8000 Ext. 244 [Subscription]

"The Journal of Commerce"

Write to: Two World Trade Center, New York, NY 10048

Phone: (800) 223-0243 [Advertising]; (800) 221-3777 [subscription]

"USA Today"

Write to: 1000 Wilson Blvd., Arlington, VA 22229

Phone: (800) 872-2528 [Classified Advertising]; (800) 242-5858 [National & Regional Advertising]; (800) 872-0001 [Subscription]

Besides having newspapers for you to study, your local library may also have other source material which may be helpful in finding potential buyers for government auction merchandise. Ask the reference librarian to assist you in finding directories and books which could provide you with a list of brokers or other potential buyers. One such source is "The Thomas Register", which can be found in the reference section of most libraries.

The library should also have the addresses and phone numbers forthe Chambers of Commerce of most major metropolitan areas. The Chambers of Commerce may be able to provide you with the names and addresses of local contacts who are potential buyers.

Making large purchases at government auctions can lead to substantial profits. It can also be a risky venture if you fail to follow the basic rule "find buyers before acquiring a large inventory".

How To Start Your Own Business Selling Wholesale Bargains

It should be apparent by now that you can buy everything you need at wholesale prices. The sources in the Guide offer every product imaginable at savings of up to 90% off manufacturers' suggested retail prices. If you take advantage of these bargains, you may never again have to pay retail prices for any purchase. It is possible to accomplish that simply as a consumer, but you can virtually guarantee that retail shopping is relegated to your past, by starting and operating your own business.

The savings you get when buying wholesale are such that instead of buying just one item for your own personal use, you can buy in quantity and resell for a substantial profit. You can sell wholesale bargains part-time to supplement your income from another job, or you can operate a full-time business. Either way, you are sure to save money on all your own personal purchases and make money on your purchases for resale.

Many of the best wholesale sources will sell only to dealers. Individual consumers are out of luck with these suppliers. However, when you start your own business, you become a dealer, and as such, you will be able to buy from many more wholesalers.

That means you'll have access to many more wholesale bargains, for yourself and for resale. Later in this chapter is information about several wholesale suppliers who sell to dealers. Many of these companies furnish catalogs from which you can sell without having to purchase an inventory. Of course, you can also purchase an inventory of products from a supplier's catalog and resell from your own business location.

Getting Started

Depending on where you live, state regulations generally require that new businesses be registered with the county clerk's office. One visit to the county clerk should be all it takes to get your business registered. Getting registered will also require that you pay a nominal registration fee. You should also contact yourstate's department of taxation and get a sales tax number. You'll need the number in order to collect sales tax from your customers. The sales tax number also makes it possible for you to avoid paying sales tax on the merchandise you purchase for resale. Contact your county clerk to find out the specific regulations in your area. And make sure you comply with those regulations.

Another important step in the start-up process is to make a small investment in professionally printed business cards and letterheads. You should represent yourself and your business as professionally as possible when dealing with suppliers and customers. Having business cards and letterheads for all your contacts and corespondence is one way to make a good impression and help establish your credibility. Your investment for cards and letterheads need not be excessive. Many printers offer wholesale prices for printing such items (see chapter 33).

Start-up is also the time to purchase a few basic but necessary office and bookkeeping supplies. You'll need invoices, record-keeping materials and other office items. You should also invest in an answering machine for your business telephone. Your recorded message to callers should include the name of your business. Again, you need not go overboard on these purchases. Many of the sources in this guide offer eveything you need at wholesale prices.

You should also open a bank account for business use only. It's important that you keep your business and personal checking accounts separate.

Your Inventory

Regardless of what items you plan to sell, you'll find plenty of wholesale suppliers that are willing to sell you samples of their merchandise. Most suppliers understand that a new business will need to "test" their products to see how well they are going to sell. That's also why many suppliers offer "no-name" or unimprinted catalogs featuring thousands of products and retail prices. You can imprint such catalogs with your own business name, and then show them to relatives, friends, colleagues, and so on. You can even offer discounts off the listed retail prices. This is a sensible and safe way to test out the marketability of products from a supplier. You sell directly from a catalog, with no, or little, investment in inventory.

In many cases, suppliers will drop-ship any orders you send them directly to your customers. All you've done is show the catalogs, receive money from your customers for the products they order, and then send in the orders. Once you find out whether or not the suppliers' products are going to sell, you can then consider ordering the products in quantity and selling from an inventory to a much wider customer base. Obviously, the more customers you have, the more money you'll make. Selling to your family and friends is a good way to test the marketability of a product line and build your confidence as a salesperson, but it will not provide enough income to make the venture worthwhile.

The important thing to remember is to not go overboard with your inventory. This is especially important when you are starting-up your business. Many of the wholesale suppliers listed at the end of this chapter provide drop shipping which means you never have to take delivery of the orders you send in. Most suppliers also provide helpful information about various proven methods of selling an inventory of their products—at flea markets and swap meets, consignment, wholesaling to retail stores, direct mail, etc. Some suppliers even offer samples and starter kits to help you get your business off the ground. Try to deal with suppliers that not only supply the products you want to sell, but also provide services designed to make it easy and profitable for you to do so.

How To Price Your Merchandise

The amount of profit you can expect to make depends on several factors. The most important factor, if you are selling from an inventory, is your costs. How much did you pay for the merchandise, and what are your operating costs?

In many cases, suppliers will provide you with suggested retail prices which you can use as guidelines to test the marketability of their products. For example, one wholesale supplier listed in this Guide has a catalog listing of Eureka upright vacuum cleaners with the suggested retail price of $149.00 each. Your wholesale price is $64.90 each.

Other pricing factors to consider include:

1) How much are your customers willing to pay?

Your success lies in your ability to price your merchandise so that your customers get a bargain and you make a good profit. In order to do that, you'll need to know your market and how much customers are willing and can afford to pay.

2) How much profit do you want to make?

Consider first, how much profit you "need" to make in order to break even. The break-even point occurs when all your costs are covered. Once you determine your break-even point, then decide on how much profit above that you "want" to make. Again, you should be realistic and find a pricing level that provides you with the biggest possible profit while still providing bargain prices for your customers.

3) What is your competition charging?

Suppose you are selling jewelry. If a customer can buy the same jewelry at a lower price from another source, he/she probably will. You should make it a point to study any competition and make sure that your prices are competitive. In other words, you should try to match or beat any of your competitors' prices.

Many people who resell wholesale bargains use the following general pricing formula:

Wholesale price (price you pay) x 2 = retail selling price per unit.

Example: Wholesale Price   Retail Selling Price

$12.50   X   2 = $25.00

This is a general distributor or retail pricing formula which represents a 100% profit.

Putting It All Together

By starting your own business, you can buy everything you need for your own personal use, as well as your inventory of merchandise for resale, at wholesale prices. You can actually cut your personal spending by 50% and make a profit of 100% and more!

Your success depends on several factors including how much time and effort you are willing to invest in marketing your merchandise, finding the right suppliers, and pricing your merchandise so that both you and your customers come out winners.

Wholesale Suppliers

Listed below are several wholesale suppliers offering virtually every type of merchandise imaginable. Most of these suppliers do not sell to individual consumers. By starting your own business you can gain access to these companies and purchase at wholesale prices an assortment of merchandise you can resell for a substantial profit.

Most of the suppliers listed below have catalogs and price lists available either for free or for a nominal fee, which is often refunded with your first order.

Alphin Wholesale Co.

419 Bankhead Hwy., S.E., P.O. Box 668, Mableton, GA 30059 Phone: (800) 228-9189 [orders] FAX: (404) 948-5379

The Alphin Wholesale Co. is the creator of the Empress Jewelry Collection. The Collection includes pierced and clip earrings, bracelets, rings (14K or 18K gold electroplate), barrettes, brooches, and necklaces. Your wholesale cost is as low as 1/4 of the suggested retail prices, providing the potential for substantial resale profits. You can take orders with your Alphin Wholesale catalog on a no-investment plan, or you can take orders by showing your catalog and/or actual samples.

For a small investment you can get sample ring assortments at below wholesale cost. You can return any unsold and unworn sample rings within 30 days and the money you paid for the rings will be returned. Ring sizers are also available. Also available is the "Perma Gold" chain selection, featuring 50 of the top selling styles of chains.

Contact the company for a free "Empress Gem" catalog and wholesale price chart. Orders may be paid for by check, money order or major credit card. There is a minimum order of $20 on credit card orders.

Anchor Specialties Co.

Dept. MM53, P.O. Box 3958, North Providence, RI 02911

Anchor Specialties offers the opportunity for big profits selling unique belt buckles and beautiful jewelry (earrings, bracelets, necklaces, rings). The Anchor catalog features more than 1000 styles of belt buckles, belts, and jewelry. All items are beautifully crafted.

Send $1.00 for the company's full color catalog and dealer's wholesale price list.

B & F System, Inc. (Maxam Wholesale)
3920 S. Walton Walker Blvd., Dallas, TX 75236-1510
Phone: (214) 333-2111
FAX: (214) 333-2137

The B & F System, Inc. is a direct source for housewares, gifts and promotional merchandise. The company, which is wholesale only and does not sell to the general public, has been in business for over 40 years. B & F services many Fortune 500 companies as well as small, family-owned companies and will make sample orders to new businesses as well as to established businesses that want to check out the quality of the merchandise before placing large orders.

The B & F System catalog, "Vista", features 100 pages of wholesale bargains, all at prices with profitable resale in mind. The catalog is available in 2 different versions—with the Vista name, and without the Vista name with space for your own imprint. The cost for either catalog is $1.50 each or $1.20 each in lots of 80 or more.

Merchandise listed in past catalogs has included 48 piece stainless steel flatware, Nikita 45 piece "Night Lily" pattern china, Sterlingcraft silver plated candy dishes, gold plated tea sets, serving trays, and 4 piece steak knife sets. Other items available for resale include Chef's Secret 10 piece cutlery sets, 16 piece stainless steel cookware, 7 piece steel cookware sets, 12" stainless 5 ply electric skillets, Brookwood German style grandfather clocks, 35mm cameras, umbrellas, sport knives, luggage, tools (114- piece Maxam tool set, wholesale price $41.90), watches, and many other items.

B & F System owns all the brands and trademarks in the Vista catalog and maintains large quantities of each item in stock. Most of the products in the catalog can be imprinted with your company name and/or logo.

The company has available a 16-page catalog, which is free upon request. Call or write the above address. There is a minimum order requirement of $50. Orders may be paid for by check, money order or major credit card.

Bosco Jewelers, Inc.
P.O. Box 8426, Albuquerque, NM 87198
Phone: (800) 967-0338 (505) 266-3222 in New Mexico
FAX: (505) 265-4003

Buying jewelry at wholesale prices for resale at retail prices can result in big profits. Bosco Jewelers offers a wide assortment of jewelry at 2/3 off the suggested retail prices, and several sample starter packages to get you going. The starter packages are priced from $100 to $200 and come with a 30-day, money-back guarantee.

The jewelry selection at Bosco's includes Indian hand-made sterling silver (rings, necklaces, earrings), genuine turquoise men's and ladies rings, non-sterling jewelry (slave bracelets, bracelets, bolo ties, and many other jewelry items. No minimum order is required, and volume discounts are available.

A recent catalog also offered several suggestions for profitable resale of jewelry items. Flea markets offer a good opportunity for instant sales. Consignment sales—placing a jewelry display in a local business—can net you 60% of the retail sales (40% goes to the business(es) allowing the display(s). Entire displays filled with jewelry can be sold to retail stores. Party plan sales can also be successful.

Call or write Bosco Jewelers and request a current catalog. Orders may be paid for by check, money order or major credit card.

Buymore Sales
87 Church Street, West Warwick, RI 02893
Phone: (401) 828-0399

Buymore features a large selection of jewelry and miscellaneous items at wholesale prices. A recent wholesale catalog featured hundreds of items with the potential for profitable resale including gold ball post earrings at just $3.75 per dozen; high \fashion pierced earrings at $5.00 a dozen; Cobra and assorted bracelets for $6.00 per dozen; high-quality pierced earrings, just $6.00 per dozen, and hundreds of other jewelry items. Starter kits, featuring 2 dozen goldstone chains; 1 dozen beaded necklaces; 2 dozen necklaces with pendants; 2 dozen goldtone bangle bracelets; and a Lucite display are priced as low as $40.Birthstone rings, necklaces, bracelets, fashion designer earrings, ladies pins, and crosses are also available.

Buymore also offers a good selection of miscellaneous items including eyelash and mascara brushes, scented boutique soap, pens, wrapping paper, key chains, perfume, combs, men's genuine leather belts, non-toxic crayons, jumpropes, kewpie dolls, soapstone trinket boxes, and hundreds of other items.

Call or write to request the current product catalog and pricing. Returns are accepted within five working days for refund or credit (shipping fees and COD fees are not refundable). All orders are shipped within 24 hours of receipt. Pay by check, money order, or major credit card.

Cook Bros., Inc.
240 N. Ashland, Dept. 110-10, Chicago, IL 60607
Phone: (312) 376-8888; (800) 621-4245 [orders]

The Cook Bros. catalog features 76 pages of famous brand-name merchandise that offers the opportunity for resale at big profits. The merchandise is all top-quality by such manufacturers as Panasonic, Texas Instruments, GE, Timex, Sanyo, Regal, West Bend, Canon, Seiko, Procter Silex, Magnavox, Sharp, Norelco, Oster, Remington, and many others. Cook Bros. also features 14 karat jewelry, clocks, cutlery, tools, novelties, religious items, carded goods, and monthly specials for even better bargains.

You can make profits by selling an inventory of merchandise or you can sell directly from the Cook Bros. full color catalog. Send $1.00 (refundable with first order) for the catalog.

El Paso Onyx Company, Inc.
1414 Common Drive, El Paso, TX 79936
Phone: (915) 591-6699; (800) 872-8411 [orders]
FAX: (915) 591-0929

The inventory at El Paso Onyx includes a huge selection of Onyx, glass, bone, jewelry, toys, Kachinas and Dream Catchers, Mandellas and Southwest art, Mexican imports, and novelty license plates. You can order wholesale by phone directly from the catalog and resell for a substantial profit.

Some items featured in a recent catalog include Onyx worry stones, pendants, rock arrowheads and spear heads, Onyx animals, Onyx fruit, ashtrays, domino sets, bookends, wine sets, and earrings. Mandellas and Southwest art including blankets (54" x 72") for $8.00 each; a 30" x 60" Navajo rug for $9.00; 16" by 20" Velvet paintings for $6.00 each; and 20" Mandellas for $20.00 each. Also available at wholesale prices are authentic Navajo artifacts, novelty license plates, flags, hats, stone washed denim caps, kids sunglasses ($3.00 a dozen), key chains, glass bead necklaces (with earrings), bracelets, Guatemala belts, Mexican shirts, and hundreds of other items.

Call or write the company to request a free catalog. El Paso Onyx will drop ship your orders. Minimum order is $50. Pay by major credit card.

Global Market Place
17220 Barlow, P.O. Box 05096, Detroit, MI 48203
(313) 371-3139

Global Market Place (GMP) offers an assortment of quality merchandise at below wholesale prices. When you buy from Global Market Place, you buy direct and eliminate the middle man. Savings can be from 50% to 75% and more. The company operates on the basis of cooperative buying. Retail items are sold at below wholesale prices, providing an opportunity for substantial profits by resale. G.M.P. offers name brand TVs, VHS recorders, home appliances, clothing, jewelry, gift items, car stereos,and many other products.

In order to take advantage of G.M.P.'s wholesale prices, you must purchase an annual membership. The membership cost is $39.95 a year. Once you have paid the membership fee, you will begin receiving G.M.P.'s catalogs. Contact the company for more details.

House Sales Company
Hwy. 18 West, P.O. 766, Dept. 234, Monette, AR 72447
Phone: (501) 486-2341

You can buy an assortment of merchandise for below wholesale prices from the House Sales Company. The inventory includes popular items with high resale potential. Choose from a selection of jewelry, leather wallets, key rings, custom printed caps, T-shirts, transfers, sweat shirts, warm-up sets, work gloves, socks, towels, wash cloths, pantyhose, panties, and much more.

Send $1.00 (refundable) for a price list.

M.B. Stevens
P.O. Box 0627
Centerport, NY 11721-0627

M.B. Stevens sells merchandise on a closeout basis only. You can order an assortment of products from the company's catalog at closeout prices, and resale at a substantial mark-up. M.B. Stevens closeout merchandise includes clothing, videos, earrings, and cosmetics. All the merchandise listed in the company's catalog is for resale purposes only.

A recent catalog listed a selection of recycled (used) clothing, including denim jackets, denim jeans ($3.50 a pair, packed in boxes of 36), ladies blouses, and football jerseys. An assortment of costume jewelry, including 144 pairs of assorted fashion earrings, and assorted fashion bracelets and necklaces were also listed at closeout prices. Other closeouts include Army/Navy Surplus including used fatigue shirts, flight shirts, used G.I. dress shirts, Air Force field jackets, U.S. Navy field jackets, and other items.

All items in the M.B. Stevens catalog are sold "Assorted Sizes/Colors", meaning you can not order specific sizes, colors, styles, etc. No single item samples are sold— you must order the minimum quantity of each item. You can order a catalog by sending $1.00 to the above address.

All orders must be in writing and mailed in (no phone orders are accepted). No refunds or exchanges are accepted. Pay by bank and postal money order or cashiers check.

Marco Novelty Company
508 South Main Street, P.O. Box 705, Ashburn, GA 31714
Phone: (912) 567-3185

Marco Novelty Company is a mail order wholesale supply house providing merchandise bargains to independent dealers and salespeople in the U.S. and Canada. The company can serve as a supplier for both full and part-time retailers. There are also special discount and bonus programs available for regular customers.

Marco's inventory includes jewelry, toys, computer labels, sunglasses, music boxes, games, fishing gear (floats, hooks, lures), pocket raincoats, screwdriver sets, wallets, leather bull-whips, and many other items. In fact, Marco Novelty Company can supply your business with everything from sewing needles to watches.

Call or write the company to request a free catalog. You get the small version of the catalog free. The complete catalog of bargains is sent to you following your first order. A minimum of $50 per order is required. Payment may be made by money order, cashier's check or certified check.

Merlite Industries, Inc.
114 Fifth Ave., New York, NY 10011
Phone: (212) 924-6440

For 40 years, Merlite Industries has been serving the wholesale buying public with quality-crafted jewelry at below wholesale. Prices are 67% and more below typical retail on a wide assortment of rings, watches, chains, pendants, earrings, and bracelets. There's also a selection of birthstone jewelry, personalized jewelry and bridal sets. Diamonds, sapphires, onyx, rubies, Cubic Zirconia, and other gemstones are also available.

Merlite's free Wholesale Jewelry Catalogue lists over 700 women's and men's styles, all at 1/3 of the nationally advertised suggested retail prices. You can take orders from the full-color catalogue and/or purchase an inventory for resale.

Satisfaction is guaranteed. Contact the company for a free copy of the Merlite Wholesale Jewelry Catalogue, and for more information.

Sheldon Cord Products
2202 W. Devon Avenue, Chicago,IL 60659
Phone: (973-7070; (800) 621-7999 [orders only]

Sheldon Cord has been in business for over 40 years offering a big selection of closeout and general merchandise at genuine wholesale prices. Items are sold to retail stores nationwide, and beginning or established retailers are welcome to order from the wholesale catalog.

The inventory at Sheldon Cord includes sunglasses (children's and adult's), fishing items (lures, hooks, swivels, reels, fishing line), men's and ladies cologne, key chains, summer beach items, toys, decorative tapestries, jewelry, cameras, T-shirts, and much more. There's also a wide assortment of furniture at wholesale prices. In a recent catalog, twin size mattress sets were listed at $49,95; a 5 piece oak bedroom set was $179.95; deluxe sleeper sofas were priced at $149.95 and up; and 5 piece wood dinette sets (with 4 matching chairs) were listed aT $149.95. There are hundreds of other furniture items to choose from.

All merchandise is sold for resale only. Call or write the company for a catalog. The minimum order from the catalog is $75. Returns are accepted within 30 days. Pay by certified check, cashier's check or money order.

S & J Products and Services
1005 N. 1st Street, Yakima, WA 98901
Phone: (509) 575-1797
FAX: (509) 575-1875

S & J Products and Services is one of the largest wholesalers of security products in the world. The company is a direct importer and manufacturer of quality personal security products. S & J Products promises to beat other competitors' prices on like products.

S & J's personal security products include key chain sprayers, fountain pen sprayers, CarGuard car alarms, personal alarms, home security systems, utility alarms, door stop alarms, first-aid and travel kits, and many other items. The company also offers 3 sample trial start-up packages, enabling potential distributors to find out what kind of retail profits are possible. You can sell these products office to office, by mail order, through flyers, in motel and hotel gift shops, and a number of other selling methods. S & J representatives can help you decide on the best selling methods.

Before ordering any personal security items, you should be aware of, and obey all applicable local, state, and federal laws in regard to possession and use of such items. Contact the company for an introductory catalog. Ask about the company's return policy. Orders may be paid by check, money order or major credit card.

Tabco International, Inc.
4342 N. Milwaukee, Chicago, IL 60641
Phone: (312) 286-4747; (800) 544-7882 [orders only]

Tabco features a large selection of general merchandise, novelties and gift items at wholesale prices. The company promises to beat any competitors' prices on like items. Tabco's inventory includes a large selection of toys, costume jewelry, T-shirts, lighters, key chains, tapestries, sweatshirts, and many other items.

Send $3.00 (refundable with first order) for Tabco's catalog. All prepaid or C.O.D. orders are shipped the same day. Minimum order is $50.

11460 N. Cave Road, Phoenix, AZ 85020
Phone: (602) 971-1243

The U.S. Gold Chain MFG. Co. supplies everything you need to start your own 14Kt. gold layered chain business. The company offers starter kits which feature gold chains, display, signs, jewelers tools, clasps, and complete instructions. The kits enable even beginners, with no previous jewelry-making experience, to set up and start selling for a profit right away. All you have to do is measure and cut the exact size to make custom necklaces and bracelets. You start by buying the highest quality 14Kt. Hamilton gold layered chain by the inch at low factory prices. You can sell at stores, malls, swap meets, and home parties for a sizable profit.

Contact the company at the above address and request a free wholesale jewelry catalog. U.S. Gold Chain MFG. also has a video tape which shows how you can make big profits by buying gold chain by the inch. The video is $10, which is refundable after 30 days. Orders to U.S. Gold Chain MFG. may be made by phone. Pay by major credit card.

W.M.S. Jewelry
120 N. Pacific St., A-4, San Marcos, CA 92069
Phone: (619) 744-8894

The W.M.S. Jewelry catalog (priced at $2.00) lists an assortment of merchandise at low wholesale prices. A recent catalog featured a selection of designer look-alike handbags, priced from $6.75, and frogskin handbags priced from $3.79. Other handbags are also available with prices starting at $3.00. These are all first-quality handbags, and no minimum order is required.

The company's inventory also includes a large selection of T-shirts and caps, fashion watches (hundreds of styles, beginning at $4.95), Eelskin products, fashion and casual shoes, costume jewelry, earrings, and other items. Some closeouts are also available.

No-name catalogs are available for your own imprint. Send $2.00 (cash only) for a catalog. Returns are accepted. Pay by money order or major credit card.

World Distributors
3420 N. Milwaukee Ave., Chicago, IL 606641
Phone: (312) 777-2345; (800) 251-0200 [orders only]
FAX:(312) 777-1445

World Distributors is an importer and distributor of general merchandise. This is a family-owned enterprise which has been in business since 1977 with an inventory of thousands of name-brand items at wholesale prices. The company's warehouse in Chicago covers more than 100,000 square feet and is filled with housewares, jewelry, clocks, novelties, cutlery, tools, gifts, toys, canned goods, watches, figurines, electronics, furniture, and many other items with great profit potential. Brand-names include Sanyo, Seiko, Regal, Canon, Texas Instruments, Sharp, Citizen, Procter-Silex, Oster, Minolta, and others.

A recent catalog featured hundreds of wholesale bargains, including 20" Toshiba Remote Control Color TVs for almost $200 below the suggested retail price; Casio AM/FM Stereo Double Cassette Recorders with remote control for less than $100 each; Craig VHS VCR with remote control for under $200; Kodak 35MM Focus Free Camera for less than $30.00; and Casio Full Feature Keyboards for under $200. The catalog also featured watches (by Seiko, Citizen, Casio, Sharp, and Benrus), jewelry (genuine 14K gold necklaces, bracelets, pendants, and rings; sterling silver earrings and pins), telephones and accessories, men's and ladies perfumes and colognes, personal care items, lamps, appliances, cookware, tableware, wallets, purses, luggage, sporting goods, and many other items.

You can order in quantity and carry an inventory or you can sell directly from the full color catalog. Catalogs are available without the World Distributors name on them so you can imprint your own. No membership fee or big investment is required.

A World Distributors catalog is available for $1.00. Write to the above address. Returns are accepted within 15 days. Minimum order requirements are $50 for U.S. customers and $100 for all international orders. Pay by major credit card.

Also see the following listings:

The Anka Co., Inc....chapter32
Bucks County Classic...chapter 21
Bob's Notions...chapter 32
Buckles of America...chapter32
Chanco Products...chapter 32
Cherry Tree Toys, Inc....chapter 6
Durham Wholesale...chapter 17
Galaxy Electronics...chapter 32
Glass Crafters...chapter 6
Hudson Glass...chapter6
Lakeside Products...chapter 32
Lou Davis Wholesale...chapter 32
Navajo Manufacturing Co....chapter 32
Oriental Trading Co....chapter 17
The Paper Wholesaler...chapter 17
The Wholesale Gift Shop...chapter 32
The Wholesale Source...chapter 32

Still More Money-Saving Wholesale Sources

Automotive

Postell Assoc., Inc.
1020 Sun Valley Dr., Roswell, GA 30076

Phone: (404) 998-777; (800) 886-RACE [7223]

In business since 1985, Postell Assoc. offers wholesale bargains on auto racing safety equipment and accessories. Call or write for a free catalog.

Brass Beds

A Brass Bed Shoppe
12421 Cedar Rd., Cleveland Heights, OH 44106
Phone: (216) 229-4900

A Brass Bed Shoppe offers brass and white iron beds at factory direct savings of up to 50% A color catalog is available free upon request.

Direct Industries
4866 W. Jefferson Blvd., Los Angeles, CA 90016
Phone: (213) 737-6865; (800) 727-6865

This company has been in business since 1969 selling brass beds and accessories at wholesale prices. Call or write for a free catalog.

Buckles

Buckles of America
4320 Anthony Ct., Suite 12K, Rocklin, CA 95677

Buckles of America offers thousands of buckles in a wide assortment of styles. Prices are below wholesale. Huge profit potential for resale. A color catalog is available for $2.00 cash). The catalog price is refundable with first order.

Carpet
American Wholesale Flooring
W. Frankfort, IL 62896.

Phone: (800) 356-6744

AWF offers mill direct carpet at wholesale prices. Most major brands are available. Also get wholesale prices on hardwood flooring and vinyl. Call the toll-free number for more information.

Carpet Wholesale Outlet
P.O. Box 1612, Exit 138, I-75, Dalton, GA 30722
Phone: (800) 235-0111

The Carpet Wholesale Outlet has been selling carpet wholesale to the public since 1967. Wholesale prices are also available on handmade and machine crafted Oriental rugs. Save up to 50% on all flooring needs while shopping at home. Call or write the company for more information.

Designer Carpets
Phone: (800) 253-7239

Designer Carpets offers most major brands of carpeting to consumers at wholesale prices. The company will deliver nationwide. Satisfaction is guaranteed. Brochures are available upon request. Call the toll-free number listed above.

Pugs Rugs Carpet N Things
Cartersville, GA
Phone: (800) 537-2943

Pugs offers wholesale mill direct savings on brand name carpeting, wood and tile flooring, and braided and Oriental rugs. Call the toll-free number listed above for complete information.

Cigars

MarkCigars
8th & Central Ave., Ocean City, NJ 08226

Phone: (609) 399-0935; (800) 257-8645

MarkCigars has been selling quality cigars at below whole-sale prices since 1947. Call or write for a free catalog.

Closeouts

Beal Textile Corp.
Lincolnton, NC 28093-0110

In business for over 20 years, Beal Textile offers closeout bargains on an assortment of merchandise. Get closeout prices on shirts, pants, socks, blouses, jeans, and much more. These closeouts are for resale only. Send $1.00 for a price list.

Cosmetics

Barnes Surplus
Rt. 2, Box 136B, Tupelo, MS 38801
Phone: (601) 840-9244

Barnes Surplus offers wholesale prices on a good selec-tion of cosmetics and perfumes. Call or write for a free catalog.

Craft Supplies

Lou Davis Wholesale
1490 Elkhorn Rd., Lake Geneva, WI 64640
Phone: (414) 248-2000 [customer service];
(800) 748-7991 [orders]FAX: (414) 248-6977

Lou Davis Wholesale offers a good selection of jewelry findings, and craft supplies. The company's inventory includes doll and teddy bear glasses, wind-up music boxes, mini quartz clocks, electrical cords and hundreds of other items. There's a selection of lampmaking accessories, carousel bases and accessories, electronic music movements, painting acces-sories, jewelry findings, air brush accessories, adhesives, clock movements and accessories, and more. Write the company to request a free wholesale ceramic and craft catalog and information.

Warner-Crivellaro
Phone: (800) 523-4242

Warner-Crivellaro offers a complete selection of stained glass supplies, tools instruction books, and glass at wholesale prices. Call the toll-free number to request a free catalog.

Electronics

Galaxy Electronics
5300 21st Ave., Brooklyn, NY 11204
Phone: (718) 258-6707: (800) 221-8924 [orders]
FAX: (718) 258-6975

Galaxy Electronics offers thousands of products at wholesale prices. Included in the company's inventory are car stereos and accessories, watches, promotional radios (as low as $3.75 each), tools, telephones, beauty aids, toys, clothing, GE and Panasonic beeperless answering machines, beaded car seats, and thousands of other items. Call the company for large quantity discounts. Minimum order is $65.00. A 178-page illustrated catalog is available for $18.

Farm & Garden

Sunshine Farm & Gardens
Rt. 5, Renick, WV 24966
Phone: (304) 497-3163

In business since 1971, Sunshine Farm & Gardens sells rare and unusual plants at wholesale prices. Send $2.00 for a catalog.

Formal Wear

Buy-A-Tux
615 W. Roosevelt Rd., Chicago, IL 60607
Phone: (800) 343-0003

Buy-A-Tux offers a huge selection of formal wear and accessories, all at wholesale prices. There are also hundreds of cummerbund and bow tie sets at discount prices. Waiter/waitstaff attire is also available. Even top designer tuxedos are available at discounts. Call the toll-free number for more information.

General Merchandise

A & B Sales Co.
Box 804, Rialto, CA 92377-0804

A & B has hundreds of wholesale bargains including cosmetics, pantyhose, tube socks, undergarmets, and much more. A wholesale catalog is available for $3.00 (refundable).

Chanco Products
P.O. Box 210550, San Francisco, CA 94121
Phone: (415) 905-6598 [24-hour recording]

Chanco offers over 2,800 products at wholesale and below wholesale prices. The company's inventory includes jewelry, watches, toys, gifts, novelties, and hundreds of other general merchandise items. Products are sold for personal use and in volume for resale. Write for free details about the company's color wholesale catalog.

Ladybucks
Box 1185, Chino Valley, AZ 86323

Ladybucks has hundreds of closeout, swapmeet, and flea market merchandise at rock bottom prices. First time buyers get a 25% discount. Send $1.00 (cash) for a 16-page whole-sale catalog.

Wilcox Sales
509 South 6th Ave.,
Paragould, AR 72450

The inventory at Wilcox Sales includes tots, novelties, automotive products, household items, combs, key chains, wallets, knives, balloons, jewelry, dolls, socks, lighters, and much more, all at wholesale prices. Some closeouts are also available. Send $1.00 for an illustrated wholesale catalog.

The Wholesale Gift Shop
Lincoln, NE 68501
Phone: (800) 847-5869

You can order gifts and other items at wholesale prices from The Wholesale Gift Shop. The company's inventory includes computers, games, watches, homewares, calculators, video games, FAX machines, cellular phones, telephone answering machines, CD's, tape decks, and more. Whether you order 1 item or 1000 you still receive wholesale prices. The company carries all major brands of merchandise. Call the toll-free number listed above for more information.

The Wholesale Source
Phone: (800) 242-4706

The Wholesale Source offers a selection of gift, personal and business items at below wholesale prices. In stock are appliances, computers, gift ideas, office supplies, electronics, toys, furniture, clothing, housewares and jewelry. You can buy direct from The Wholesale Source and save. Corporate and personal accounts are welcome. Call the toll-free number for a catalog and information.

Gifts

A & S Gift
P.O. Box 451072, Garland, TX 75045

A & S Gift offers below wholesale prices on hundreds of great gift ideas. The company's inventory includes jewelry, porcelain, household items, solid brass, knives, combs, automotive items, tools, toys, and many other gift items. Send $3.00 (refunded with first order) for a wholesale catalog.

Tender Heart Treasures, LTD
10525 "J" St., Omaha, NE 68127-1090
Phone: (402) 593-1313; (800) 443-1367

THT offers a selection of country style gifts at wholesale prices. Call or write for a catalog and information.

Gourmet Coffee

International Country Store
P.O. Box 1789-C, Redway, CA 95560
Phone: (707) 923-2661

The ICS sells gourmet coffees at wholesale prices. Call or write for a free catalog.

Hardware & Tools

Grainger
333 Knightsbridge Pkwy., Lincolnshire, IL 60069
Phone: (708) 913-8333

Grainger sells commercial and industrial equipment, parts and related merchandise. The company has been in business since 1927. A wholesale catalog is available free upon request.

Wholesale Tool Co., Inc.
P.O. Box 68, Warren, MI 48090
Phone: (313) 754-9270

The name tells the story. This company sells all kinds of tools at wholesale prices. Call or write for a free catalog and more information.

Health

Abunda Life Laboratories
Asbury Park, NJ
Phone: (800) 443-5649

Abunda Life manufactures 500 unique health products, powders, supplements, homeopathics, herbs, and vitamins. Call the toll-free number for wholesale information.

Hosiery

YES Trading
4471 N.W. 36 St., Miami Springs, FL 33166
Phone (305) 888-8055

YES Trading offers wholesale savings on hosiery, lingerie, and briefs. Buy undergarmets for women, men and children, and resell for a big profit. Send $1.00 (cash) for a catalog. The $1.00 is refundable with your first order.

Jewelry

A. J. Jewel's & Gifts
P.O. Box 502, McKeesport, PA 15134
Phone: (412) 673-3259

A. J. Jewel's has been selling wholesale jewelry and gifts since 1987. Send for a free catalog.

Anka Co., Inc.
40 Freeway Drive, Cranston, RI 02920
Phone: (800) 556-7768

The Anka Co. offers a selection of 14K gold, sterling silver, diamonds, gemstones, rings, earrings, and necklaces at wholesale prices. This line of jewelry offers a great money-making opportunity. Call the toll-free number to request a free color catalog.

Bob's Notions
2341 Boston Road, #5, Suite 502,
Wilbraham, MA 01905

Bob's Notions offers 14k gold at below wholesale prices. You can buy below wholesale and resale at a huge profit. In stock are Italian beveled herringbone, solid rope, rings, earrings, charms, bracelets, diamonds, and watches by Citizen and Seiko. Send $4.00 for a catalog, wholesale price list and information.

The Collection
Rd. 1, #216 Steelmanville Rd., Linwood, NJ 08221
Phone: (609) 927-4686

The Collection is fashion jewelry at wholesale prices. No minimum order is required. The company has been in business since 1984. Send $2.00 for a catalog.

Fort Worth Gold & Silver
3417 Hulen St., #109, Fort Worth, TX 76107-6100
Phone: (800) 433-5668

Fort Worth Gold & Silver offers an outstanding selection of wholesale jewelry. Send for a free catalog.

Gail's
Rt.8, Box 761, Fairmont Acres,
North Wilkesboro, NC 85738

If you are into horoscopes, Gail's has a great selection of jewelry for you. Unique pins, necklaces, charms, paperweights, and plaques are all available at wholesale prices. Send $5 for a sample and wholesale prices.

Gem Express
150 West 34th St.,
New York, NY 10001
Phone: (800) 552-4463

The Gem Express manufactures a collection of 14K gold and gemstone jewelry which is sold by the nation's leading retailers. You can get the same fine quality jewelry and save up to 50% by buying direct from the factory. Satisfaction is guaranteed. Call Gem Express at the toll-free number listed above and request a catalog.

Jim's Wholesale Supply
400 E. 10th Ave.,
Mitchell, SD 57301
Phone: (605) 996-7972

Jim's Wholesale sells gold and sterling silver findings and chains at wholesale prices. The company has been in business since 1989. Send $3.00 for a catalog.

Navajo Manufacturing Co.
501 Logan St., Denver, CO 80216
Phone: (303) 292-8090; (800) 525-5097

The Navajo Manufacturing Co. has over 700 authentic handmade Navajo and Zuni jewelry items. Send your name, address, phone number, and type of business, plus $2.00 for a color wholesale catalog.

Surprises & Jewelry
P.O. Box 1052,
Orange, CT 06477
Phone: (203) 934-8886

This company sells a fine selection of wholesale jewelry, and no minimum order is required. Send for a free catalog.

Novelties

Lakeside Products Co.
6646 N. Western Ave.,
Chicago, IL 60645
Phone (312) 761-5495; (800) 777-4404 [orders]

Lakeside Products has been serving the wholesale trade for over 30 years, offering a large selection of novelties and unusual items. Products include animal air refreshers, electronic TV antennas, automatic needle threaders, whoopee cushions, electric yoyos, removable tattoos, door stop alarms, power water guns, and hundreds of other wholesale novelty items with good resale potential. No minimum order requirement. Send $1.00 (refundable) for a wholesale catalog.

Office Furniture & Equipment

Alfax Wholesale Furniture
370 7th Ave., Ste. 1101,
New York, NY 10001
Phone: (212) 947-9560; (800) 221-5710

Since 1946, Alfax Wholesale has been selling institutional furniture designed for heavy use. Send for a free wholesale catalog.

ATD-American Co.

135 Greenwood Ave.,
Wyncote, PA 19095
Phone: (215) 576-1000; (800) 523-2300

For over 60 years, ATD has been offering wholesale bargains on office furniture and equipment. Send for a free catalog.

Wholesale Supply Co.

P.O. Box 23437,
Nashville, TN 37202
Phone: (800) 962-9162

Almost 10,000 office supply products are available at wholesale prices at Wholesale Supply. Call or write to request a catalog and more information.

Printing

Press Express

528 E. Andrews Ave., Ozark, AL
Phone: (205) 774-3794

The Press Express offers circulars, letterheads, envelopes, booklets, catalogs, business cards, rubber stamps, typesetting, and graphic design all at wholesale prices. Contact the company and request a free wholesale catalog.

Pet Supplies

Hercules Wire & Metal Products

7300 Radford Ave., North Hollywood, CA 91605
Phone: (201) 423-2222; (800) 526-0388

Hercules Wire & Metal specializes in animal and pet cages

and exercise pens. The company has been in business since 1956. Send for a free wholesale catalog.

Rubber Stamps

Arben Stamp Co.
413 Main Street, P.O. Box, 353, Evansville, IN 47703

Arben Stamp Co. has all the newest designs as well as hearts, dolls, holidays, and more. Also available are Rollagraphs, embossing powders, and glitter glue. Write the company and request wholesale information.

Silk Plants

Silk Plants Wholesale
14885 N. 83rd Pl., Scottsdale, AZ 85260

Buy silk plants, flowers and trees at wholesale prices from Silk Plants Wholesale. Save up to 60% on some items. A catalog is available for $3.00.

Wallcoverings

AAA Wallpaper
Sturgis, MI
Phone: (800) 882-6867

AAA Wallpaper features all wallpaper from any book in any pattern at wholesale prices. The company also offers discount prices on Graber blinds. Satisfaction is guaranteed. Call the toll-free number for prices.

Cleveland Wholesale Wallcoverings
Cleveland, OH
Phone: (800) 321-9933; (800) 362-2609 [in Ohio]

Cleveland Wholesale offers wholesale prices on all quality

brands of fabrics. Save 40% to 70% on all your wallcovering needs. Call the toll-free number for more information.

Price Is Right
374 Hall St., Phoenixville, PA 19460
Phone: (800) 336-WALL [9255]
FAX: (215) 933-3930

The Price Is Right has been serving the wallpaper industry for over 50 years. Save 40% to 72% on the top brands of wallpaper. You can buy what you need direct by phone at wholesale prices. Save up to 65% on window treatments by Bali, Kirsch, Hunter, and Douglas. Call the toll-free number and ask for a free order and information kit.

How To Buy Thousands Of Products Below Wholesale Direct From Secret Sources In Hong Kong And Taiwan

Most of the wholesale sources in this Guide are located within the United States. Many of the products offered by these suppliers are manufactured in this country. However, some products are manufactured overseas and imported into the U.S. Two of the most popular markets for U.S. importers are Hong Kong and Taiwan. These markets are popular product sources for big U.S. importers because they can provide thousands of products at incredibly low prices. The products are then sold in the U.S. for three or four times their cost to import.

The good news is that you don't have to be a big American importer in order to buy products directly from previously secret Hong Kong and Taiwan manufacturers. In fact, there are hundreds of manufacturers who are more than willing to sell their products to you, many at almost giveaway prices. Some products are imported at prices as low as 10 cents each and then sold for four times that amount in the United States. Your profits can be just as big on electronics, clothing, textiles, cameras, watches, andthousands of other items direct from manufacturers in Hong Kong and Taiwan.

You don't have to travel to Hong Kong and Taiwan to find these sources. You can find the addresses and product information for hundreds of manufacturers while sitting in your office or your own home. This special chapter of the Wholesale Bargains & Free Stuff Guide will provide some very basic information that will give you access to these "secret" sources in Hong Kong and Taiwan.

Hong Kong

There are nearly three hundred small factories in Hong Kong which manufacture over 8,000 products that you can purchase direct for well below typical wholesale prices. These manufacturers do not advertise in the U.S. and, with the exception of big importers who send representatives to Hong Kong, their addresses and product information are virtually a secret. That can be frustrating for a small business, since Hong Kong manufacturers specialize in textiles, finished clothing, assembly electronics, cameras, and thousands of other products that can be resold for big profits.

Here is a small sample of the products available at factory direct prices from Hong Kong manufacturers: radios, watches, jewelry, fashion accessories, lingerie, hardware, toys, calculators, hats, clothing for adults and children, vacuum cleaners, tools, machinery, footwear, food items, decorations, cameras and a variety of photographic equipment, home furnishings, personal care products, plastic products, novelties, TVs, and thousands of other items. These are all top-quality products which you can order factory-direct.

Now, the important part. How can you find current and

accurate information about these sources? To answer that question it may be worthwhile to consider how you would go about finding similar information about manufacturers in specific locations within the United States. For example, suppose you want to obtain the current addresses and product information for manufacturers in Anytown, U.S.A. You could get an Anytown phone directory and make a list of all the manufacturers. Better yet, you could contact the Anytown Chamber of Commerce which should be able to provide you with the information you need. Explain to the Chamber that you are a buyer, looking to do business in their city. After the Anytown Chamber of Commerce has given you the appropriate names and addresses, you can begin contacting the factories that manufacture the products you want to buy.

Since you are interested in Hong Kong manufacturers from whom you can buy direct, you can contact the Hong Kong General Chamber of Commerce (see address below). There are some U.S. produced directories which you can buy that may provide you with some information, but by contacting the Hong Kong General Chamber of Commerce you can be assured of getting current and accurate information. Your letter to the General Chamber of Commerce in Hong Kong should be clear and concise. It should be, after all, a business letter. Explain who you are, the types of products you wish to buy, and request any information (addresses, contacts,etc.) about manufacturers you can contact. Once you have this information, you can begin writing letters to individual manufacturers.

To contact the Hong Kong General Chamber of Commerce, write to the following address:

Hong Kong General Chamber of Commerce
22/F United Center, 95 Queensway, Hong Kong
Phone: 001-852-5-299-229

Taiwan

You can also contact the General Chamber of Commerce of Taiwan and request information about manufacturers from whom you can buy. There are many small manufacturers in Taiwan that offer thousands of products at prices well below typical wholesale. You can contact these manufacturers by letter, and buy factory direct a wide assortment of products including electrical goods, clothing and textiles, which are Taiwan's main exports.

The over 4,000 products you can buy direct include toys, electrical appliances and other electronic equipment, sporting goods, porcelain figurines, silk flowers, sun glasses, novelties, leather products, clocks, handbags, footwear, clothing for men women and children, art work, and thousands of other items. In many cases, you maybe able to order samples of merchandise, find out if it meets your satisfaction, and then order items in larger quantities.

You can contact the General Chamber of Commerce in Taiwan by writing to:

6/F, 390 Fu Hsing South Rd., Section 1,
Taipai, Taiwan

Phone: 001-886-2-701-2671

XXXIII

Factory Outlets

Factory Outlets have become very popular with time. Factory Outlets started out in the boom of the 80's and continue to grow and thrive during the hard economic times of the 90's. These discount Outlets offer name-brands, and quality for much less than department store prices. Factory Outlets continue to survive because they offer the high quality products people are looking for at discount prices. Outlet stores can afford to offer such good prices because they are factory or manufacturer owned, which cuts out the cost of the middleman and allows for a savings of 20% to 70% to be passed on to the customer, though the average discount is 30% to 40%.

Many people believe that the merchandise sold at Factory Outlets is damaged or in poor condition. The truth is, most of the merchandise sold is high quality with some of the merchandise being seconds or irregulars with flaws that are often times not noticeable. Discount Outlets sell fashions that are in season or one season behind. Outlets receive merchandise that is being discontinued, or overstocked. A manufacturer will sell what is needed to regular department stores and then place the extra stock in their outlet mall stores which is sold for much less than you would pay for the same item in a department store. Factory Outlets accept checks and credit cards and will usually allow you to return merchandise within a certain amount of time. When making a purchase, ask the store what their return policy is, don't assume that they will take returned merchandise.

Factory Outlets are usually not located nearby. Many department stores and other full-priced retailers require the manufacturer to sell discount items on an average of 15 to 30 miles away from the department or retail stores. Sometimes an Outlet will subsidize part of a bus tour for shoppers. Not all Outlets do this for their customers. If you belong to an organization that may be interested in a bus tour to a Factory Outlet, call the Outlet first to see if they will help with the cost. The cost can run anywhere from $20 to $120 depending on the extent of the trip. A bus tour is a good idea and often times those participating will receive free discount coupons that can be spent at the Outlet stores. Outlet shopping is definitely the best way to save money while still getting the high quality merchandise you want, without paying department store prices.

The following is a list of various Factory Outlets throughout the country. In order to locate an Outlet store nearest to your home, call 1-800-555-1212 for a toll free number. If the store you are trying to contact does not have an 800 number, call directory assistance (411) of the largest metropolitan area near your home. If the number you are looking for is still not found, try to locate the phone number of another Outlet store that may be near your home. If you are able to find a number for another Outlet store, chances are they may be located near or have the telephone number of the original store you were trying to locate.

APPAREL-CHILDREN'S
Baby Bliss Outlet Store
Benetton
Boston Traders Kids

Brooks Brothers Factory Store
The Eagle's Eye Kids
Farah Factory Store-Men's and Boy's
Hang Ten
Jessica McClintock
Kids Xpress
LaPetite Factorie
Today's Child

APPAREL-FAMILY
B.U.M. Equipment
Forsyth Factory Outlet
Fruit of the Loom
The Gap Outlet
Generra
Gitano Factory Stores
Great Outdoor Clothing Company
Guess? Factory Store
Jockey
Jordache
L.L. Bean Factory Outlet Store
Levi's Outlet
Levi's Outlet by Design
Levi's Outlet by Most
London Fog Factory Stores
Osborn Specialty Sewing
OshKosh B'Gosh Factory Stores
The Patagonia Outlet

APPAREL-MEN'S
Arrow Factory Stores
Banana Republic Outlet
Britches Great Outdoor Outlet
Brooks Brothers Factory Stores
Bugle Boy Outlet

Calvin Klein Outlet

Colours by Alexander Julian
Country Road Australia Outlet
Donna Karan Company Stores
Dickies Factory Outlet
Eddie Bauer Outlet Store
European Designer Outlet
French Connection Outlet
Geoffrey Beene Company
J. Crew Factory Store
John Henry & Friends for Men
Liz Claiborne Outlet Stores
Woolrich

APPAREL-WOMEN'S
Adrianna Papell Outlet Stores
Ann Taylor Clearance Centers
Anne Klein Factory Stores
Albert Nipon Factory Store
Banana Republic Outlet
Clavin Klein Outlet
Cambridge Dry Goods Company
Carroll Reed Catalog Outlet
Donna Karan Company Stores
Eddie Bauer Outlet Stores
Ellen Tracy
Esprit
Euro Collections
First Choice
Formfit
French Connection Outlet
Iguana Ltd.
J. Crew Factory Store
Jessica McClintock
J & F Factory Outlet
Jones New York
Large Sizes for Less
Laura Ashley
Liz Claiborne Outlet Stores

Maternities Factory Outlet
Oxford Sportswear Outlet
The Peruvian Collection

SHOES/SPORTING GOODS
Converse Factory Outlet Stores
Fila Factory Outlet
Hyde Factory Outlet
Nike Factory Store
The North Face
Russell Outlet Stores

BOOKS/RECORDS
Better Homes and Gardens
Books and Crafts
Book Warehouse
Publishers Warehouse

DRUGS/HEALTH/COSMETICS
Bubbles & Scents
Perfume Boutique
Prestige Fragrance & Cosmetics
Vitamin World Inc.

ELECTRONIC/APPLIANCES
Black & Decker Factory Outlet
Farberware
Kitchen Collection
Magnavox Factory Outlet
Regal Factory Outlet
Regal Outlet Stores
West Bend Company

FABRIC/YARN/CRAFTS
Coats & Clark
Nettle Creek
The Rag Shop
The Ribbon Mill

HANDBAGS/LUGGAGE/LEATHER GOODS
American Tourister Factory Outlet
Bagmaker Factory Stores
Bally of Switzerland Outlet
Bruce Alan Bags Etc.
Georgetown Leather Design
Griffco Leather Factory Outlet
Hahn Shoe Outlet
Hahn Shoe Rack
Leather Loft
Leather Manor
Samsonite
Satchels
Timberland Factory Outlet

HOME DECOR/FURNISHINGS
Brass Factory
Designer Wicker by Tribor Int'l.
Drexel Heritage Furniture Outlet
Lighting Factory Outlet
The NoJo Company Store
Polo/Ralph Lauren Factory Store

HOUSEWARES/TABLEWARES/POTTERY
Action Housewares Outlet
The Chicago Cutlery Factory
Corning/Revere Factory Stores
Crystal Works Factory Outlet
Famous Brands Housewares
Farberware
Flemington Cut Glass
Fostoria Glass Factory Outlet
General Housewares
Gorham Factory Outlet

Kennedy Brothers Woodenware
Kirk Stieff Factory Outlet Store
The Lenox Shop
Mikasa Factory Store
Oneida Factory Store
Reading China & Glass Inc.
Waterford/Wedgewood

JEWELRY/ACCESSORIES
Charles Jourdan Factory Outlet
Coro Fashion Jewelry
Crystal Brands Retail
L'ccessory
London Fog Factory Stores
Time World
Tower Jewelry Outlet

LINENS
American Classic Wovens, Inc.
Beacon Outlet
Chatham Country Store Outlet
Curtain Factory Outlet
Dan River Outlet
Fieldcrest Cannon
Home Fashions Outlet
Linen Factory Outlet
Mikasa Factory Store
The NoJo Company Store

LINGERIE/UNDERWEAR/HOSIERY
Appel-Jones New York Intimates
Barbizon Lingerie Co., Inc.
Carole Hochman Lingerie
E.J. PLUM Socks
Formfit
Jockey

Komar Stores
LaLingerie
Natori
The Robe Outlet
The Sox Market

PAPER GOODS/CARDS/GIFTS
Current Factory Outlet
Factory Card Outlet
Greeting Cards Outlet Store
Greetings-N-More
The Paper Factory

SHOES
Acme Boot Company Factory Outlet
Bass Company
Bostonian Factory Outlet
The Branded Store
Brands Factory Outlet
Buster Brown
Clark's Shoes
Endicott Johnson
Florshein Factory
Joan & David
Johnston & Murphy
Naturalizer Outlet
9 West & Co. Outlet
Perry Ellis Shoes
Timberland Factory Outlet

XXXIV

Free Stuff

**Books, Reports, Posters, Toys, Recipes, Product
Samples, and Hundreds of Other Goodies
You Can Get Free!**

There are literally hundreds of things you can get free, if you know where and how to get them. This special section of the Wholesale Bargains & Free Stuff Guide features listings of many companies, as well as groups and organizations that have something to give you, absolutely free. In many cases, companies will give away free products and samples for the promotional benefit. A number of groups, organizations, and agencies (Governmental, nonprofit, etc.) offer a wide assortment of educational and "how-to" manuals booklets, and pamphlets. All you have to do is write and ask for the free items. Usually, you'll be asked to submit a small postage and handling fee, and in some cases a specified size SASE, but you'll pay nothing for the items themselves. Please note that giveaways are usually available in limited quantities, so if you see something you want you should send for it right away. Don't be disappointed if a particular "freebie" is no longer available. Some of the free items listed in this section may no longer be available by the time you read this catalog.

To request any of the free items listed below, you must follow all directions and instructions exactly as each listing specifies. Be sure to include specified postage and SASEs when required.

CONSUMER AND BUSINESS INFORMATION

Information on how to protect yourself against credit card fraud is available in a free booklet titled "Who's Got Your Number?" To get the booklet send a #10 SASE to: Consumer Affairs Office, 19th Floor, American Express Co., 125 Broad St., New York, NY 10004.

To get consumer guidelines for shopping by mail send a #10 SASE to: Bess Myerson's Consumer Guidelines, Direct Marketing Association, 6 East 43rd St., New York, NY 10017.

"Saving Energy Wisely", is a 16 page booklet which provides suggestions and advice for home energy efficiency. To get a free copy of this booklet, write to: AARP, Consumer Affairs Section, Program Coordination and Development Department, 1909 K.St., NW, Washington, DC 20049.

A free copy of "A Citizens Guide To Radon" is available by writing to: Public Information Center, E.P.A., 401 M St., SW, PM-211B, Washington, DC 20460.

For a free booklet on nuclear energy write to: U.S. Council for Energy Awareness, P.O. Box 66080, Dept. TR05, Washington, DC 20035.

"Stripping Paint From Wood", a booklet which provides information detailing the best (and safest) way to apply and remove chemical paint strippers, is available free upon specific request from the Consumer Information Center, Department 571Y, Pueblo, CO 81009.

A 21 page booklet, written to help you manage your budget and suggest ways to invest in the future is available free by writing to: Financial Planning, American Council of Life Insurance, 1850 K. St., N.W. Washington, DC 20006.

A free home employment report, describing several potentially profitable home- based business opportunities is available from Consumer Network. The report provides information about specific home-based opportunities as well as how to get started in such a business. The report is free when you send a long SASE to: Consumer Network, Dept. M2, BOX 8138, St. Paul, MN 55108.

Women who want to start or expand a small business can get free information about 25 demonstration centers across the country that charge small fee for advice and counsel. To get a free list of the 25 demonstration centers, write to: SBA, Office of Women's Business Ownership, Demonstration Project Sites, 409 Third St. S.W., Washington, D.C. 20416.

The Enforcement Division, Federal Trade Commission (FTC), 6th & Pennsylvania Ave., NW, Washington, DC 20580, has available free information about what to do upon receiving unordered merchandise through the mail. Write to the FTC and ask for a copy of "Unordered Merchandise Statute".

To get a free copy of the booklet, "Master Laws Administered by the U.S. Department of Labor That Affect Small Business", write to: Office of Small and Disadvantaged Business Utilization, U.S. Department of Labor, Washington, DC 20210.

Information on the FDA's packaging and labeling regulations for food and drug products is available free by writing for a copy of "A Small Business Guide To the FDA". Write to: Small Business Coordinator, Food and Drug Administration, 5600 Fishers Lane, Room 1372, HFC 50, Rockville, MD 20857.

Free information on how to start your own mail order and

merchandising business can be obtained from the Specialty Merchandise Corporation. The Information is contained in a cassette, "20 Minutes To Financial Success" and a booklet titled, " A Professional Guide to Specialty Wholesaling". Both are free upon written request to: Mr. C.L. Priesel, Specialty Merchandise Corp., 9401, De Soto Ave., Dept. 12-39, Chatsworth, CA 91311-4998.

For a free copy of "Blake's Natural: Non-Irradiated Herbs & Spices", write to 505 N. Railroad, Ellensburg, WA 98926— or call 1-800-932 HERB.

A 56 page herbalist catalog is available free by writing to: Herbalist, P.O. Box 5 Dept. ADCG, Hammond, IN 46325.

A free color catalog featuring a selection of wild bird, animal, and marine mammal mobiles is available from Skyflight Mobiles, P.O. Box 974, Dept E, Woodinville, WA 98072.

"RockWare Scientific Catalog", featuring a selection of earth science software, is available free from RockWare, 4251 Kipling St., Suite 595, Wheat Ridge, CO 80033.

An environmental catalog, "A Better Way", is available free by writing to: A Better Way, P.O. Box 1045, San Carlos, CA 94070-1045.

To get a free Earth Science Catalog write to: ASC Scientific, 2075 Corte del Nogal, Ste. 1, Carlsbad, CA 92009— or call 1-800-272-4327.

Free Engine Help: To get a free brochure titled, "How to Treat Your Engine Right", write The Shaler Company, P.O. Box 471, Waupun, WI 53963 or call 1-800-452- 2888.

A free catalog of business books for sale by the U.S. government is available by writing to: Free Business Catalog, U.S. Government Printing Office, Office of Marketing— Stop SM, Washington, DC 20401.

A PBS home video color catalog is free from PBS Home Video, Dept. 2G137, 11858 La Grange Ave., Los Angeles, CA 90025— or call 1-800-538-5856.

Complete guide to exercise videos catalog is available free of charge from : Video Exercise Catalog, Dept. DC2, 5390 Main St. NE, Minneapolis, MN 55421.

To get a free monthly newsletter, "Memo To Mailers", which provides timely information about changes in postal rates and classifications, write to: Marketing Department, Regular Mail Services, 475 L' Enfant Plaza, SW, Washington DC 20260-6336.

A free booklet, "Postal Crime Prevention: A Business Guide", is available from the Public Affairs Branch, Postal Inspection Service, U.S. Postal Service, 475 L' Enfant Plaza, SW, Washington DC 20260.

A free book, providing information on home-based business is available by writing to: Mountain Publishing Co., Sunnyside Rd., Lenore, Idaho 83541.

A free pamphlet titled, "How To Start A Home Based Business", is available by writing to: Office of Business Development and Marketing, Small Business Administration, Washington, DC 20416.

A free copy of "Homebased Business: Child Care and Running a Child Care Business" is available by writing to: County Cooperative Extension Service, 6707 Groveton Dr., Clinton, MD 20735. Also get a free copy of "How To Select Quality Day Care For Your Child", by writing to the same address.

To get a free copy of "Business Use Of A Car (#917), write to: Taxpayer Services, Internal Revenue Service, U.S. Department of The Treasury, 1111 Constitution Ave., NW,

Room 2422, Washington, DC 20224

PRODUCT SAMPLES

Lactaid—a product designed as a supplement to help make dairy foods more digestible. Get a free test and sample kit by calling toll free, 1-800-HELP- KIT (1-800-435-7548).

K-Y Brand Jelly— for information and a free sample, call 1-800-547-2300, ext. 202.

Beano— a product which contains a food enzyme that helps to break down the hard-to-digest sugars in gassy foods, preventing gas after eating beans and other foods. For more information and a free sample, call 1-800-257-8650 (In Canada, call 1-800-668-8968).

Estraderm— available by prescription only, this product is a clear patch that delivers a form of estrogen through the skin into the blood stream. It is also used to help prevent osteoporosis. To get a free "non-medicated" sample patch and information kit, call toll free, 1-800-521-CIBA.

A free sample import and a free report which shows how to make money with a mail order home import business is available from B.L. Mellinger III, The Mellinger Co., Dept. N2369, 6100 Variel Ave., Woodland Hills, CA 91367.

To Get a free list of the Juvenile Products Manufacturers Association's certified products, send a SASE to the association, Directory of Certified Products, 2 Greentree Center, Suite 225, P.O. Box 955, Marlton, NJ 08053.

FOOD STUFF, RECIPES, REPORTS

Free recipes for the kids! With a little help, kids can be creative in the kitchen and learn to make great tasting chicken. Send a business size S.A.S.E. to Delmarva Poultry Industry,

R.D. 2, Box 47, Georgetown, Del. 19947. Ask for: "Prize Winning Chicken Recipes."

Learn about the "History of Ice Cream." This beautifully illustrated book is yours free by writing to International Association of Ice Cream Manufacturers., 888 16th Street N.W., Washington, D.C. 20006.

Here is a free guide to help you learn the health benefits of diet and exercise. It is called "A Recipe for Fitness" and describes an easy-to-follow exercise program and contains 21 diet recipes for healthy main dishes. Just send $.50 for postage and handling to Mazola Corn Oil, Dept.RF, Box 307, Coventry, CT 06238. Ask for: A Recipe For Fitness.

Free "Kids-Can-Do-It" Cookbook from Kellogg's. 13 Recipes for desserts and main course meals made out of cereal. Just send a postcard to Kellogg Company, Department G-9, One Kellogg Square, Battle Creek, MI 49016. Ask for Kellogg's Cereal Recipe Collection.

Salad recipes are available by writing to: T. Marzetti Company, Dept P, Box 29300, Columbus, OH 43229.

Free recipes, using pork, are available for a legal-sized SASE. Send to: RECIPES, Box 10383-WM, Des Moines, IA 50306.

To get free recipes for fat-free family desserts, send your name and address to: Karo Fat-Free Recipes, P.O. Box 307, Dept. K-FF, Coventry, CT 06238.

For delicious seafood recipes send a SASE to: New Bedford Seafood, Box 307, Fairhaven, MA 02719.

You can get Mexican and Tex-Mex recipes free by writing to: Pace Recipe Cards, P.O. Box NB169, El Paso, TX 79977.

For a selection of recipes using tomatoes, send a SASE to: Favorite Tomato Recipes, Florida Tomato Committee, Box 140533, Suite CL, Orlando, FL 32814- 0533.

Delicious recipes using soy sauce are available for a SASE— send to: Kikkoman International Inc., Dept. CS8Q, P.O. BOX 427084, San Francisco, CA 94142-0784.

"Sensibly Delicious Recipes", using Nestle Toll House Morsels, are available free by writing to: Sensibly Delicious Recipes, P.O. Box 1898, Young America, MN 55594-1898.

The National PTA and Educational Testing Service have produced a booklet titled, "What Every Parent Should Know About Testing". The booklet is free with a business-sized SASE. Write to: National PTA Orders, 700 N. Rush St., Chicago, ILL 60611.

Videos: A free video and brochure for people who wear wigs is available by writing to: The Wig Company, Dept. 9093, Box 112650, Pittsburgh, PA 15241— or call 1-800- 446-4047.

Videos:To get a free video and a brochure on how to get relief from back pain, write to: Back Technologies, 2525 West Casino Road, Everett, WA, 98204— or call 1- 800-433-5599.

Videos:For a free video and brochure about an aerobic exerciser write to: NordicTrack, Dept. #105C2, 141 Jonathan Blvd. N., Chaska, MN 55318— or call 1-800-328-5888, ext 105C2.

FREE PUBLICATIONS

Consumer Information Catalogs offering a variety of facts and information are made available through the government. Many catalogs are made available to you free of charge, others for a very minimal fee. To receive your free publication send your requests to write to:

S. James, Consumer Information Center-3C
P.O. Box 100,
Pueblo, Colorado 81002.

To receive publications for a minimal fee write to:
R. Woods, Consumer Information Center-3C
P.O. Box 100,
Pueblo, Colorado 81002.

Auto Service Contracts. Helpful tips on avoiding duplicate coverage, making claims, using reconditioned parts and more. Publication no. 401Z. $.50.

Buying a Used Car. Learn your rights when buying from an individual and the "Buyer's Guide" sticker required on all used cars sold by a dealer. Publication no. 479Z. $.50.

Consumer Tire Guide. Learn how to check for proper air pressure and signs of uneven wear; how and why to rotate your tires; special care in cold weather; and more. Publication no. 403Z. $.50.

New Car Buying Guide. Discusses pricing terms, financings options, and various contracts. Includes a worksheet to help you bargain. Publication no. 405Z. $.50.

Recycling Used Oil. Explains how and why oil recycling helps the environment and saves energy. Publication no. 503Z. Free.

Auto Warranty Claims: What you should know about your Auto emissions warranty. Learn how to make a claim, what parts and repairs are covered, and more. Publication no. 407Z. $.50.

Help Your Child Learn to Write Well. Simple strategies for adults to help encourage children who are just learning to express their ideas through writing. Publication no. 413Z. $.50.

Helping Your Child Learn Geography. Designed to teach children geography in a style that's challenging and fun. Publication no. 414Z. $.50.

Helping Your Child Learn Math. 26 meaningful and fun activities to help you child (ages 5-13) see math as a positive and interesting part of life. Publication no. 612Z. Free.

Helping Your Child Learn to Read. Fun and practical activities to help you and your child lay a foundation for a lifetime of reading. Primarily for children under 10, but helpful for older children too. Publication no. 617Z. Free.

Helping Your Child Learn Science. Step-by-step guide to many fun and creative activities for 3-10 year olds. Lists resources for parents who want more help and information. Publication no.143Z. $3.25.

Help Your Child Improve in Test-Taking. Simple techniques to help children at all grade levels avoid "test anxiety" and prepare for various types of tests. Publication no.412Z. $.50.

Helping Your Child Succeed in School. 15 fun

activities to do with your children (ages 5-11) to help expand their imagination, obey, organize, help others, and much more. Publication no. 478Z. $.50.

Helping Your Child Use the Library. Highlights programs and activities for children of all ages as well as those with special needs. Tips to get children interested in books. Publication no. 415Z. $.50.

FREE TRAVEL GUIDES, MAPS, POST CARDS

Free Maps, Postcards. Write to tourism department of each state and they'll send you a packet of free maps, brochures, tourist attractions, and postcards. So you can travel all over the U.S. without ever leaving your home. Send a postcard to the state of your choice and ask for: Tourist Information.

Alabama Bureau of Tourism and Travel
532 South Perry Street   800-252-2262
Montgomery, Ala. 36104

Alaska Division of Tourism   907-465-2010
Box E
Juneau, Alaska 99811

Arizona Office of Tourism   602-255-3618
1100 West Washington Street
Phoenix, Ariz. 85007

Arkansas Department of Parks & Tourism   800-643-8383
1 Capitol Mall
Little Rock, Ark. 72201

California Office of Tourism   800-862-2543
1121 L Street
Sacramento, Calif. 95814

Colorado Tourism Board   800-433-2656
1625 Broadway, Suite 1700
Denver, Colo. 80202

Connecticut Department of
Economic Development
210 Washington Street   800-243-1685
Hartford, Conn. 06106

Delaware Tourism Office
99 Kings Highway - Box 1401   800-441-8846
Dover, Del. 19903

District of Columbia Visitors Association   202-789-7000
1575 Eye Street N.W.
Washington, D.C. 20005

Florida Division of Tourism   904-487-1462
126 Van Buren Street
Tallahassee, Fla. 32301

Georgia Tourist Division   800-847-4842
Box 1776
Atlanta, Ga. 30301

Hawaii Visitors Bureau   808-923-1811
2270 Kalakaua Avenue, Suite 801
Honolulu, Hawaii 96815

Idaho Travel Council   800-635-7820
700 West State Street
Boise, Idaho 83720

Illinois Tourist Information   800-223-0121
310 South Michigan Avenue
Chicago, Ill. 60604

Indiana Tourist Development   800-292-6337
1 North Capitol, Suite 700
Indianapolis, Ind. 46204

Iowa Tourism Office   800-345-4692
200 East Grand Avenue
Des Moines, Iowa 50309

Kansas Travel and Tourism Division   800-252-6727
400 West Eighth Street, Suite 500   913-296-2009
Topeka, Kan. 66603

Kentucky Department of Travel Dvlp.   800-225-8747
Capital Plaza Tower - 22nd Floor
Frankfort, KY 40601

Louisiana Office of Tourism   504-342-8119
Box 94291   800-334-8626
Baton Rouge, LA 70804

Maine Publicity Bureau   800-533-9595
97 Winthrop Street
Box 23000
Hallowell, ME 04347-2300

Maryland Office of Tourism Development   800-331-1750
217 East Redwood Street - Ninth Floor
Baltimore, MD 21202

Massachusetts Office of Travel & Tourism
100 Cambridge Street   800-533-6277
Boston, Mass. 02202

Michigan Travel Bureau   800-543-2937
Box 30226
Lansing, Mich. 48909

Minnesota Office of Tourism
375 Jackson Street   800-328-1461
250 Skyway Level
St. Paul, Minn. 55101-1810

Mississippi Department of Tourism   800-647-2290
Box 22825
Jackson, Miss. 39205

Missouri Division of Tourism   314-751-4133
Box 1055
Jefferson City, MO 65102

Montana Promotion Division
1424 Ninth Avenue   800-541-1447
Helena, Mont. 59620

Nebraska Division of Travel and Tourism
301 Centennial Mall South   800-228-4307
Box 94666
Lincoln, Neb. 68509

Nevada Commission on Tourism   800-638-2328
600 East Williams, Suite 207
Carson City, Nev. 89710

New Hampshire Office of Vacation Travel   603-271-2666
Box 856
Concord, NH 03301

New Jersey Division of Travel and Tourism 800-537-7397
C.N. 826
Trenton, NJ 08625

New Mexico Tourism and Travel Division
1100 St. Francis Drive   800-545-2040
Santa Fe, NM 87503

New York Department of Econ. Development
1 Commerce Plaza   800-225-5697
Albany, NY 12245

North Carolina Division of Travel & Tourism
430 North Salisbury Street   800-847-4862
Raleigh, NC 27611

North Dakota Tourism Promotion   800-437-2077
Capitol Grounds
Bismarck, ND 58505

Ohio Division of Travel and Tourism   800-282-5393
Box 1001
Columbus, Ohio 43266-0101

Oklahoma Tourism and Recreation Department
215 Northeast 28th Street   800-652-6552
Oklahoma City, Okla. 73105

Oregon Tourism Division   800-547-7842
595 Cottage Street NE
Salem, Ore. 97310

Pennsylvania Division of Travel Marketing   800-847-4872
439 Forum Building
Harrisburg, PA 17120

Rhode Island Department of
Economic Devlelopment
7 Jackson Walkway   800-556-2484
Providence, RI 02903

South Carolina Division of Tourism   803-734-0122
Box 71
Columbia, SC 29202-0071

South Dakota Department of Tourism   800-843-1930
711 Wells Avenue
Pierre, SD 57501

Tennessee Tourist Development   615-741-2158
Box 23170
Nashville, Tenn. 37202

Texas Tourism Division   800-888-8839
Box 12008
Austin, TX 78711

Utah Travel Council   801-538-1030
Council Hall - Capitol Hill
Salt Lake City, Utah 84114

Vermont Travel Division   802-828-3236
134 State Street
Montpelier, VT 05602

Virginia Division of Tourism   800-847-4882
202 North Ninth Street, Suite 500
Richmond, VA 23219

Washington State Department of   206-586-2088
Trade and Economic Development
101 General Administration Building
Olympia, WA 98504-0613

West Virginia Tourism Division   800-225-5982
2101 Washington Street East
Charleston, W. VA 25305

Wisconsin Division of Tourism Development
123 West Washington Avenue   800-432-8747
Box 7970, Madison, WI 53707

Wyoming Travel Commission   800-225-5996
I-25 and College Drive
Cheyenne, Wyo. 82002

TOYS AND OTHER ITEMS
FOR CHILDREN

Coloring Books, Posters, Photographs: An assortment of coloring books, litter bags, song sheets, photographs, posters, and bike stickers are available by writing to: Woodsy Owl, Forest Service, Department of Agriculture, Room 3248, South Building, P.O. Box 2417, Washington, D.C. 20013— Or call 202-447-7013.

Coppertone Suntan Lotion: Coppertone Suntan Lotion offers a free sample of their famous Coppertone Suntan Lotion "4". Simply send $.50 for postage and handling to: Coppertone Sample Offer, P.O. Box 377, Memphis, TN 38151.Be sure and ask for: Free Sample of Coppertone Suntan Lotion #4.

Become a Pen Pal: Here is a freebie for all of those pen pals out there, or those who would like to become pen pals. To find a student to write to in any state or country, send a business size S.A.S.E. to the Student Letter Exchange Bureau, 215 Fifth Ave.S.E., Waseca, MN 56093. And ask for:Student Letter Exchange Information.

The Declaration of Independence: This document can be yours free! Just send $1.00 for postage and handling to Historical Documents Co., 8 N. Preston St., Philadelphia, PA 19104. Ask for: The Declaration Of Independence & Bill of Rights Set.

Bicycle Safety: "Cycling Safety Rules" can be very important to you if you have a youngster who rides a bike. It's free when you send a postcard to Employers Insurance of Wausau, Safety and Health Services Department, WI 54401. Ask for: Cycling Safety Rules.

How to be a good Fisherman: Send for this free booklet with valuable advice on how to improve on your sport. Send $.25 for postage and handling to Sheldon's, Inc., Antigo WI 54409 and ask for: The Fisherman's Guide.

Washington Redskins Fan-Mail Package: Football Fans! "The Washington Redskins" are giving away a free fan mail package including a team decal and photos of your favorite team stars. Send a postcard to Washington Redskins Public Relations Department, 13832 Redskin Drive, Herndon, VA 22070. Ask for: Fan Mail Package.

Kite Flying: Here's a free booklet with every style of kite for your pleasure. Send a postcard to Into the Wind Co.,1408 Pearl St.,Boulder,CO 80302-5307. Ask for:Into the Wind Catalog.

Scale Model Railroading: Free! Everything you need to know is in this booklet. Send $.25 for postage and handling to Model Railroader Magazine, 1027 North 7th St., Milwaukee, WI 53233. Ask for: Introduction to Scale Model Railroading.

Study Abroad: If you would like to become a Foreign Exchange student and study abroad in a foreign school. Write to ASSE International Student Exchange Program, 228 N. Coast Highway, Laguna Beach, CA 92651. Or, write to AFS Intercultural Programs, 313 E. 43rd St., New York, NY 10017.

Easy Ways to Earn Money: This free booklet provides lots of fundraising ideas for your school or church, or any group. Send a postcard to Revere Company, Fund Raising Department, Scranton, PA 18504-1491. Ask for: Fund Raising Ideas.

Learn about the Weather: This free booklet explains all about the weather and how it affects our lives. Send a business size S.A.S.E. to Air France Distributing Center, 2039 9th Avenue, Ronkonkoma, N.Y. 11779. Ask for: "What's the Weather" Pamphlet

Postage Stamp Collecting: Learn how to collect postage stamps, free! To get started in this fascinating hobby, send a postcard to Littleton/Mystic Stamp Company, 96 Main Street, Camden, N.Y. 13316. Ask for: Beginners "How to Collect Stamps" booklet..

Free Iron-Ons: Get a great set of 10 animal iron-ons, free, that can be put on a t-shirt, hat, jacket, or anything. Send $.75 for postage and handling to Dog's World, 498 New Rochelle Road, Bronxville, N.Y. 10708. Ask for: Animal Iron-Ons.

Exercise Booklet: Youngsters can benefit greatly from a regular exercise routine. Get a free pamphlet that presents a physical exercise program that is fun for kids to do. Send a business size S.A.S.E. to Jim Johnson, Hershey Youth Program, P.O. Box 814, Hershey, PA 17033-0814. Ask for: Team Up for Fitness.

Emergency & First-Aid Chart: Here's a free chart that will help kids identify emergencies and learn some first-aid. It is full of detailed instructions on how to treat most common emergencies. Send a postcard to Council on Family Health, 420 Lexington Avenue, New York, N.Y. 10017. Ask for:

First Aid Wall Chart.

Music Appreciation for Children: Enjoy a symphony and learn the fundamentals of symphonic music appreciation for kids, free! Send a business size S.A.S.E to How to Enjoy a Symphony c/o Hershey Chocolate USA, P.O. Box 800, Hershey, PA 17033-0800.

Make Your Own Paper: With just a few common things found around the house and this free pamphlet, you can make your own paper. Send a postcard to American Paper Institute, Inc., 260 Madison Avenue, New York, N.Y. 10016. Ask for: How You Can Make Paper.

Free Blistex Sample: Blistex is offering a free sample of their "Soothing Berry" lip balm with sunscreen protection - perfect for dry, chapped lips. Send $.50 for postage and handling to Blistex Sample Offer, 1800 Swift Drive, Oak Brook, IL 60512. Ask for: Blistex Soothing Berry Sample.

Put on Your own Puppet Show: You can learn how to have your own puppet show and have lots of fun. By writing to the address below, you can have your very own mitten hand puppets, both in different designs. Simply send $1.00 for postage and handling to Mr. Rainbows, P.O. Box 27056, Philadelphia, PA 19118. Ask for: Mitten Hand Puppets.

Greeting Cards from the President: How about surprising someone special with a greeting card from the President of the United States? Anyone who is at least 80 years old or has been married for 50 years or more can get a free greeting card from the White House. At least a one month advance notice is required. Send a postcard to The President c/o Greeting Office, The White House, Washington, D.C. 20500.

Science Project Ideas: Here is a pamphlet of 150 ideas that your high school teacher can get free for you. It has ideas for projects for all students from chemistry and biology to geology and math. Send a business size S.A.S.E. to Mr. Michael Farmer, teacher, P.O. Box 193, Tigerville, SC 29688. Ask for: Science Fair Project Idea Folder.

Free Batteries. You can get free batteries, one every month for a whole year, by walking into any Radio Shack store and asking for a free battery card. You don't have to buy anything. Just present your card once a month, and you will have a choice of a 9 volt, AA, C, or D cell battery, free! You don't need to write anywhere for this great offer.

Gold Necklace: Girls, you can have your very own 18-inch necklace made of 14-karat enhanced gold. It looks and feels like pure gold, but it's not. You can sell the jewelry and earn money or great prizes. Send $2.00 for postage and handling to A.T.H. Co., P.O. Box 70-FT, Stroudsburg, PA 18360.

Free Coloring Book. How to have fun with different types of pets. For your free coloring book and poster, send a postcard to Pets are Wonderful Council, 500 North Michigan Avenue, Suite 200, Chicago, IL 60611. Ask for: Pets are Wonderful Companions.

Roller Skating. How about picking up a sport that is great fun and great exercise too? It's Roller Skating and you can learn lots of safety tips, hints, stunts, and games by sending away for this free booklet. Send a postcard to Chicago Roller Skate Co., 4458 West Lake Street, Chicago, IL 60424. Ask for: How to Roller Skate and Fun & Games on Roller Skates.

United States Flag. Send for this free, 32-page booklet that tells all about it by sending a postcard to U.S. Marine Corps, Department of the Navy, Washington, D.C. 20380. Ask for: How to Respect and Display our Flag Booklet.

Free Rainbow Glasses, that burst with color when sunlight, or any light,, hits them. The secret is the laser-created halograms that cause a 3-D effect. Just send $1.00 for postage and handling to Mr. Rainbows, P.O. Box 27056-RB, Philadelphia, PA 19118. Ask for Rainbow Glasses.

Coin Collecting: Learn about coin collecting from a magazine with lots of articles and features aimed towards the beginner - Free. Just send $.50 for postage and handling to Coins Magazine Sample Offer, Dept. CG, 700 E. State Street, Iola, WI 54990. Ask for: Sample Copy of Coins Magazine.

Kids Games, Puzzles, & Crafts: Have fun with kids with over 40 fun things to do.Just send a business size S.A.S.E. to Kid's Fun Pak, The Children's Museum, 533 16th Street, Bettendorf, IA 52722. Ask for: Kid's Fun Pak.

Free Information Booklets from NASA: These free booklets include: Space Shuttle Facts; What About U.F.O.s?; America's Spaceport; Exploring Inner Planets; All About The Moon; and Space Launch Vehicles. Send a postcard to Public Affairs Office, John F. Kennedy Space Center, NASA Cape Canaveral, FL 32899. Ask for any of the booklets from the above list.

Free Coloring Book: This free 26-page coloring book takes you from your baby teeth all the way up to the proper brushing of your teeth. Just send $.25 for postage to American Dental Association, 211 E. Chicago Avenue, Chicago, IL 60611. Ask for the ABC's of Good Oral Health.

Jesse James Poster: Get a genuine replica of the famous Jesse James poster. Send $1.00 for postage and handling to Historical Documents Co., 8 N. Preston St., Philadelphia, PA 19104. Ask for: Jesse James & Billy The Kid Reward Posters.

Free Coloring Book: This book tells you about honey bees. How they make honey and all about their families. Send

$.60 for postage and handling to Dadant & Sons, Inc. Hamilton, IL 62341. Ask for: Honey Bee Coloring Book (M50).

YO-YO Tricks: Get a free pamphlet on how to do YO-YO tricks. Send a business size S.A.S.E. to Duncan Toys Company, P.O. Box 165, Baraboo, WI 53913. Ask for: YO-YO Trick Pamphlet.

George Washington: This beautifully illustrated free book tells of the life and times of our first president. Just send a postcard to Washington National Insurance Company, Consumer Education Dept., Evanston, IL 60201. Ask for: Booklet on the Life of George Washington.

National Geographic: National Geographic World for Kids has great articles on nature, science, and world events, and it's yours free. Send a postcard to National Geographic World, 17th and "M" Streets, Suite 687, Washington DC 20036. Ask for: A Sample Copy Of National Geographic World.

Free Mini-Sewing Kit: Includes everything you need to fix a button, safety pins, needles, thread, a needle threader, and a 25" measuring tape. All of these items come in a small box. Send $1.00 for postage and handling to Assiduity Industries, P.O. Box 1147, Willits, CA 95490. Ask for the Sewing Kit Keychain.

Pet Care Bookmarker: Get a bookmark that tells you how to care for your favorite pet. Send a business size S.A.S.E. to Animal Protection, P.O. Box 22505, Sacramento, CA 95822. Ask for: Animal Bookmark and tell them which pet bookmark you would like to have.

First-Aid Chart: Receive a free first-aid chart that contains basic information that every child and adult should know. Send a postcard to Johnson & Johnson Consumer Education Department, New Brunswick, NJ 08903. Ask for: First Aid

Facts Chart.

Electrical outlets can be very dangerous for children. A way to protect against this danger is with safety "plugs" that will child-proof your home. For 10 free safety plugs, send $1.00 for postage and handling to F&H Baby Products, P.O. Box 2228, Evansville, IN 47714-2228. Ask for: Set of 10 Safety Outlet Plugs.

Hair Care and Styling Tips: Here is a guide for you young girls full of all kinds of shampooing and drying tips, and of course, setting and styling ideas. Send a postcard to Goody Products, P.O. Box 524, Kearny, N.J. 07032. Ask for: Hair Styling Booklet.

Jog and Run Safely: Jogging can be a fun , but if done improperly, can hurt you. Send for your free safety tips on jogging and running by sending a business size S.A.S.E. to American Running & Fitness Assn., 9310 Old Georgetown Rd., Bethesda, MD 20814. Ask for: Safety Tips for a Safe Workout.

Bicycle Care & Safety: Riding a bike can be easy, but taking care of a bike and learning the safety rules is also important. Send for this free guide to show you how. Send a business size S.A.S.E. to Aetna Life & Casualty, Consumer Information Department, 151 Farmington Avenue, Hartford, CT 06156. Ask for: Bicycle Safety Pamphlet.

Learn to play chess: Send for your free 32-page booklet that tells you how to play by sending a postcard to Dover Publications, Inc., 31 East Second St., Mineola, N.Y. 11501. Ask for: "How Do You Play Chess" beginners booklet.

Birds: Get two free books on birds. "HOMES FOR BIRDS" and "BACKYARD BIRD FEEDING." For these free booklets, write to Consumer Information Center(Free Booklets), P.O. Box 100, Pueblo, CO 81002.

Coca-Cola Stickers. You can get a whole set of peel-off labels with the "Real Thing" trademark in foreign languages from all over the world by sending a postcard to Consumer Information Center, The Coca-Cola Co., P.O. Drawer 1734, Atlanta, GA 30301. Ask for: Foreign Coca-Cola Stickers.

Badges,Stickers: Badges stickers and other items of interest for children are available upon request from: Smokey Bear Headquarters, Washington, D.C. 20252- - or call 202-235-8160.

Noise Quiz Book: A free coloring book and noise quiz is available from the Office of Noise Abatement and Control, Environmental Protection Agency, ANR 471, Washington D.C. 20460.

Coloring Books: To get coloring books which show the nutritional value of foods, write to: Public Information, Food and Nutrition Service, 500 12th St. S.W. #764, Washington, D.C. 20250.

How to become a Junior Fire Ranger: Become an Honorable Junior Fire Ranger and get a free Smokey Bear Kit. Send a postcard to Smokey Bear Headquarters, Washington, D.C. 20252. Ask for the Smokey Bear Fire Ranger Kit.

Advice for First-Time Babysitters: Send a postcard to Johnson & Johnson Consumer Products, Inc., P.O. Box 1112, Somerville, NJ 08876. Ask for (#B-478) Guide for the First-Time Babysitter. (Or, Spanish Edition #B-479).

Safety Coloring Book for Kids: Send a business size S.A.S.E. to Aetna Life & Casualty Co., Consumer Information Department, 151 Farmington Avenue, Hartford, CT 06156. Ask for: Play It Safe Coloring Book.

Free Home Eye-Chart: Check your family's eyes with this free home eye test chart. Send $.25 for postage to Prevent Blindness, 759 Milwaukee Street, Milwaukee, WI 53202. Ask for:Family Home Eye Test.

Free Posters: Get two posters that teach history the fun way. One shows all of the presidents, the other shows 16 different flags used to represent the United States. Send $1.00 for postage and handling to Historical Documents Co., 8 N. Preston St., Philadelphia, PA 19104. Ask for: Presidents of the U.S. and History of American Flags.

Activity Book: Kids will enjoy this Healthy Teeth Activity Book loaded with crossword puzzles, follow-the-dot pictures, secret codes, and lots more. Simply send $.25 for postage to American Dental Association, Health Education Department, 211 E. Chicago Avenue, Chicago, IL 60611. Ask for: Casper's Dental Health Activity Book.

Russia: Learn about the life and people of Russia. Just send a postcard to the Embassy of the U.S.S.R., 1125 Sixteenth Street N.W., Washington, D.C. 20036. Ask for: Literature on Russian Life and the Russian People.

The Wright Brothers: Learn all about the Wright Brothers, Wilbur and Orville, and their quest to build the first airplane in 1903. You can send away for a free pamphlet that explains the whole story. Send a postcard to Wright Brothers National Memorial, P.O. Box 457, Manteo, NC 27954. Ask for: The Story of the Wright Brothers.

History of the Railroads: Learn about our American Railroads that have been an important part of our history. Write to the following two addresses for information about our railroads. Association of American Railroads, 50 "F" Street N.W., Washington, D.C. 20001. Or, Santa Fe Railroad Lines, Public Relations Department, 80 E. Jackson Blvd., Chicago, IL

60604. Ask for: Educational Material on U.S. Railroads.

Information on Boy Scouting: Free information on joining the boy scouts available by writing to Boy Scouts of America, 1325 Walnut Hill Lane, Irving, TX 75062.

"Houston Oilers" Fan-Mail Package: Free fan-mail package for "Houston Oilers" NFL Fans. Send a postcard to Houston Oilers Public Relations Department, 6900 Fannin Street, Houston, TX 77030. Ask for: Fan Mail Package.

NFL Fan-Mail Package: If you want your own NFL fan-mail package complete with decals, posters and souvenirs, then send a postcard to NFL Fan Mail, P.O. Box 25, Trenton, NJ 08650. Ask for an NFL Fan Package for your favorite team.

Free Coloring Book and Poster: This coloring book and poster are created for latchkey kids, with ways to have fun with pets, and lots of safety tips. Write to Pets Are Wonderful Council, 500 North Michigan Avenue, Suite 200, Chicago, IL 60611.

Publishing A School Newspaper: Students can get a free booklet (#AT-13) on picture-taking and different printing methods for publishing school newspapers. Write to Eastman Kodak, 343 State St., Rochester, NY 14650.

Girl Scout Information: Get free information of girl scouting by writing to Girl Scouts of the U.S.A., 830 Third Ave., New York, NY 10022.

FREE CHILDREN'S MAGAZINES

Sample copies of various children's magazines are available free upon written request. Most sample copies, while free, will require a SAE (signed, addressed envelope) and sufficient return postage. A request for a free sample copy of a children's magazine does not place you under any obligation to subscribe. The sample copy is yours to keep at no charge, regardless. Here are several popular children's magazines which provide free sample copies upon written request:

ASPCA Animal Watch Magazine: This magazine is concerned with animal issues such as care and protection. To get a sample copy, send a 9 x 12 SASE to: ASPCA, 424 East. 92nd St., New York, NY 10128.

Career World: Published once a month (during the school year). This magazine provides a guide to careers. It is aimed at students in grades 7-12. A free sample copy is available for a 9 x 12 SAE and 3 first class stamps. Write to: Career World, Curriculum Innovations Group, 60 Revere Drive, Northbrook, ILL 60062.

Clubhouse Magazine: Published six times a year. A free sample copy is available by sending a business (#10) SAE and 3 first class stamps to: Clubhouse, Your Story Hour, P.O. Box 15, Berrien Springs, MI 49103.

Day-care and Early Education: This is a quarterly magazine for both children and parents. A free sample copy is available by writing to: Day Care And Early Education, 351 Pleasant St., Suite 330, Northampton, MA 01060.

Exploring: Published four times a year, this magazine is aimed at members of the Boy Scouts of America's Exploring program. A free sample copy is available for an 8 1/2 x 11 SAE and 5 first class stamps. Write to: Exploring, Boy Scouts of

America, P.O. Box 152079, 135 W. Walnut Hill Ln., Irving, TX 75015- 2079.

FFA New Horizons: Published bi-monthly. A sample copy is available for a 9 x 12 SAE and 5 first class stamps. Send to: FFA New Horizons, The Official Magazine of the National FFA Organization, 5632 Mt. Vernon Hwy, Alexandria, VA 22309.

Guide Magazine: This is a weekly magazine written for 10 to 14 year old readers. A free sample copy is available by sending a 5 x 9 SAE and 2 first- class stamps to: Guide Magazine, Review and Herald Publishing Association, 55 West Oak Ridge Dr., Hagerstown, MD 21740.

High Adventure: A quarterly magazine designed to provide positive leisure reading for young boys. For a free sample copy, send a 9 x 12 SASE to: High Adventure, Assemblies of God, 1445 Boonville Ave., Springfield, MO 65802.

Noah's Ark: A free sample copy of this monthly tabloid is available by sending a #10 SAE and 1 first-class stamp to: Noah's Ark, A Newspaper for Jewish Children, 8323 Southwest Freeway, #250, Houston, TX 77074.

Pockets: This magazine is published 11 times a year and is designed for children ages 6 to 12. For a free sample copy, send a 7 x 9 SAE and 4 first- class stamps to: Pockets, Devotional Magazine For Children, The Upper Room, 1908 Grand, P.O. Box 189, Nashville, TN 37202.

Scienceland, To Nurture Scientific Thinking: Published 8 times a year, this is a "reading and picture book" for children K-3rd grade. For a free sample copy, send a 9 x 12 SASE to: Scienceland, To Nurture Scientific Thinking, Scienceland Inc., #2108, 501 Fifth Ave., New York, NY 10017-6102.

The Young Crusader: Published 10 times a year, this magazine is geared to readers ages 6 to 12. A free sample copy is available by writing to: The Young Crusader, National WCTU, 1730 Chicago Ave., Evanston, IL 60201.

FOR YOUR FAMILY'S HEALTH

Healthy Foods: The Food Marketing Institute has available two free brochures which provide advice and tips on grocery shopping and healthful eating. The Brochures— Eating For Life: A Supermarket Guide, and Eating Right With Dietary Guidelines— are free when you send a legal-sized SASE to: Consumer Affairs

Free Eyecare: Needy senior citizens can get cost-free eye care by calling toll-free, 1-800- 222-3937. Doctors, who are members of the American Academy of Ophthalmology, will provide a comprehensive medical eye examination and care for any eye condition diagnosed, free of charge to any U.S. citizen or resident 65 or older. (This cost-free eye care does not cover prescription drugs, hospital care, or eyeglasses.)

Cold Sore Information: A Booklet titled, Cold Sores, Fever Blisters & Canker Sores is available free by sending a business SASE to: American Academy of Otolaryngology-Head and Neck Surgery, "Fever Blisters", One Prince St., Alexandria, VA 22314.

Toll Free Health Line: The Arizona Heart Institute & Foundation provides a nationwide toll-free information line called "Hartline". Nurses are available to take calls from 10 a.m. to 7 p.m. and answer any questions callers have about any aspect of heart disease. The toll-free Hartline number is 1-800-345-4278.

Cataract Information: To get a free copy of "A Patient's Guide: Cataract In Adults", write to: Agency for Health Care Policy and Research, Publications Clearinghouse, P.O. Box 8547, Silver Spring, MD 20907— or call 1-800-358-9295.

Vitamin C Menus: A free booklet that provides information on vitamin C and gives ideas on vitamin C menu planning is available from: Vitamin C, P.O. Box 148, Dept. A, Lakeland, FL 33802-0145.

Alzheimer's Disease: To get a 12 page pamphlet titled, "Q & A: Alzheimer's Disease (No. 81-1646)", write to the National Institute on Aging Information Center, 2209 Distribution Circle, Silver Springs, MD 20910.

Phony Weight Loss Programs: For a free pamphlet providing tips on how to spot phony weight-loss programs and products, and information on how to choose a diet plan, write: "Weight Loss,", Federal Trade Commission, Washington DC 20580.

Medicine Safety: Information on medicine safety is available free from the National Council on Patient Information and Education. To get the brochure, "Get the Answers About Your Medicines", send a business SASE to: NCPIE, 666 11th St. N.W., Suite 810, Washington, D.C. 2001.

Drug Interactions: Free, from the Food and Drug Administration, are brochures titled, "Food and Drug Interactions, Know the Right Way To Take Your Medicines", and "Some Things You Should Know About Prescription Drugs". To get the brochures write to: Leonard Genova, 900 Madison Ave., Baltimore, MD 21201.

Free Brochures: The brochure "Using Your Medications Wisely" is available by writing to the National Institute on Drug Abuse, Information Systems, P.O. Box 2345— or call 1-800-729-6686.

Computer Hazards: Information about potential hazards from working in front of computer screens, are available from the Occupational Safety and Health Administration (OSHA). To get the publications titled, "Display Terminals", and "Working Safely With Display Terminals", write to: Information and Consumer Affairs, Occupational Safety and Health Administration, U.S. Department of Labor, Washington, DC 20210.

Birth Defects Information: A ten-page booklet titled, "Genetic Counseling", with information on heredity, genetic counseling and testing, is available from the national headquarters of the March of Dimes Birth Defects Foundation. Write to: Dept. RD, 1275 Mamaroneck Ave., White Plains, NY 10605— or contact your local March of Dimes Chapter.

Consumer Information Catalogs offering a variety of facts and information are made available through the government. Many catalogs are made available to you free of charge, others for a very minimal fee. To receive your free publication send your requests giving the publication no. to:

S. James, Consumer Information Center-3C
P.O. Box 100,
Pueblo, Colorado 81002.

To receive publications for a minimal fee write to:
R. Woods, Consumer Information Center-3C
P.O. Box 100,
Pueblo, Colorado 81002.

Cancer Tests You Should Know About. A Guide For People 65 and Over. Describes six simple tests that can help detect cancer early. Includes checklists for men and women to keep track of the tests needed. Publication no. 619Z. Free.

Clearing the Air. No-nonsense tips on how to quit

smoking for keeps. Publication no. 529Z. Free.

Cosmetic Safety. Learn which cosmetic products are regulated and what terms such as "hypoallergenic" and "natural" really mean. Publication no. 614Z. Free.

Getting The Lead Out. Learn which household items can cause poisoning, symptoms, treatments, why infants and children are most at risk and how to reduce exposure. Publication no. 532Z. Free.

Guide to Choosing a Nursing Home. Here is help for evaluating your need with information on services, Medicare/Medicaid coverage, insurance, contracts and more. Publication no. 533Z. Free.

Hocus-Pocus as Applied to Arthritis. Discusses fraudulent cures and medically sound treatments for arthritis, rheumatism, and gout. Publication no. 535Z. Free.

Hope or Hoax? Unproven Cancer Treatments. How to investigate treatments outside of mainstream medicines, including experimental therapies. Publication no. 597Z. Free.

AIDS. How AIDS is spread, prevention tips, and what to do if you think you've been infected. Publication no. 548Z. Free.

Chronic Fatigue Syndrome. Learn the physical and psychological symptoms and what treatments are being studied. Publication no. 422Z. $.50.

Dizziness. Explains the various causes, diagnostic tests and treatments for people suffering from dizzy spells. Publication no. 119Z. $1.00.

Getting a Second Opinion. Answers questions you

might have and includes a toll-free number for locating specialists. Publication no. 550Z. Free.

Headaches. Information on possible causes and treatments of headaches, including migraines. Publication no. 120Z. $2.00.

Lyme Disease. Symptoms, treatment and tips to prevent contracting this disease that often resembles arthritis. Publication no. 467Z. $.50.

A Consumer's Guide to Mental Health Services. Answers common questions, helps identify warning signs, discusses treatments and lists resources for help and information. Publication no. 556Z. Free.

Depression. Nine million people suffer from this illness during any six month period. Learn symptoms and causes, how it's diagnosed and treated, and how to help. Publication no. 557Z. Free.

Eating Disorders. Anorexia and bulimia affect at least 3% of girls and young adult women in the U.S. Learn to dangers of this illness, symptoms, treatments, how to help and resources for more information. Publication no. 613Z. Free.

HOUSING & HOME IMPROVEMENT GUIDES

A Consumer's Guide To Mortgage Refinancing. What the costs are, and how to tell if the time is right to refinance you home. Publication no. 470Z. $.50.

The Home Inspection & You. 11 questions with answers about how and why to get a professional home inspection before you buy or sell. Publication no. 480Z. $.50.

Home Improvement Guides: Other great home improvement and home furnishings guides can be obtained by writing to the addresses below.

Construction Complaints: A Consumer Guide To Filing Construction Complaints." Contractor's State Licensing Board, P.O. Box 26000, Sacramento, CA 95826.

Consumer's Guide To Hiring An Architect. State Board of Architectural Examiners, 400 R St., Suite 4000, Sacramento, CA 95814-6200.

Consumer's Guide To Hiring A Landscape Architect. State Board of Landscape Architects, 400 R St., Suite 4020, Sacramento, CA 95814-6200.

Flammability of Consumer Products. (Available in English or Spanish) Bureau of Home Furnishings and Thermal Insulation, 3485 Orange Grove Ave., North Highlands, CA 95660.

Tips On Purchasing A Waterbed. (Available in English or Spanish) Bureau of Home Furnishings and Thermal Insulation, 3485 Orange Grove Ave., North Highlands, CA 95660.

Tips On Purchasing Feather And Down Products. (Available in English or Spanish) Bureau of Home Furnishings and Thermal Insulation, 3485 Orange Grove Ave., North Highlands, CA 95660.

Tips On Purchasing Mattresses: (Available in English or Spanish) Bureau of Home Furnishings and Thermal Insulation, 3485 Orange Grove Ave., North Highlands, CA 95660.

Helpful Hints On Purchasing Upholstered Furniture. (Available in English or Spanish) Bureau of Home Furnishings and Thermal Insulation, 3485 Orange Grove Ave., North Highlands, CA 95660.

Finding a Good Moving Company: For help in moving including all aspects such as finding a good moving company and filing damage and loss claims, write to "Consumer's Guide To Moving," Moving Fact Sheet, P.O. Box 310, Sacramento, CA 95802.

Guide for Renting Californians: "California Tenants: Your Rights And Responsibilities." Is a great guide for the Californian who is renting. For a free copy, send a business size S.A.S.E. to California Tenants, Box 310, Sacramento, CA 95802.

Questions about Pests: "Frequently Asked Questions Regarding Structural Pest Control Inspections" is yours free by writing to Structural Pest Control Board, 1422 Howe Avenue, Sacramento, CA 95825-3280.

Biological Pollutants in Your Home. Pollen, dust mites, molds, and animal dander can cause illness and allergies. Learn symptoms and what to do to control them. Publication no. 430Z. $.50.

Buying a Home Water Treatment Unit. Discusses various units for purifying drinking water and how to protect yourself from deceptive sales practices. Publication no. 431Z. $.50.

MISCELLANEOUS FREEBIES

How to Grow Great Tomatoes: Get free tomato seeds, so you can grow big juicy plump tomatoes. Send $.25 for postage and handling to Stakeless Tomato Seed Offer, Gurney Seed Company, 3101 Page Street, Yankton, SD 57079. Ask for: Stakeless Tomato Seeds.

Bowling Instructions for Beginners: Bowling can be a fun and inexpensive means of recreation. For a free beginners booklet, send a business size S.A.S.E. to American Bowler's Association, 5301 So. 76th Street, Greendale, WI 53129. Ask for: Tips for Young Bowlers.

How to have a Garage Sale: Have a garage sale and earn some money! Learn how, free! Send a business size S.A.S.E. to United Van Lines, Consumer Services Department, One United Drive, Fenton, MO 63026. Ask for: How to Hold a Garage Sale Booklet.

Free Refrigerator Magnets: You can get a free refrigerator magnet with a Disney Character on it by sending $.75 for postage and handling to Hick's Specialties, 1308 68th Lane North, Brooklyn Center, MN 55430. Ask for: A Disney Refrigerator Magnet. (They select the character for you)

Lose Weight Eating Popcorn: here is a fun way to lose weight with popcorn. It is a plan developed by a doctor called "How to Use Popcorn to Lose Weight." Just send a business size S.A.S.E. to Popcorn Diet, P.O. Box 482, South Station, Framingham, MA 01701. Ask for: Mini Outline of Popcorn Diet.

Traveling with Pets: This free brochure will tell you some dos and don'ts of handling your pet before and during the trip. Send a business size S.A.S.E. to American Veterinary Medical Association, 930 North Meacham Road, Shaumburg, IL 60196. Ask for: Traveling With Your Pet Brochure.

A Travel and Fashion Guide: To help make your trip more enjoyable, write: Union Label, 275 Seventh Avenue, New York, NY 10001.

Aspiring Writers: To receive a free "writing evaluation" and an illustrated brochure describing "Breaking Into Print", a correspondence study program for aspiring writers, send a written request to: Long Ridge Writers Group, Long Ridge Road, West Redding, CT 06896-1123.

Can I really get Free or Cheap Public Land (#632G) -- from: Consumer Information Center, Pueblo, CO 81009, (Note: When ordering from this source, write the word "FREE" on the outside of your envelope. No more than 20 different titles may be ordered at any one time.)

Health Guides: For various health guides, write Pharmaceutical, Raritan, NJ 08869

Managing Your Families Credit (send stamp) write: Everybody's Money, Credit Union National Association, Box 431, Madison, WI 53701

9 to 5 Office Worker Survival Guide: Write to 9 to 5, 1224 Huron Road, Cleveland, OH 44115

Help for Car Owners: Write National Highway Safety Administration, 400 Seventh Street, SW, Washington, DE 20590

Investing in Oil, Gas, and Coal: (635G) Consumer Information Center, Pueblo, CO 81009

Borrowing Money from Your Bank: From SBA, 1441 L St., NW, Wash., DC 20416

Fishing Tips: Write Cisco Kid, 2630 NW First Ave., Boca Raton, FL 33432

Information & Sample for Contact Lens Wearers: Write to Unisol Sample, Coppervision Pharmaceuticals, 455 East Middlefield Rd., Mountain View, CA 94043

First-Aid Facts: From Consumer Services, J & J, 501 George St., New Brunswick, NJ 08903

Retirement Plans for Small Businesses: SBA, 1441 L St., NW, Washington, DC 20416

Moving Handbook: Includes inventory sheets, schedules and other tips. Write to Red Ball Movers, P.O. Box 1127, Indianapolis, In 46206

Do-it Yourself Remodeling Ideas: Send 25 cents to: Georgia-Pacific Corp., 133 Peachtree St., NE, Atlanta, GA 30303

Retirement Money Guide: Write to American Association of Retired Persons, 215 Long Beach Blvd., Long Beach, CA 90801

Attitude of Bankers towards Small Business Financing: From Small Business Administration, 1441 L St., NW, Washington, DC 20416

Directory of Consumer Information Sources: From Center for Study of Responsive Law, P.O. Box 19367, Washington, DC 20036

Own A Shoe Business: From Mason Shoe Company, Chippewa Falls, WI 54774

Silver Polish: From W.J. Hagerty Ltd., P.O. Box 1496, S. Bend, IN 46624

Save on Taxes: From Lebenthal & Co., One State Street Plaza, New York, NY 10013

How to Add Hours to Your Day: From Day-Timers, Inc., Box 2368, Allentown, Pa 18001

Become a Wholesaler: Write Specialty, 9401 DeSoto Av., Chatsworth, CA 91311.

Historical Documents: A sample from Historical Documents Co., 8 N. Preston St., Philadelphia, PA 19104

Getting Started in Farming: Write Farm Credit Administration, Wash., DC 20225.

Road Maps: From Texaco Travel Service, Box 1459, Houston, TX 77001

How to Start a Cooperative: (FCS-ED-C-18) Food, Dept. of Agr., Wash., DC 20250

Burglar Proof Your Home: Free booklet on evaluating your home's defense. Aetna, 151 Farmington Ave., RWAC, Hartford, CT 06156

The Catalyst (career opportunity catalog for woman): Write The Catalyst, 14 East 60th St., New York, NY 10022

Items and Books on Cars & Trucks: Write Automobile Manufactures Assoc., 320 New Center Bldg., Detroit, MI 48202

Catalog on Gifts & Gadgets: From Miles Kimball, 251 Bond St., Oshkosh, Wi 54901

Shopping Club Guide: Available from Popular Club Plan, Passaic, NJ 07055

U.S. Export Financing Program: For a book on export/import write, Public Affairs Office, Export-Import Bank of the U.S., 811 Vermont Ave. NW, Washington, DC 20571

What can You do about Family Living Costs?: Write for a free book from the Office of Information, Cooperative Ext. Serv., Ohio State Univ., 2120 Fyffe Rd Columbus, OH 43210

Travel & Vacation Parks: Free guides from Mobile Home Manuf. Assoc., 20 N. Wacker St., Chicago, IL 60606

Tips on How to Sleep Better: Available from better Sleep Inc., New Providence, NJ 07974

How to Panel a Room: A free booklet from Masonite Corp. P.O. Box 311, Towanda, PA 18848

Wedding Invitations & Stationery Samples: For free samples write to Dawn Stationery, 300 Main Street, Lumerton, NJ 08048

Indian and Eskimo Arts & Crafts: Source directory of how to and where to obtain everything. Indian Arts & Crafts Board, Dept. of Interior, Wash, DC 20240

A Collection of Liqueur Recipes: Dozens of cocktail and cooking recipes using liqueurs are available free from: Le Roux Liqueurs, General Wine And Spirits Co., 375 Park, New York, NY 10152

What kind of Money do You need?: A booklet from SBA , 1441 L St., NW Wash, DC 20416

How to Give Up Cigarettes: Write the American Cancer Society, 19 West 56th Street, New York, NY 10001.

Sewing Charts: From Butterick Co., Educational Dept., Box 1752, Altoona, PA 16603.

Business Letterhead Samples: Write Hammermill Paper Co., 1475 E. Lake Rd., Erie, PA 16507.

Sales Prospector: For a free sample monthly newsletter providing sales leads write: Herbert Ireland, Prospector Research Services, 751 Main St., Boston, MA 02154.

First-Aid Guide: From Prudential Ins. Co., Public Relations, Box 549, Newark, NJ 07101.

The Pleasures of Wine: Write to Wine Inst., 165 Post St., San Francisco, Ca 94108.

The Poets Guide to getting Published: A how to on getting your poetry published for profit. Write American Poetry Assoc., P.O. Box 2279, Santa Cruz, CA 95063.

Land Use Digest: A Newsletter from Urban Land Inst., 1200 18th St., NW, Washington, DC 20036.

Free Tickets to see Live T.V. Shows: Write to Guest Relations Dept. of the following, ABC, 1330 Ave of the Americas, New York, NY 10019, CBS, 51 West 52nd St., New York, NY 10019, NBC, 30 Rockefeller, New York, NY 10020.

Government Surplus Sales: Large variety of surplus items for sale by U.S. govt to clear inventories. Write to Surplus Sales Center, Washington Navy Yard, Wash. DC 20406.

Profits- What are They?: Write the Federal Info Center, POB 25006, Denver, CO 80025.

Catalog of Free Publications: Thousands of free publications available just for the cost of shipping. Write to Cooperative Extension Service, Michigan State U, E. Lansing, MI 48824.

Forest Recreation for Profit: Write the U.S. Dept. of Agr., Washington, DC 20425.

Freedom of Information Act: What it is and how to use it. Write the Center for Study of Responsive Law, P.O. Box 19367, Washington, DC 20036.

Retirement Legal Guide: Write to NRTA-AARP, P.O. Box 2400, Long Beach, CA 90801.

Easy to Make Gifts: Free from Johnson's Wax, Consumer Svc. Dept., Racine, WI 53401.

Business Quarterly Review: Subscribe to, Fed. Reserve Bank 33 Liberty St., NY 10045.

Nursing as a Profession: Write to National League for Nursing, 2 Park Ave., NYC 10016.

Gas Watchers Guide: From AAA, 8111 Gatehouse Rd., Falls Church, VA 22047.

The Handbook of Cat Care: A 76 page book for 25 cents from: Cat Care Handbook, Checkerboard Square, St. Louis, MO 63188.

Consumer Quick Credit Guide: Write the U.S. Dept. of Agriculture, Washington, DC 20250.

Prospecting on Government Owned Land: Write The Forest Services, Box 2417, Washington, DC 20013.

What Everyone should know about Stocks & Bonds: From Merrill, Lynch, Pierce, Fenner & Smith, 70 Pine St., New York, NY 10014.

Basic Picture Taking (#L-15): From Eastman Kodak Service Dept., Rochester, NY 14604.

Put More Personality into Your Business Letters: Advice worth having from Pitney-Bowes Inc., Walnut & Pacific Sts., Stamford, CT 06904.

Bond & Money Market Review: First Ntl. Bank., 38 S.

Dearborn St., Chicago, Il 60603

Insurance as a Career: Write Casualty & Surety Co, 60 John St., New York, NY 10038.

Answers to Your Questions: Need answers to your questions or advice and don't know where to go for it? Write the Library of Congress LA5122, 10 First St. SE, Wash, DC 20540.

Self Hypnosis: Improve your life, increase creativity, shed bad habits, etc, Write to Potentials Unlimited, 4808 Broadmour SE., Grand Rapids, MI 49508.

Break the Smoking Habit: Write The American Cancer Society, 4 w. 35 St., N.Y., NY 10001.

The Furniture Finishing Guide: For a free copy write Johnson Wax company, 525 Howe Street, Racine, WI 53403.

Studying Tips & Hints: For a free copy write to, Cliff Notes, Inc., P.O. Box 80728, Lincoln, NE 6850.

Retirement Information: Write the American Association of Retired Persons, DuPont Circle Bldg., 4th Floor, Washington, DC 20036.

World Time Chart: Write the Manufacturers Hanover trust Co., International Banking Dept., 55 broad St., New York, NY 10015

Free Cookbook: From Quaker Oats. Write, Wholegrain Cookbook, Box 14077, Baltimore, MD 21268.

How to get the most Food for Your Money: College of Agriculture and Home Economics, Office of Information and Aids, 2120 Fyffe Rd., columbus, OH 43210.

Anderson Home Remodeling Guides: Write the Anderson Corp., Bayport, MN 55003.

Herbs: A free chart from: R.T French Co., 1 Mustard Street, Rochester, NY 14609.

Health and Safety Aids Poster: Available from Health and Safety Education Div., Metropolitan Life Insurance Co., One madison Ave., New York, NY 10010.

The Art and Secret of Chinese Cooking: From LaChoy Food Prod., Archbold, OH 43502.

Start a Flea- Market Business: For information on what and how to sell at flea markets) write to: Flea Market Forum, 355 Great Neck Rd., Great Neck, NY 11021.

Cook Book: From Metropolitan Life Insurance Co., 1 Madison Ave., NYC 10010.

Power of the Printed Word Series: Learn to write a better business letter, read faster, improve your vocabulary, etc. Write, Power of the Printed Word, International Paper Co., P.O. Box 954, Madison Square Station, New York, NY 10010.

How to help Your Child become a Better Writer: Specify English or Spanish. Send a SASE to National Council of Teachers, 1111 Kenyon Rd., Urbana, IL 61801.

Entertainers Wine Recipes: Write to Taylor Wine Co., Hammondsport, NY 14840.

Outdoor Guide to Holiday Fun: From Coleman Co. P.O. Box 1762, Wichita, KS 67201.

How to Control Your Weight: From Metropolitan Life Insurance Co., 1 Madison Ave., New York, NY 10010.

Learning with Cassettes: Self-improvement, money-making, etc. Write Nightingale-Conant Corp., 7300 N. Lehigh Ave., Chicago, IL 60648.

A Career in Banking: For details write to Comptroller of Currency, Administrator of National Banks, Washington, DC 20219

Working Abroad: A monthly newsletter listing current openings in foreign employment. For a current copy send 39 cents postage to Mr. Information, 2515 Rainier Avenue South, Suite 307, Seattle, WA 98144.

Free Mini-flashlight on a keychain. Simply send $1.00 for postage and handling to Swope's Economy Hut, 632 Pine Street, Johnstown, PA 15902. Ask for: Mini Keychain Flashlight.

Overseas Pen Pal. You or your teacher can get this free information by sending $1.00 for postage and handling to International Pen Friends, Attn.Guidelines, P.O. Box 43904, Tucson, AZ 85733-3904. Ask for: Pen Pal Information Package.

Grow Your Own Healthy, Nutritious Vegetables: Free vegetable garden seeds. Send $1.00 for postage and handling to Butterbrooke Farm, 78 Barry Road, Oxford, CT 06483. Ask for: Kids Salad Garden Seeds.

Free Q-Tip Dispenser: Receive a free Q-tip dispenser in your choice of blue, white, green, or yellow. Send $.25 for postage to Q-Tip Dispenser Offer, P.O. Box 1009, Jefferson City, MO 65102. Ask for Q-Tip Swab Dispenser (Specify Color).

Seashells Booklet: Learn about seashells in this free booklet. Send a postcard to Shell Oil Company, Public Affairs

Department, Room 1535, P.O. Box 2463, Houston, TX 77001. Ask for:Let's Collect Shells.

Historical Civil War Documents: Civil War Confederate Banknotes (replicas) that is. The set of 12 is printed on antiqued parchment paper and then processed to look and feel old. Just send $1.00 for postage and handling to Historical Documents Company, 8 N. Preston Street, Philadelphia, PA 19104. Ask for 12 Different Confederate Banknotes.

Free Travel Games Booklet: Fun for children while traveling in the car. Send for your free 32-page booklet of travel games by sending $1.00 for postage and handling to the Beavers Star Route, Box 537, Laporte, MN 56461. Ask for: Travel Games.

Refrigerator Magnets: Refrigerator magnets in the shape of your state. All 50 states are available. Just send $.75 for postage and handling to Hick's Specialties, 1308 68th Lane North, Brooklyn Center, MN 55430. Ask for: State Magnet Stamp.

Backpacking Tips: Send for this free pamphlet that contains lots of tips on "Backpacking with Ease." Just send a postcard to Dow Chemical Company, Consumer Products Division, P.O. Box 68511, Indianapolis, IN 46268. Ask for: Backpacking with Ease.

Grow Tropical Hawaiian Plants: Get your free tropical Hawaiian plant seeds by sending $1.00 for postage and handling to Hawaiian Ti Plant, P.O. Box 34989, San Rafael, CA 94902. Ask for: Hawaiian Ti Plant.

Free Foreign Paper Money: Money from a variety of countries including Korea, Brazil, and Argentina. Send $1.00 for postage and handling to The Jolie Company, P.O. Box 399, Roslyn Heights, NY 11577-0399. Ask for the Foreign Paper Money Starter Collection.

How to Win Playing Chess: Receive a free 16-page booklet with ten tips and suggestions on how to win the game and beat your partner. Send a business size S.A.S.E. to U.S. Chess Federation, 186 Route 9W, New Windsor, NY 12550. Ask for: Ten Tips to Winning Chess.

Gettysburg Address Replica: Get an exact replica of Lincoln's Gettysburg Address. It is printed on antiqued parchment paper and then processed to look and feel like the real thing. Send $1.00 for postage and handling to Historical Documents Co., 8N. Preston St., Philadelphia, PA 19104. Ask for Lincoln's Gettysburg Address and Lincoln's Portrait.

14 Gourmet Recipes: Try 14 delicious gourmet recipes from Country Inn Recipes. Send a postcard to Uncle Ben's Country Inn Recipes, P.O. Box 11166, Chicago, IL 60611. Ask for the Country Inn Recipe Packet.

How to Identify Counterfeit Money: Here is a guide to help you recognize counterfeit money and keep you from being cheated. Send a postcard to United States Secret Service, Room 805, 1800 "G" Street N.W., Washington, D.C. 20226. Ask for: How to Recognize Counterfeit Money.

Cooking with Eggs: With this free recipe booklet, you can get all sorts of new ideas about cooking eggs. Just send a business size S.A.S.E. to American Egg Board, 1460 Renaissance, Park Ridge, IL 60068. Ask for: Egg Cooking Recipe Booklet.

Color Film: Improve your photography with film that produces sharp, bright colors and amazing detail. Just send $2.00 for postage and handling to Signature Color Film, 5311 Fleming Court, Austin, TX 78744. Ask for: Free Film Offer.

Free Sandwich Recipes: The recipes in this free 20-page booklet are from the winners of a national kid's contest.

Simply send a postcard to Bread Winners c/o Ziplock Sandwich Bags, P.O. Box 78980, New Augusta, IN 46278. Ask for the Bread Winner's Booklet.

Free Iron-on Decal: Get a free 8'x7' "GIVE ME A SQUEEZE" iron-on decal from Heinz Ketchup. It's bright and colorful. Just send a business size S.A.S.E. to Heinz Ketchup, P.O. Box 28, Pittsburgh, PA 15230. Ask for: Give Me A Squeeze Iron-On Decal.

Free Lip Ointment From Blistex: Take care of those dry chapped lips with this free offer from Blistex. Send a business size S.A.S.E. to Blistex Sample Offer, 1800 Swift Drive, Oak Brook, IL 60521. Ask for: Sample Packets of Blistex Lip Ointment.

Horseshoe Pitching: It's a great sport and lots of fun. To learn how, write for your free rules and regulations of horseshoe pitching to National Association of Horseshoe Pitchers c/o Horseshoe Pitcher's News Digest, 1307 Solfisburg Avenue, Aurora, IL 60505. Ask for: Horseshoe Pitching Rules.

Grow a Flower Garden: You can start a beautiful garden with this free packet of flower seeds and your parent's permission. Just send $.50 in coin to Alberta Nurseries, P.O. Box 20, Bowden, Alberta, Canada TOM-OKO. Ask for a packet of flower seeds.

Attend a Live T.V. Show: See your favorite "NBC" television show live in Los Angeles or New York. Write to:

National Broadcasting Company,
Guest Relations Department,
30 Rockefeller Plaza, New York, NY 10020 or,
3000 West Alameda Ave., Burbank, CA 91523.

Broadcasting System,
Guest Relations Department,

524 W. 57th Street, New York, NY 10019 or,
7800 Beverly Blvd., Los Angeles, CA 90036.

American Broadcasting Company,
Guest Relations Department,
7 West 66th Street, New York, NY 10023 or,
4151 Prospect Ave., Hollywood, CA 90027.

Learn to Play the Harmonica: This free beginner's booklet makes it fun and easy. Send a business size S.A.S.E. to Hohner, Inc. P.O. Box 15035, Richmond, VA 23227-5035. Ask for "How To Play The Harmonica."

Free Nature & Ecology Booklets: Get free booklets on nature and ecology fromThe National Wildlife Federation. Just send a postcard to National Wildlife Federation, Educational Servicing Department, 1412 16th Street N.W., Washington, D.C. 20036. Ask for: The 12-Page Wildlife Sanctuary Pamphlet.

Sign Language Communication: Learn to communicate with the deaf by using sign language. Send for a free card that shows you the whole sign-language alphabet and how to use it by sending a business size S.A.S.E. to Keep Quiet, P.O. Box 361, Stanhope, NJ 07874. Ask for: Sign Language Alphabet Card.

Replica of the Constitution: This wonderful replica is printed on antiqued parchment paper and then processed to look and feel old. Just send $1.00 to Historical Documents Co., 8 N. Preston St., Philadelphia, PA 19104. Ask for the U.S. Constitution and Star Spangled Banner.

Hair Care Sample: Get 3 different types of oil treatment from the makers of Alberto VO5. Just send $.50 for postage to VO5 Hot Oil Sample, P.O. Box 7745, Mount Prospect, IL 60056-7745.

Tennis Guide: Beginners can learn to play with this free guide of correct rules. Send $1.00 for postage and handling to U.S. Tennis Association, Publications Department, 707 Alexander Road, Princeton, NJ 08540. Ask for: Introduction to Tennis Rules.

Racing Decals: Get decals like the "PENNZOIL" decal seen in famous races such as the Indy 500. Send a postcard to Pennzoil Products Company, Customer Service Department, 1630 W.Olympic Blvd., Los Angeles, CA 90015-3850. Ask for the Racing Decals.

Table-Tennis Guide: Send for this guide that tells you all you need to know about the sport from how to grip the handle to how to make a forehand chop. Send $.25 for postage to U.S. Table Tennis Association, P.O. Box 815, Orange, CT 06477. Ask for: Table Tennis Rules & Guide.

Louisville Slugger Bat: A pen shaped like a miniature baseball bat that'll help you bat away at that homework. Just send $1.00 for postage and handling to H&B Promotions P.O. Box 10, Jeffersonville, IN 47130. Ask for:Louisville Slugger Baseball Bat Pen.

Vegetable Garden: A free guide to Vegetable Gardening John Deere Company, 1400 Third Avenue, Moline, IL 61265. Ask for: Starting Your Own Garden Booklet.

Chicken Recipes: Learn to make award winning chicken with these free recipes. Send $1.00 for postage to Recipe Book, Zacky Farms, 2000 Tyler, South El Monte, CA 91733. Ask for:Chicken Recipes Book.

Waterskiing: A free waterskiing guide will show you everything from how to stand up to how to fall down. Just send a business size S.A.S.E. to American Water Skiing Association, 799 Overlook Drive, Winter Haven, FL 33884. Ask for: Guide to Safe Waterskiing.

Fishing : Find when it's the best time to go fishing, what type of bait to use, and the best types of equipment. Send a postcard to Cisco Kid Tackle, 2630 N.W. First Avenue, Boca Raton, FL 33432. Ask for: Fishing Tips Booklet.

Traveling: Tips on what to do in an emergency from Travelers Insurance Company that will help prepare you for certain situations. Send a postcard to The Travelers Insurance Company, Women's Information Bureau, One Tower Square, Hartford, CT 06115. Ask for: First Aid Chart and Emergency Telephone Number Card.

Grilling Guide: Webers Guide to Great Grilling provides you with all the helpful hints you need to have a great barbeque, everything from basics and food preparation tips, to cooking times and wonderful barbeque recipes. To order, write to Weber Guide to Great Grilling, P.O. Box 962, Palatine, IL. 60078-0962.

Wood Projects: You can create simple do-it-yourself wood projects, such as planters and bench toy boxes, with easy step-by-step instructions from Redi-cuts. To order, write to Georgia Pacific, P. O. Box 1763, Norcross, GA. 30091.

Thirty Delicious Chicken Recipes.: For great recipes send a postcard to Perdue Cookbook, P.O. Box 1537, Salisbury, MD 21801. Ask for: Thirty Delicious Chicken Recipes.

Sunscreen Samples: Protect yourself from the sun and avoid skin cancer, by getting this free sample of "SunSense" Sunscreen. Send a business size S.A.S.E. to SolarCare, Inc., Ben Franklin Technology Center, 115 Research Drive, Bethlehem, PA 18015. Ask for Sunsense Towelette Sample.

United Nations: Learn about the organization that works for international peace and security. Get a free book about the UN by sending a postcard to United Nations Information

Center, 1889 "F" Street N.W., Washington, D.C. 20006. Ask for:Basic Facts on the UN Booklet & UN in Brief Pamphlet.

Columbian Coffee Sample: Receive a generous sample of 100% Columbian Coffee. Send a business size S.A.S.E. to 100% Columbian Coffee Sample Offer, P.O. Box 8545, New York, NY 10150. Ask for: Free Coffee Samples.

Foreign Exchange Students: Hosting a foreign exchange student can be a lot of fun and bring countries closer together. For information about being a host family, or for information about sending your children to a foreign country to study, send for this free 60-page booklet that explains all about it. Just send a postcard to Consumer Information Center, Pueblo, CO 81009. Ask for: Youth Exchange Program Booklet.

Stain Remover: Remove stains or spots fast. Send for this free chart that tells you how to remove over 35 different stains. Just send a postcard to Consumer Information Department, The Maytag Company, Newton, IA 50208. Ask for: Stain Removal Chart.

Shampoo Sample: Get a free sample of Neutrogena shampoo. Just send $1.00 for postage and handling to Neutrogena Shampoo Offer, Dept. 1765, P.O. Box 45062, Los Angeles, CA 90045. Ask for: Neutrogena Shampoo Sample.

United States Flags: Learn all about The United States Flag. Where the name came from, who made the first flag, and a lot more. Send for your free information by sending $.50 for postage and handling to the Star-Spangled Banner Flag Association, 844 East Pratt Street, Baltimore, MD 21202. Ask for: History of the American Flag.

College Survival Tips: Learn how to hang in there with this free 32-page booklet titled "How to Survive Your Freshmen

Year at College." Send a postcard to How to Survive the Freshmen Year, Loyola University of Chicago, 820 N. Michigan Ave., Suite 1500, Chicago, IL 60611. Ask for: How to Survive Freshmen Year Booklet.

Tennis Racquet Pen: Get a free Mini-Tennis Racquet Pen. A ballpoint pen in the shape of an actual tennis racquet, like the pros use only smaller. Send $1.00 for postage and handling to United States Tennis Association Publications, 707 Alexander Road, Princeton, NJ 08540. Ask for: Tennis Racquet Pen.

Obedience Lessons For Your Dog: Teach your dog to be obedient. The makers of Ralston Purina dog food present a booklet that tells you how to teach your dog important lessons. Just send a postcard to Ralston Purina Co., Dog Food Division, Checkerboard Square, St. Louis, MO 63164. Ask for: Your First Year With Your New Dog.

Sugar Substitute Samples: Get free samples of "Sweet'N-Low," the low calorie sugar substitute. Just send $.25 for postage to Sweet'N-Low Sample Offer, 2 Cumberland Street, Brooklyn, NY 11205. Ask for: Sweet'N-Low Samples.

Pasta Recipes: Great Pasta recipes everyone will love. Get this free recipe booklet by sending a business size S.A.S.E to Mueller's Endless Pastabilities, P.O. Box 307, Coventry, CT 06238. Ask for: Endless Pastabilities Recipes. Manga!

Tour the White House: Take a tour of the White House without even leaving your home. It's a free book showing every beautiful room in the White House in full color. Send a postcard to White House Tour Booklet, The White House, Washington, D.C. 20500. Ask for: Photo Tour Booklet.

Hieroglyphics: Learn how to write using Hieroglyphics. Get this free brochure that tells you all about the Hieroglyphic

Alphabet, as well as the pyramids, temples, and tombs. Just send a postcard to Egyptian Tourist Authority, 630 Fifth Avenue, New York, NY 10111. Ask for: Egypt Tourism Brochure.

Bear Poster: Get a free poster of a stuffed baby bear. This large poster, 22"x28", has a slogan that reads "LOVE LASTS," and is so cute. Send $1.00 for postage and handling to Love Lasts Poster, Oneida Silversmiths, P.O. Box One, Oneida, NY 13421. Ask for: Love Lasts Poster.

Make-Up: Get a mascara sample from "Lush-Lash." It's longlasting, smudgeproof, waterproof, and it's free. Just send $.75 for postage and handling to Del Laboratories, Lush-Lash Department, 565 Broad Hollow Road, Farmingdale, NY 11735. Ask for Lush-Lash Sample (Specify Color - Black or Brown/Black).

Photography Tips: Improve your photo-taking skills with the help of an expert - Eastman Kodak. Send for a free guide that tells you all about how to take better pictures. Send a post-card to Eastman Kodak Company, Dept. 841, Rochester, NY 14650. Ask for: 29-Page Picture Taking Guide #AC-2.

Evergreen Trees: Grow beautiful Evergreen trees right in your backyard with these free seeds. Send away for these seeds today (Planting Instructions Included). Send $.50 for postage and handling to Waukesha Seed Company, P.O. Box 1820, Waukesha, WI 53187. Ask for: Colorado Spruce Tree Seeds.

Feminine Hygiene: Get a free sample of Maxi-Thins, and free booklet that comes with it. Send a postcard to Consumer Services Department, Tambrands, Inc., Bridge and Springfield Streets, Palmer, MA 01069. Ask for: Maxi-Thins Sample Offer.

Party Planning: Learn how to throw creative parties with this free booklet from Reynolds Wrap, "Entertaining Ease." Send $.50 for postage and handling to Reynolds Wrap Entertaining Ease, P.O. Box 6704, Richmond, VA 23230. Ask for: Entertaining Ease Booklet.

Fitness Award: Get a Free Presidential Fitness Award from the President of the United States! for walking 125 miles in four months. It's a lot of fun. For more information, send a business size S.A.S.E. to Presidential Sports Award Program c/o Prevention Readers Service, 33 E. Minor St., Emmaus, PA 18098. Ask for: President's Award Program.

Gold Certificate: Get a Free Replica of a Million Dollar Gold Certificate. It's yours when you send away for the "Fun House" catalog of Jokes, Tricks, Magic Items, and Novelties. Send a business size S.A.S.E. and $.25 (coin) to The Fun House Catalog, P.O. Box 1225, Newark, NJ 07101. Ask for: Million Dollar Certificate.

Prevent Smokers: How to stop someone from smoking around you. Send a postcard to the American Lung Association, GPO Box 596, New York, NY 10001. Ask for: #0121 Lungs at Work Sign.

Paneling: Learn to panel a room, step-by-step. Write to Masonite Corp., P.O. Box 311, Towanda, PA 18848.

Archery: Get several books on Archery, "Archery Made Easy," "Helpful Hints on Archery Shooting," and "Bow Fishing," by writing to Ben Pearson, Inc., Pine Bluff, Arkansas 71601.

Retirement Information: Get a list of free AARP Publications covering every phase of retirement, from financial, to social, by writing to the American Association of Retired Persons, 1909 "K" Street N.W., Washington, D.C. 20049. Make sure to ask for the free list.

Starting Your Own Business: Find out how to start your

own business by writing to the U.S. Small Business Administration, Office of Public Information, Washington, D.C. 20416. Ask for: Free Listings of Publications and Videotapes.

Traveling with Pets: Order your free 20-page booklet on how to travel with your pet. Write to Alpo Pet Center, P.O. Box 4000, Allentown, PA 18001-4000. Ask for: "Pets On The Go."

Puppy Care: This free booklet lists 30 tips on caring for your puppy. Send a business size S.A.S.E. to MSD-AGVET, P.O. Box 931, Whippany, NJ 07981-9990.

Office Supplies: Send for this free 48-page booklet on "How To Save Money On Office Supplies." Send a postcard to Quill Corporation, P.O. Box 464, Lincolnshire, IL 60069-0464.

Laundry Tips: Learn to wash clothes right with dozens of tips. Send for "The Way To Wash Clothes," Dow brands Dept.180, P.O. Box 78980, New Augusta, IN 46278.

Touring Washington D.C.: Send for this free 36-page guide called "Welcome to Washington," by writing to your own state's U.S. Senator, U.S. Senate, Washington, D.C. 20510. It's loaded with tourist attractions.

Granite: Learn "The Story of Granite." Write to Barre Granite Association, Box 481, Barre, VT 05641. You'll learn all about the history and uses of granite.

Preparing A Living Will: Protect yourself and your loved ones in the case of an incurable illness or injury that may take your life. Get a free copy from your state's attorney general or by writing to Society of Right to Die, 250 W. 57th Street, New York, NY 10107.

Steel Manufacturing: Learn how steel is made with this great folder called "The Steel Making Process," offered by the Bethlehem Steel Corp., Bethlehem, PA 18015.

Sun Protection Booklet: Get a free booklet on protecting yourself and your family from the sun by sending a business size S.A.S.E. to Skin Cancer Foundation, Box 561, New York, NY 10156.

Human Development: Mothers can get help discussing development into womanhood with their daughters by sending for this free guide titled "How Shall I Tell My Daughter," Personal Products, Box 1001, Milltown, NJ 08850.

Silver Polish Sample: Get a free sample of Hagerty's Silver Polish by writing to W.J. Hagerty Ltd., Box 1496, 3801 W. Linden Ave., So. Bend., Ind. 46624.

History of Aluminum: Learn about aluminum with "A Brief Story Of Aluminum And Alcoa," and "Story Of Aluminum," by writing to the Aluminum Company of America, 1501 Alcoa Bldg., Pittsburgh, PA 15219.

Salad Recipes: Get a free recipe book with unusual ideas for salads. Write to "Salad Tour of the U.S.A." H.J. Heinz Co., P.O. Box 57, Pittsburgh, PA 15230. Be sure to send $.25 for postage.

Free Poster: Get a free wall poster of the founder of the famous "Jack Daniels" Tennessee Whiskey. Write to the Jack Daniel Distillery, Route 1, Lynchburg, TN 37352. Ask for: Jack Daniel's Founders Poster.

Toothbrushing Tips: A free booklet is offered to you on the proper techniques of toothbrushing by the American Dental Association, 211 E. Chicago Ave., Chicago, IL 60611.

Relieve Arthritis Pain: Relieve the pain of arthritis with a free sample of Myoflex. Write to "Myoflex Sample Offer," Warren-Teed Labs, P.O. Box 2450, Columbus, OH 43215.

Information on Meat: Get free educational material on the raising of meat animals and meat preparation. Write to American Meat Institute, P.O. Box 3556, Washington, D.C. 20007. Or, write to the National Livestock and Meat Board, 444 North Michigan Avenue, Chicago, IL 60605. Both are good sources of information.

Free Meat Recipes: Get a recipe book for chicken, beef, and fish from Lea & Perrins Worcestershire sauce. Write to Free Recipe Book, Lea & Perrins, Fairlawn,NJ 07410.

Free Jewelry: Send for a free pair of beautiful 14k gold or simulated diamond stud earrings. Send your name, address, and zip, choice of earrings, and $1.50 for postage and handling for each pair ordered, to Karat Club of America, 405 Tarringtown Rd., Suite 215, White Plains, NY 10610.

Strokes Treatment: Learn what causes a stroke and how can it be treated. Send for this valuable source of information about strokes by writing to the American Heart Association, Box SG, Greenville Ave., Dallas, TX 75231.

Facts About Diabetes: "Keeping Well With Diabetes," is an excellent handbook that gives facts on diabetics and their diets, urine testing, insulin, and much more. Write to Novo Nordisk Pharmaceuticals, Consumer Education, 100 Overlook Center, #200, Princeton, NJ 08540-7810.

Currency Exchange Guide: This free exchange guide includes currency conversion charts for 23 European, Asian, and Latin American Countries, and other helpful information. Send a business size S.A.S.E. to Foreign Currency Guide, Ruesch International,1350 "1" St.NW, 10th Floor, Washington, D.C. 20005-3305.

Prune Recipes: For a free Prune Recipe Book, write to Prune Recipe Ideas, P.O. Box 882168, San Francisco, CA 94188-2168.

Educational Material for Teachers: Learn about coal and pass the knowledge along to your students. Write to the American Coal Foundation, 1130 17th Street N.W., Room #220, Washington, D.C., 20036-4604. Remember only teachers can get this great big packet of educational material.

Insurance Information: Learn about the many different types of insurance with the different booklets provided to you by Insurance Information Institute, 110 William Street, New York, NY 10038.

Vineyards: Locate vineyards that permit public access (guided tours and wine tasting), by writing for the free book "California Wine Wonderland," Wine Institute, 425 Market Street, #1000, San Francisco, CA 94105.

Automobiles: Get free booklets and materials on the subject of automobiles and trucks by writing to the Motor Vehicle Manufacturers Association, 300 New Center Building, Detroit, Michigan 48202. Address the Communications Department and ask for their list of educational items.

Moving Booklet: Prepare your children for moving with this 16-page booklet, "Moving With Children," is yours free, by sending a business size S.A.S.E. to Consumer Services Department, United Van Lines, One United Drive, Fenton, MO 63026.

20 Italian Recipes: 20 Delicious Italian Recipes From Prego. Write to Prego's Easy Italian Cooking, Box 964, Bensalem, PA 19020.

Learn about Chinese life and culture: Write to Chinese Information Service, 159 Lexington Ave., New York, NY 10016. Ask for any of the following: Chinese "Calligraphy" (artistic writing), Chinese Art of "Paper Cutting," Chinese Painting, Chinese Opera, Chinese Festivals, Chinese Ceramics, and

The Story and Life of "Confucius."

Card Games: Learn Point-Count Bidding. Send a business size S.A.S.E. for Charles Goren's "Point Count Bidding" & Free Bookmark to U.S. Playing Card Co., Cincinnati, OH 45212.

Information on Trucking: For free educational material on trucking, write to the American Trucking Association, Office of Public Affairs, 2200 Mill Road, Alexandria, VA 22314.

Funeral Planning Booklet: If you must plan the funeral of a loved one, get help from The National Selected Morticians. They have written a booklet that provides helpful information about prices and options. Write to the Consumer Information Bureau, National Selected Morticians, 1616 Central Street, Evanston, IL 60201.

Free Skin Cream Sample: Get a free sample of "Balmex," a special treatment cream for skin irritations. Send $.25 for postage to Balmex Sample Offer, 1326 Frankford Avenue, Philadelphia, PA 19125.

Free Bumper Stickers: Get free colorful bumper stickers that read "Go Navy" or "Sailors Have More Fun?" Check with your local U.S. Navy Recruiting Office, probably listed in the yellow pages, to get these stickers free.

Wine Tasting Tour: Take a free wine tasting tour of the Hudson Valley Wine Company in upstate New York. Write to the winery for more information and directions.

Credit Card Fraud Protection: Protect yourself against credit card fraud. This free booklet titled "Who's Got Your Number?" has loads of suggestions. Send a business size S.A.S.E. to Consumer Affairs Office, 19th Floor, American Express Co., 125 Broad St., New York, NY 10004.

Health & Beauty Booklet: Learn the beauty secrets and diet tips from a professional models' booklet titled "Health & Beauty Booklet." It's yours free if you write to Health & Beauty Booklet c/o Castle & Cooke Foods, Box 7758, San Francisco, CA 94119.

Free Blueberry Recipes: For Blueberry Recipes Send $.15 for postage to Blueberry Council, P.O. Box 38, Tuckahoe, NJ 08250.

Free Apple Recipes: Free recipes and diet ideas from The Washington State Apple Commission, P.O. Box 18, Wenatchee, WA 98801.

Free Insulation Booklets: Get some free information booklets on insulation from the Consumer Inquiry Dept., Owens-Corning Fiberglass Corp., P.O. Box 901, Toledo, OH 43601. Be sure to ask for their list of educational material.

29 Apple Juice Recipes: Get 29 recipes using apple juice for salads, meats, and desserts? Write to "29 Recipes Using Apple Juice," Speas Co., 2400 Nicholson Ave., Kansas City, MO 64120.

Spot & Stain Removal Guide: Get a free "Guide To Spot & Stain Removal Chart For Carpets & Upholstery," by writing to Duraclean International, 2151 Waukegan Rd., Deerfield, IL 60015.

24 Recipe Books from Best Foods: Best Foods is offering 24 different recipe books, free. Write for your list of these books to Best Foods, Dept.LL, Box 307, Coventry, CT 06238.

Treasure Hunting: Learn how to treasure hunt. Write for this free book from Garrett Electronics, 2814 National Drive, Garland, TX 75041.

Turkey Recipes: Get a free collection of great turkey recipes. Write to the National Turkey Federation, Consumer, Dept., 11319 Sunset Hills Road, Reston, VA 22090.

Science Literature: Get free educational literature from the American Chemical Society, Pre-high School Science Program, Room 814, 1155 16th Street N.W., Washington, D.C. 20036.

Free Bumper Sticker: Get a free, colorful bumper sticker with the logo of "Lazy Bones," offered to you by Juvenile Shoe Company, 331 Carnation Dr., Aurora, MO 65605-0331.

Money-Making Ideas: If you are a salesmen interested in making money on your spare time, then send away for a free sample copy of Spare Time Magazine, loaded with money-making ideas. Write to Spare Time Magazine, 5810 W. Oklahoma Ave., Milwaukee, WI 53219. Be sure to include $.50 for postage and handling.

Wedding Invitations & Stationary: Brides-To-Be - Here is your free kit of wedding invitations & stationary samples. Write to: "Rexcraft," Rexburg, Idaho 83441, or, Dawn Stationery, 300 Main Street, Lamberton, NJ 08048.

The History of Measuring: Learn about the history of measuring. It's all here in this big, colorful chart of A History Of Measurement. It's free, but only for teachers. Write to: Ford Motor Company, Educational Affairs Dept., The American Road, Dearborn, Michigan 48121.

Defensive Driving Booklet: Send for your free booklet on "Defensive Driving Tips." Send a business size S.A.S.E. to National Safety Council, P.R. Dept., 444 N. Michigan Ave., Chicago, IL 60611.

Free Dog Care Books: The makers of Friskie Dog Food are offering the following books: Care & Feeding Your Puppy;

Care & Feeding Your Dog; Care of the Older Dog;Health Record of My Dog;and Pedigree Blanks - 5 Generations. Each booklet is $.25 with a minimum order of 4 ($1.00) Send your order to Friskie Pamphlets, P.O. Box 220A, Pico Rivera, CA 90660.

Free Bladder Protection: If you are an adult woman suffering from a bladder problem, then get your free sample of "Serenity" pads. You have a choice between 3 regular or 3 super absorbency pads. Please specify when writing to J&J Serenity Offer, P.O. Box 5250, Clifton, NJ 07015.

Free Flower Seeds: Get a free sample of colorful annual flower seeds from Alberta Nurseries, P.O. Box 20 Bowden, Alberta, Canada TOM-OKO.

Camping and Traveling Booklets: Get three booklets that make camping and traveling easier, from the makers of Ziploc Storage Bags. "Camping," "Backpacking," and "traveling." Send $.25 for each or $.50 for all three to Nan Collinson, The Dow Chemical Company, P.O. Box 68511, Indianapolis, Indiana 46268.

Spices: Add some spice to your meals, with McCormick Spices. Write for your free subscription to "Spice 'Xpress" Consumer Affairs Dept., McCormick & Co., 211 Schilling Circle, Hunt Valley, MD 21031. Along with the periodic newsletter filled with hints, tips, and recipes, you'll get free samples of their products from time-to-time.

Learn To Milk A Cow: Send for "Handbook of Milking," De Laval Separator Co., Poughkeepsie, NY 12602.

Free Chess Magazine: Get a free copy of Chess Life & Review from the U.S. Chess Federation, 186 Rt. 9W, New Windsor, NY 12550.

Feminine Hygiene Samples: Get a free sample of

Tampax Tampons. Write to Tampax Tampons Sample Offer, P.O. Box 4138, Monticello, MN 55565-4138.

Jogging and Running Tips: Learn tips on jogging and running safely. Send a business size S.A.S.E. to American Running & Fitness Assn., 9310 Old Georgetown Road, Bethesda, MD 20814.

Wallpapering Tips: "Learn How To Wallpaper." It's easy and fun when you send for this booklet with lots of tips. Send a business S.A.S.E. to Red Devil Tools Co., Box "W" Union, New Jersey 07083.

Free Yogurt Recipes: Get a free recipe book full of diet recipes using Columbo Yogurt. Send a business S.A.S.E. to Columbo, Dept. ZW, Methuen, Massachusetts 01844.

32 Page Microwave Cookbook: Get a 32-page creative microwave cookbook by sending $.50 for postage & handling to Reynolds Wrap Kitchens, Box 6704, Richmond, VA 23230.

Ocean Spray Recipes: Get an Ocean Spray recipe book for cranberry and grapefruit drinks and desserts. Send $.25 for postage to Ocean Spray, P.O. Box 237B Hilliard, OH 43026.

Fitness Recipes: How about a healthy cooking and exercising booklet? Write to "Recipes For Fitness," Mazola Dept., Box 307, Coventry, CT 06238.

Ski Together as a Family: Get the "Guide To Skiing As A Family Sport." Send a business S.A.S.E. to Campho-Phenique Skiing as a Family Sport, 101 Fifth Ave., 9th Floor, New York, NY 10003.

Choosing and Caring for Tools: If you are a "do-it-your-selfer," send for your free book on "How To Choose, Use, And Care For Tools," H.K. Porter Co., Hardware Division, Porter Building, Pittsburgh, PA 15219.

Health & Safety Literature: To get a complete list of free health and safety literature available to you, write to The Metropolitan Life Insurance Co., Health & Safety Education Dept., One Madison Avenue, New York, NY 10010-3690.

Information About the Constitution: Learn more about The Constitution of our founding fathers. Write to: The Constitution Commission, Washington, D.C. 20599.

Educational Wildlife Material: Teachers! get lots of educational material on wildlife, conservation, and birdwatching. Write to the National Wildlife Federation, Educational Services Dept., 1412 16th NW, Washington, D.C. 20036.

16 Microwave Cheese Recipes: Free - 16 delicious cheese recipes for your microwave use. Write to: Wisconsin Milk Marketing Board, 8414 Excelsior Dr., Madison, WI 53717.

How to Decorate Cakes & Cookies: Learn fancy ways to decorate your cakes, cookies, and cupcakes, with Cake Mate's "Easy Does It Idea Book." Send a business S.A.S.E. to McCormick Easy Does It Booklet, P.O. Box 208, Hunt Valley, MD 21031-0208.

Learn all about your eyes: Write for this free booklet from American Optometric Association, 243 N. Lindbergh Blvd., St. Louis, MO 63141.

Silver Coin Chart: Get a free Silver Value Chart for U.S. and Canadian Coins from Numismatic News Weekly, Iola, WI 54945.

What to Feed Your Baby: For babies less than 2 years of age, diets are very important according to the U.S. Pediatric Association. So send for this free booklet, "Dietary Guidelines For Infants," from Gerber Products Co., Dept. "L," P.O. Box 5530, Fremont, MI 49413.

Fitness Guide & Exercise Program: Get a free "Physical Fitness Guide And Exercise Program" from the Tea Council of U.S.A., 230 Park Avenue, New York, NY 10169.

How to Shop By Mail: Learn the right way to shop by mail from Bess Myerson. Send a business S.A.S.E. to Bess Myerson's Consumer Guidelines, Direct Mail Marketing Association, 6 East 43rd St., New York, NY 10017.

How to find the Right College to Attend: Looking for a good college? Then send for "College Prospecting." It tells you all you need to know about looking for the right college. Send a business S.A.S.E. to Office of Univ. Communications, University of Rochester, Rochester, NY 14627.

Checks and the Federal Reserve System: Learn how checks and the Federal Reserve System work together in, "The Story of Checks." Write to Federal Reserve Bank of N.Y., 33 Liberty St., New York, NY 10045.

How to Pay for College: How will anyone ever be able to afford college? If this is a question bothering you, then send for this free booklet that tells you how. Write to Consumer Information Center, Dept. MB, Pueblo, CO 81009. Ask for: The Student Guide - Federal Financial Aid Programs (Item 513).

Cancer Prevention: Prevent cancer with a good diet. All doctors agree that cancer prevention starts with a balanced diet. So send for this 50-page "Cancer & Diet Booklet" complete with menus and recipes. Write to Food Choices, National Cancer Institute, Bethesda, MD 20205.

Free Neutrogena Samples: Get a free sample of Neutrogena Cleansing Bar, Drying Gel, or Acne Mask. Just send $.50 for shipping for each sample plus an additional $.75 for handling. Neutrogena Sample Offer, P.O. Box 45062, Los Angeles, CA 90045.

The History of Money: Learn about money - how it evolved and how it is used. Send for this free 24-page booklet "Coins and Currency" that gives a splendid story about money. Write to Coins and Currency Booklet, 33 Liberty St., New York, NY 10045.

Cycling for Exercise: Exercise by cycling. It's great for your heart. Send for "Cycling For A Healthy Heart," American Heart Association, Box C, 7320 Greenville Ave., Dallas, TX 75231.

Seafood Recipes: Free "Choice Seafood Recipes." Send a business S.A.S.E. to New Bedford Seafood, Box 307, Fairhaven, Massachusetts, 02719.

Marketing Grain and the Grain Exchange: Learn about marketing grain through a grain exchange. Learn the hand signals and the workings of the Grain Commodity Exchange. Write to the Chicago Board of Trade, Public Information Dept., 141 W. Jackson Blvd., Chicago, IL 60604.

Baby Shoes that Fit: Find the right size shoe for your baby or toddler. Send a business S.A.S.E. to Baby-Bottle, Parent's Guide, P.O. Box 25715, Salt Lake City, Utah 84125.

Family First-Aid Guide: Here is a great first-aid guide for the whole family called "Home Care Bandaging." Send a business S.A.S.E. to Home Care Bandaging, "3M" Co., 530 Fifth Ave., 15th Floor, New York, NY 10036.

Tips fro Relieving Tension & Stress: Relieve tension and stress with eleven tips. Send a business S.A.S.E. to National Mental Health Assoc. 1021 Prince St., Alexandria, VA 22314-2971.

Information on Houses: Thinking about purchasing a house? Get a free copy of the "Househunter's Scorecard" full of advice on the house itself, the surrounding community, things you should take note of, the mortgage, etc. Offered to you by Chicago Title Insurance, Consumer Affairs, 111 West Washington St., Chicago, IL 60602.

Learn About Democracy in America: Send for this free booklet "Making Your Voice Heard In Washington." Learn about democracy and the American Way. Write to: Mobile Corp., Public Relations Dept., 3225 Gallows Rd., Fairfax VA 22037.

How to Care for Your Pet Dog: Learn to properly take care of your pet dog or cat. Write to Feline & Canine Friends, 505 North Bush St., Anaheim, CA 92805. Ask for: Tips on Animal Care.

Free Bumper Sticker: Would you rather be dancing? Then get a free bumper sticker that says so. Send $.25 and a business S.A.S.E. to "I'd Rather Be Dancing," Capezio Ballet Makers, One Campus Rd., Totowa, NJ 07512.

Guide to Kitchen Tools: Ekco's Guide To Tools Of The Trade (includes recipes) is yours free by writing to Ekco Housewares, Consumer Service Dept., Franklin Park, IL 60131.

Financial Planning Booklet: Get a free 21-page booklet, written by money columnist Grace Weinstein, on Financial Planning, Especially For Women. Write to Financial Planning, American Council of Life Insurance, 1001 Pennsylvania Ave., NW, Washington, D.C. 20004.

Booklet on Avoiding Plumbing Problems: Avoid plumbing problems. Send for this free 11-page booklet by writing to "How To Avoid Plumbing Problems," Copper Development Association, Inc., Greenwich Office, Park 2, Box 1840, Greenwich, CT 06836-1840.

A Guide to Japan: Planning on visiting Japan? Then send for your free booklet titled "Your Guide To Japan," from Japan National Tourist Organization, 45 Rockefeller Plaza, New York, NY 10020.

Booklet on How to Buy a Used Car: If you want to buy a used car, don't until you read the information in this free 12-page booklet on "How to Buy a Used Car." Send a business size S.A.S.E. to How to Buy a Used Car, P.O. Box 1013, Maple Plain, MN 55348.

Free Wallchart: Get a free, colorful wallchart that tells the "Story of Cotton." Write to National Cotton Council of America, P.O. Box 12285, Memphis, TN 38112.

Free Booklet about the Stars and Space: If your interested in learning about the stars, send for your free sample copy of "Sky & Telescope." You won't just learn about stars, though. You learn about the sun and the moon, the planets and galaxies, and our entire universe. Write to Sky Publishing Corp., 49 Bay Street Road, Cambridge, Mass. 02138.

NBA Fan-Mail Packages: Get a fan-mail package from your favorite NBA basketball team. Fan-mail packages include team decals and photos of the team's stars. Send a business size S.A.S.E. to any of the teams listed below and ask for the Fan Mail Package.

Atlanta Hawks Public Relations Department,
One CNN Center #405, Atlanta, GA 30303.

Boston Celtics, 151 Merrimac St., 5th Floor,
Boston, MA 02114. Attn: Fan Mail Department.

Chicago Bulls, 980 N. Michigan Avenue, Room #1600,
Chicago, IL 60611-4501.

Cleveland Caveliers, 2923 Streetsboro Rd.,
Richfield, OH 44286. Attn: Fan Mail Department.

Denver Nuggets Public Relations Department,
1635 Clay St., Denver, CO 80204.

Detroit Pistons, 2 Championship Dr.,
Auburn Hills, MI 48326. Attn: Fan Mail Department.

Golden State Warriors, Oakland Arena Coliseum,
Oakland, CA 94621-1995.

Houston Rockets Public Relations Department,
P.O. Box 272349, Houston, TX 77277.

Indiana Pacers, 300 E. Market Street,
Indianapolis, IN 46204. Attn: Fan Mail Department.

Los Angeles Clippers, LA Sports Arena, 3939 S. Figueroa,
Los Angeles, CA 90037.

Los Angeles Lakers Public Relations Department,
P.O. Box 10, Inglewood, CA 90306.

Milwaukee Bucks Public Relations Department,
1001 N. Fourth St., Milwaukee, WI 53203.

New Jersey Nets, Brendan Byrne Arena,
East Rutherford, NJ 07073.

New York Knicks, Madison Square Garden,
Four Penn Plaza, New York, NY 10001.

Orlando Magic, 1 Magic Place, Orlando Arena,
Orlando, FL 32801. Attn: Fan Mail Department.

Phoenix Suns Public Relations Department,
P.O. Box 1369, Phoenix, AZ 85001.

Sacramento Kings Public Relations Department,
1515 Sports Dr., Sacramento, CA 95834.

San Antonio Spurs, 600 E. Market St., Room #102,
San Antonio, TX 78205.

Seattle Supersonics Public Relations Department,
Box C900911, Seattle, WA 98109.

Utah Jazz, 5 Triad Center #500, Salt Lake City,
UT 84180. Attn:Fan Mail Department.

Washington Bullets Public Relations,
Capital Centre, Landover, MD 20785.

Job Opportunities for Women: Find out what job oppor-
tunities will be available in the future. The business & profes-
sional Women's Foundation offers "Jobs Of The Future For
Women." Send a self-addressed mailing label to Women's
Bureau, Dept. "P", Department of Labor, 200 Constitution
Avenue N.W., Washington, D.C. 20210.

Federal Government Summer Jobs: You can get a
great summer job with the Federal Government. Everything
from office jobs to park ranger positions are open. Write for
"Summer Jobs In Federal Agencies" U.S. Civil Service
Commission, Washington, D.C. 20415.

Stamp Collecting: Learn how to collect stamps! Write to
Littleton Mystic Stamp Co., 96 Main St., Camden, NY 13316
and ask for their beginner's booklet "How To Collect Stamps."

Garden Tools & Accessories: Write to Gardner's Supply
Company, 128 Intervale Road, Burlington, VT 05401 for a catalogue of their wide selection of tools and garden accessories,
including season-extending materials. You may also call (802)

863-1700.

English Garden Tools & Equipment: Kinsman Co., River Road, Point Pleasant, PA 18950 offers a free catalogue of English garden tools and equipment, compost bins, shredders, and cold frames. Phone (215) 297-5613.

Tools, Garden Equipment, and Seeds: For a free catalogue of fine, high-quality tools and garden equipment, as well as a wide variety of seeds, then write to Johnny's Selected Seeds, Foss Hill Road, Albion, ME 04910 or call (207) 437-4301.

Garden Tools: The finest in domestic and European garden tools are shown in this beautiful catalogue from Langenbach, P.O. Box 453, Blairstown, NJ 07825.

Asbestos Awareness: "A Consumer's Guide To Asbestos" is yours free by writing to Contractor's State Licensing Board, P.O. Box 26000, Sacramento, CA 95826.

How to Repair Credit Troubles: Are you close to financial ruins because of your credit card? Then send for "From Credit Despair to Credit Repair" to help you get back on your feet. Write to Credit Repair, P.O. Box 310, Sacramento, CA 95802.

Obtaining & Managing Credit: "California Immigrants and Credit" provides information on how to obtain credit and manage it as well. It's available in 10 different languages (Please Specify). Write to California Immigrants, P.O. Box 310, Sacramento, CA 95802.

Hiring a Contractor: Here's a great booklet about "What You Should Know Before You Hire A Contractor." Write to the Contractor's State Licensing Board, P.O. Box 26000, Sacramento, CA 95826.

Child Car Safety Booklet: Keep your child safe. Get "Children & Car Safety" by sending a business size S.A.S.E. to the American Academy of Pediatrics, 141 N.W. Point Blvd., Elk Grove, IL 60007.

How to File and Insurance Claim: Learn how to file an insurance claim. Call the Insurance Institute at 800-221-4954.

Contact Lens Booklet: Get a free booklet on "The Contact Lens." Write to Bausch & Lomb Soft-lens Division, Room 101-S, Rochester, NY 14602.

Avoid Money Blunders: Learn to avoid 15 of the most common money blunders. Write to Aetna Life & Casualty, 151 Farmington Ave., Hartford, CT 06156. Attention: Public Relations Department.

Free Moving Guide: Don't plan on moving without this free guide that tells how. Write to Moving Guide, P.O. Box 21503, Phoenix, AZ 85036.

Piano Music Simulator: Create the music of a grand piano with The Yamaha Clavinova. A free demo cassette is offered by Yamaha Music Corporation, U.S.A., P.O. Box 28570, Santa Ana, CA 92799-8570.

Free Guide to Drugs, Medications, and Cleaning Products: Get a free 272-page "Guide to Consumer Product Information" that tells all about different types of drugs and pain medications, personal-care and household cleaning products. Write to Bristol-Myers Company Guide to Consumer Product Information, Box 14177, Baltimore, MD 21268.

Guide to Health Problems & Preventive Care: A free, 50-page guide on health problems & preventative care for the elderly is offered to you by writing to "Wellness Guide,"

Pennsylvania Hospital Marketing Services, 800 Spruce St., Philadelphia, PA 19107.

10 Spicy Tomato Sauce Recipes: If you like spicy foods, then send for 10 free recipes made with spicy tomato sauce. Write to Free Pace Recipe Cards, Box 169, El Paso, TX 79977.

Free Bumper Sticker: Get free bumper stickers and reference guide books on the American Quarter Horse. Write to American Quarter Horse Association, Amarillo, TX 79168.

Booklet on Carpet: "Everything You Wanted To Know About Carpet But Were Afraid To Ask," is yours free by send $.25 for postage and handling to Advertising Department, Bigelow-Sanford, Inc., P.O. Box 3089, Greenville, SC 29602.

Nutrition & Exercise Booklet: Send for this great booklet that deals with nutrition and exercise and "Shaping Up For The Long Run." Write to: Nutrition For The Way We Live, P.O. Box 307, Coventry, CT 06238.

Free Music Booklet that can Improve Relationships: Let music bring you and your child closer together. Send for this free booklet, "How Music Can Bring You Closer To Your Child" by writing to Leblanc Corp., 7019 30th Avenue, Kenosha, WI 53140.

Tips on Planning A Reunion: "How To Plan A Reunion!" It's easy with this free booklet from Yardley of London. Send $1.00 for postage and handling to Yardley Family Reunion Planner, P.O. Box 14851, Chicago, IL 60614.

Learn about youth hostels all over the world. Write to American Youth Hostels, 891 Amsterdam Avenue, New York, NY 10025.

How to Eat Better for a Healthy Heart: Get a free chart

on "Guide To Eating For A Healthy Heart" by sending a business size S.A.S.E. to Merck Sharp & Dohme, Health Information Department, P.O. Box 1486, West Point, PA 19454.

Free Trees Available: Get free trees! In honor of Arbor day and to encourage the planting of trees, The National Arbor Day Foundation, 100 Arbor Avenue, Nebraska City, NE 68410 is offering a free tree as part of their "Trees For America" program.

Learn about carpeting: Send for "Understanding Carpet Quality" by writing to Armstrong Consumer Dept., Box 3001, Lancaster, PA 17604.

A Family Guide to Fire Safety: "Fire Safety In Your Home" can prevent any harm from coming to your family. Send for your free guide on fire safety instructions along with a free "Fire Pail" label by send a business size S.A.S.E. to Arm & Hammer, P.O. Box 7648, Princeton, NJ 08543-7648.

Guide to Planning Wedding Photographs: "How to Plan Your Wedding Photographs" is free from Eastman Kodak Co., Dept. 12, 343 State St., Rochester, NY 14650.

Free Catalog of Certificates: Teachers - Get a free catalog with beautiful 8x10 certificates for your students, grade 1-8. Many subjects are available, so write to Achievement Certificates, P.O. Box A, Clarence, NY 14031.

Decorating Ideas Booklet: Get this free 29-page booklet that provides you with lots of decorating ideas for all rooms of the house. Send $.25 for postage to Georgia-Pacific Corp., 900 S.W. Fifth Ave., Portland, Oregon 97204.

Retirement Activities & Information Booklet: "The Aging And The Community" contains facts on the problems of retiring, leisure activities, and about the subject in general.

Write to AFL-CIO Department of Community Services, 815 16th St. N.W., Washington, D.C. 20006.

Free Popcorn Recipes Booklet: Get a free popcorn recipe booklet plus a popcorn-ball maker by sending $1.00 for postage and handling to Jolly Time Popcorn, Dept. WB1, Sioux City, IA 51102.

Wine Tour & Tasting: Tour & Taste the Wine in the oldest and most beautiful winery. It's in New York State. Write for a free map and brochure on the tours to "Brotherhood" Winery, Washingtonville, NY 10992.

Floor Design Booklets: Get a number of booklets on Kitchen & Bathroom and Floor & Room Design are offered to you by the makers of Armstrong Floor Tile. Write to Armstrong Consumer Affairs Dept., P.O. Box 3001, Lancaster, PA 17604.

Timeless Chicken Recipes: Get a free recipe book from "Timeless Chicken Recipes...In No Time," Swanson Chunk Chicken, Box 964 Bensalem, Pennsylvania 19020.

History of the Helicopter : Free - The Story of the Helicopter. Write to Sikorsky Aircraft, Division of United Aircraft Corp., Stratford, CT 06602.

How to Make & Bake Bread: Learn how to bake terrific bread with this free booklet from Fleischmann's Educational Services, P.O. Box 2695, Grand Central Station, New York, NY 10017. Be sure to ask for your free "Bake-A-Bread" Books.

Free T-Shirt Decal: If you don't like guns, then order this free t-shirt decal and sew-on patch. Write to Ban Handguns Coalition, 100 Maryland Avenue, N.E., Washington, D.C. 20002. You will also receive a free booklet.

Help Protect the Environment: Learn to protect our fragile environment with this free booklet that tells you everything that you can do to help. Write to Mobil, Box EL, 3225 Gallows Rd., Fairfax, VA 22037. Ask for "Protecting The Environment" Booklet.

Learn How to Get Rid of Household Pests: Send for this free booklet called "Household Pests & How To Get Rid Of Them." Just send $.50 for postage and handling to the National Pest Control Association, 8100 Oak Street, Dunn Loring, VA 22027.

Information on Buying a New Car: Get a free 16-page guide to ensure that you are not missing any important features when buying a new car. To get a copy of "What Every Woman Should Know Before Buying A Car," write to Ford Motor Co., Marketing Programs, P.O. Box 2959, Detroit, Mich. 48202.

Hand Cleaner Sample: Get a free sample of "Fast Orange" Hand Cleaner by writing to Fast Orange Sample Offer, Loctite Corp., Public Relations Dept., 4450 Cranwood Parkway, Cleveland, OH 44128-4084.

Advice For Rape Victims: If you have been a victim of rape, order this helpful booklet that offers practical advice. Write to the Rape Treatment Center, 1225 Fifteenth St., Santa Monica, CA 90404. Ask for: Taking Action; What To Do If You Are Raped. Send a business size S.A.S.E. to Caffeine, P.O. Box 1144, Rockville, MD 20850 for a free booklet called "What You Should Know About Caffeine."

Cooking with Yogurt: "The Dannon 100: 100 Tips For Cooking With Yogurt" is yours if you send $.50 for postage to The Dannon 100, P.O. Box 5809, Kalamazoo, Michigan 49003-5809.

Protect Your Money with the Consumer Resource

Handbook: How you can avoid being cheated or ripped-off of your money. Send for this free, 93-page Consumers Resource Handbook that tells who to contact to assist you with your problems. Write to the Consumer Information Center, Dept. 568X, Pueblo, CO 81009. (1990 OCA) #568X.

Free Veteran Services: Find out about the many free services available to you. Write to the Veterans Administration, Information Service, Washington, D.C. 20420

Picture Framing Tips: Learn tips on grouping, mounting, and framing pictures from Eastman Kodak. Send a business size S.A.S.E. to Eastman Kodak Co., Dept. 841, 343 State Street, Rochester, NY 14650.

Maps & Information on Washington D.C.: Send for free brochures and maps on the Washington D.C. area that are offered by The Washington Area Convention Visitors Bureau, 1212 New York Ave. N.W., Washington, D.C. 20005. Also ask for the Washington D.C. Calendar of Events.

Postage Stamp Booklets: Get free booklets on United States Postage Stamps by writing to the U.S. Postal Service, Consumer Affairs Dept., Washington, D.C. 20260.

Pickling Information & 43 Relish Recipes: Free information on pickling from Heinz. This booklet also includes 43 recipes for relishes, fruits, and vegetables. Write to "Pickling Guide," Heinz U.S.A., P.O. Box 28, Pittsburgh, PA 15230.

Booklet on the History of the Buffalo: Learn the history of "The American Buffalo." Get this free book from the U.S. Department of the Interior, Fish & Wildlife Service, Washington, D.C. 20240.

200 Free Booklets: Get a list of over 200 booklets you can receive free. Write to the Consumer Information Center, Pueblo, CO 81009.

Handling Winter Driving Hazards: Learn how to handle the various hazards of winter driving. Send for "Winter Driving or Survival of the Fittest," Midas International, Box 11172, Chicago, IL 60611.

Free Booklets on Bird Feeders: Attract more wild birds to your yard. Send $.25 for postage and handling for each booklet to Hyde Bird Feeder Co., 56 Felton St., Waltham, Mass. 02254. Other booklets include how to make bird feeding and bird watching more fun.

Free Toothpaste and Booklet: Want a beautiful smile? Then write to Lever Brothers Company, Consumer Education Department, 390 Park Avenue, New York, NY 10022 for a free AIM Toothpaste booklet called "Tooth Wars."

Free Birth Announcements: Let everyone know your having a baby. Get a free sample of birth announcements that tie in with your work or hobby. Send $.25 for postage to Birth-O-Gram, Coral Gables, FL 33134.

Free Guide to Training & Riding Horses: Get a free 30-page guide on "Training Riding Horses." Write to the American Quarter Horse Association, P.O. Box 200, Amarillo, TX 79105.

Free Booklet on Dieting & Wight Control: Get a free "Diet & Weight Control Book" offered to you by Metropolitan Life Insurance, Health & Welfare Dept., 1 Madison Ave., New York, NY 10010.

How To Use Your Electronic Gizmos: Get a free 52-page booklet that takes the headache out of using today's electronic "gizmos." Send a business size S.A.S.E. with (3) 1st class stamps to Electronic Industries Association, P.O. Box 19100, Washington, D.C. 20036. Ask for: "How to Install, Connect, & Expand Electronics."

Free information on Walking & Your Health: Walking can save your life! Get this free information booklet by sending a business size S.A.S.E. to Walking Brochure, Rockport Co., 72 Howe St., Marlboro, MA 01752.

The History of Gold: Get free literature on the history of "Gold." Write to The Gold Information Center, 900 Third Ave., New York, NY 10022.

Indian & Eskimo Arts & Crafts: Here's a free source directory of Indian & Eskimo Arts & Crafts. Write to Indian Arts & Crafts, Room 4004, U.S. Dept. of Interior, Washington, D.C. 20240.

Free Copy of the "Bill of Rights": Get a free copy of the "Bill of Rights" by writing to the Veterans of Foreign Wars, Americanism Dept., Broadway at 34th Street, Kansas City, MO 64111.

Long-Distance Moving Booklet: If you're planning to make a long-distance move in the near future, Allied Van Lines publishes a helpful 27-page booklet. "Guide to a Good Move" explains how long-distance moving operates, how moving charges are determined, how to file a claim if your goods are damaged or delivered late, and how to prepare children and pets for a move. Get the booklet by writing to: Allied Van Lines, P.O. Box 4403, Chicago, IL 60680.

Energy Conservation: The Conservation and Renewable Energy Inquiry and Referral Service (CAREIRS) has over 300 free fact sheets and other publications on energy conservation. You can get a condensed publication list by writing to CARIERS, Box 8900, Silver Spring, MD 20907, or by calling (800) 523-2929.

Free Earrings: Simply Whispers are 100% hypoallergenic, alleviating the hassle of irritation. You can get a free introductory pair of these earrings and a catalog by writing to: Simply Whispers, Department 93M7-0805, 33 Riverside Drive,

Pembroke, MA 02359.

Quilting Catalog: This quilters "wishbook" features over 100 pages of quilting books, patterns, notions, fabric medleys, quilting aids, scrap bags, and more. Send your name and address to: Keepsake Quilting, Department CM, Dover Street, P.O. Box 1459, Meridith, NH 03253.

Tennis-Racquet Pen: You can get a free ball-point pen that looks just like a mini-sized tennis racquet by writing to: United States Tennis Association Publications, 707 Alexander Road,Princeton, NJ 08540. Ask for a Tennis Racquet Pen. Include $1.00 to cover postage and handling.

Gold Prospecting: A free booklet titled, "How to Mine and Prospect for Gold", is distributed by the publications department of the Bureau of Mines. Write to: Publications Department, Bureau of Mines, U.S. Department of the Interior, 18th and C Sts., NW, Room 2647, Washington, DC 20240.

Rock Collecting: A free booklet titled, "Collecting Rocks" is available from the U.S. Geological Survey. The booklet is of interest to anyone interested in pursuing rock collecting as a hobby and learning more about geology. Write to: U.S. Geological Survey, Book and Report Sales, Box 25425, Denver Colorado 80225.

Beginners Stamp Collecting: Anyone interested in collecting and studying stamps should send for this free booklet called, "Introduction to Stamp Collecting". Write to: Stamp Division, U.S. Postal Service, 475 L'Enfant Plaza West, SW, Washington, DC 20260.

Weight Guidelines Information: If you think you have a weight problem, Send for your free guidelines by sending a long business size S.A.S.E to Height & Weight Chart, Health & Safety Education Department, Metropolitan Life, One Madison Ave., New York, NY 10010.

Free Samples for Denture-wearers: Receive a free sample of Sea Bond for either Uppers or Lowers or both (Please Specify). Write to Sea Bond Free Offer, Combe, Inc., 1101 Westchester Ave., White Plains, NY 10604.

Use Light Efficiently: Learn to use light properly with "See Your Home in a New Light." Write to General Electric Lamp Division, Inquiry Bureau, Nela Park, Cleveland, OH 44112.

Guide to Carving a Turkey or Roast: Learn to carve a turkey or a roast the right way with the free 32-page "Carving Guide" from "Cutco Carving Guide" at Cutco Cutlery Dept.33, Wear-Ever Aluminum Company, 1089 Eastern Avenue, Chillicothe, OH 45601.

Free Christmas Decorating Booklet: Get this free "Christmas Decorations" booklet that shows you how to bake your own decorations. Write to Morton Salt Co., Consumer Affairs Dept., 110 N. Wacker Dr., Chicago, IL 60606.

Free Booklet on Window Ideas: If you're planning on remodeling your home, then send for your free "Window Idea Booklet" from Pella Windows Co., 100 Main St., Pella, IA 50219.

Food Safety Tips: Determine how safe the food you buy really is with the help of this free booklet. Write to Americans For Safe Food, 1501 16th Street N.W., Washington, D.C. 20036.

Creative Math Activities: Teach your kids how to figure out math problems the fun way. Send a business size S.A.S.E. to the National Council of Math Teachers, 1906 Association Dr., Reston, VA 22091. Ask for: Family Math Activities Brochure.

Figure Your Net Worth with Free Checklist: Find out

how much money you are worth with this free checklist and worksheet called "What Is Your Net Worth? Send a business size S.A.S.E. to Net Worth Brochure, First Investor's Corp., 120 Wall Street, New York, NY 10005.

The Peace Corps: Find out about "Peace Corp Facts" with this free material from the Peace Corps, Information Office, Washington, D.C. 20525.

Do-it Yourself Home Plans: Get a list of Do-It-Yourself Plans For The Home Craftsman. Write to Home Craftsman Plan, Department of Western Wood Products Association, 1500 Yeon Building, Portland, Oregon 97204.

Childproof Your Refrigerator & Freezer: Learn how to childproof old refrigerators & freezers to prevent children from climbing inside and getting trapped. Send a business size S.A.S.E. to Home Appliance Manufacturers, 20 North Wacker Dr., Chicago, IL 60606.

Oat-Bran Tablets: Get a free 30-day supply of Swanson Oat Bran Tablets - Proven to reduce blood cholesterol levels. Send $1.00 for postage and handling to Swanson Health Products, P.O. Box 2803, Fargo, ND 58108.

Protect Yourself Against All Types of Crime: Write for your free Crime Resistance Booklet, Public Affairs Dept., Room 6236, F.B.I., 10th and Pennsylvania Ave., Washington, D.C. 20535

Save Money with Refunds & Coupons: Get a free brochure to find out how Refunding can save you as much money as couponing can, and perhaps more! Write to Tropicana Products Consumer Center, P.O. Box 338, Bradenton, FL 34206. Ask for: "Refunding For Fun And Profit."

Feminine Hygiene Samples: Get a free e Tampax Teen Kit complete with a sample of Tampax Tampons, a purse container, and a helpful booklet on the subject. Write to Dr. C.L. Thomas, Tampax, Inc., P.O. Box 271, Palmer, Mass. 01069.

Information About Your Heart: The American Heart Association offers free information including; "Your Heart & How It Works"; "The Circulatory System"; About Your Heart & Bloodstream"; and a puzzle called "How The Heart Works Puzzle." Write to The American Heart Association, 205 East 42nd St., New York, NY 10017.

Help for Snorers: Get help if you're a chronic snorer. Send a business size S.A.S.E. to Snoring Brochure, New York Eye & Ear Infirmary, 2nd Ave. at 14th St., New York, NY 10003.

Remodel Your Yard or Garden: Get a free "Yard & Garden Remodeling Kit" by sending $1.00 for postage and handling to The Garden Council, 500 N. Michigan Ave., Suite 1400, Chicago, IL 60611.

Health Tips for Seniors: Seniors - Here's a great handbook called "Help Yourself To Good Health" and it's yours free from Pfizer Pharmaceuticals, P.O. Box 3852, Grand Central Station, New York, NY 10163.

Make Your Bathroom Safe: "Play It Safe In The Bathroom" was published to help you safety-proof your bathroom to make it safe for children and seniors. Write to Scrubbing Bubbles, Dept. 400, P.O. Box 78980, New Augusta, IN 46278.

Turkey Menus: Turkey Leftover Menus are yours free when you write to Louis Rich Co., Box 7188, Madison, WI 53704.

Tree Care: Plant and care for your trees with "Spunky's Tree Care Check List." Send a business size S.A.S.E. to American Forestry, P.O. Box 2000, Washington, D.C. 20013.

Renters Guide: Free-"A Guide to Renting An Apartment." Write to State Farm Insurance, Public Relations Dept., One State Farm Plaza, Bloomington, IL 61701.

Healthcare Booklets for Women: Get a list of the free health care booklets offered to women. Write to Beecham Products U.S.A., Consumer and Public Affairs Dept., P.O. Box 1467, Pittsburgh, PA 15230.

Vitamin Sample: Get a free sample of "Green Magma." It's a nutritional vitamin that mixes with water and lets you drink your vegetables. Send $1.00 for postage and handling to Green Foods Corp., 620 Maple Ave., Torrance, CA 90503-5001.

Home Security: Test the security in your home with the free Home Security Test from the New England Lock Co., Box 544, South Norwalk, CT 06856.

Free Booklets Available: To get a list of free booklets, write to the National Safety Council, 425 North Michigan, Chicago, IL 60611.

Boating Rules & Water Safety: Learn everything you need to know about boating safety & rules of the waterways with a free booklet called "Don't Make Waves" from State Farm Public Relations, One State Farm Plaza, Dept. R, Bloomington, IL 61701.

Bicycle Safety Coloring Book: Kids can get a free coloring book that will teach them about bike safety and how to take care of their bike. Write to Sandoz-Triaminic, Route 10 East, E. Hanover, NJ 07936. Ask for: The Bike Safety Coloring Book.

Free Healthcare Items: To get a list of free healthcare items titled, "Consumer Healthcare Series List." Write to Pfizer

Pharmaceuticals, P.O. Box 3852, Grand Central Station, New York, NY 10163.

Travel & Fashion Guide: Get a free "Travel And Fashion Guide" from the Consumer Affairs Department, ILGWU-Garment Worker's Union, 1710 Broadway, New York, NY 10019.

Financial Booklets: To get a list of American Express free "Lifecycle Brochures,"on many financial subjects, write to American Express, Consumer Affairs Department, World Financial Center, New York, NY 10285.

Tennis Guide: Learn to play tennis with "Mr. Peanut's Guide To Tennis." Write to Standard Brands Educational Dept., Box 2695, Grand Central Sta., New York, NY 10017.

Reynolds Recipes: Send for the free "Reynolds Cooking Fold" recipes by writing to The Reynolds Wrap Kitchens, P.O. Box 27003, Richmond, VA 23261.

Information on the United Nations: Get free material on the United Nations by writing to The United Nations Educational Services Department, United Nations, NY 10017.

The Interstate Commerce Commission: Get free material on the duties of the Interstate Commerce Commission, Public Information Office, Washington, D.C. 20423.

The Federal Land Bank System: Get free information on the Federal Land Bank System. Write the Farm Credit Administration, Washington, D.C. 20578.

Set Up a Personal Financial Plan: Get the help of a life insurance underwriter to help you set up a personal financial plan with "Shaping Your Financial Fitness." Send a business size S.A.S.E. to Fitness Brochure, National Association of Life Underwriters, Dept. C, 1922 F Street, Washington, D.C.

20006-4387.

Free Ruler/Bookmark: Get a free 6-inch plastic ruler that also serves as a bookmark. Send a business size S.A.S.E. to Union Label Department, ILGWU, 1710 Broadway, New York, NY 10019.

Money-making Ideas: "Ways & Means Handbook" is offered to help you with money-making ideas for your club or organization. Just send $.50 for postage and handling to Sperry & Hutchinson Co., Consumer Services, 2261 Brookhollow Plaza Dr. #207, Arlington, TX 76006.

Denture Adhesive Sample: Get a free sample of "Klutch" denture adhesive powder by writing to Klutch Free Sample Offer, I.Putnam, Inc., P.O. Box 444, Big Flats, NY 14814.

Free Booklet about Vision at an Older Age: Get a free booklet on "Seeing Well As You Grow Older." Send a business size S.A.S.E. to Inquiry Clerk, American Academy of Ophthalmology, Box 7424, San Francisco, CA 94120.

Moving Guide: Here's a great guide if you are planning on moving. Write to Ryder Truck Rentals, P.O. Box 020816, Miami, FL 33102. Ask for: Mover's Guide.

Learn About the Stock Market: Learn how the stock market works with "Journey Through A Stock Exchange." Write to American Stock Exchange, Publications Department, 86 Trinity Place, New York, NY 10006.

Recycling: Learn all about Recycling in a free booklet called "Recycling." Send $.25 for postage and handling to Educational Servicing, National Wildlife Federation, 1412 16th Street NW, Washington, D.C. 20036.

Collect Picture Postcards: Learn how to start collecting

Picture Postcards! Get a free Beginner's Set of 5 Picture Postcards plus an information booklet by sending $1.00 for postage and handling to Joan Nykorchuk, 13236 N. 7th Street (#4), Suite 237, Phoenix, AZ 85022. Be sure to ask for the Beginner's Postcard Collector's Set.

How to Quit Smoking: Stop smoking with this free guide called "How To Give Up Cigarettes." Write to the American Cancer Society, Booklet Distribution Department, 19 West 56th Street, New York, NY 10019.

How to Finish Furniture: "Recipes For Finishing Furniture" is yours, free, by writing to Johnson Wax Co., Box 567, Racine, WI 53403.

Free Wall Poster: Get a free, colorful wall poster titled "Freedom From Hunger" by writing to The Food and Agriculture Organization of the U.N., 1325 "C" Street S.W., Washington, D.C. 20437.

Valicium Information Kit: Get a free Valicium Information Kit that includes a facts brochure, a 4-tablet sample, a calcium counter, and a $.50 coupon for Caltrate. Send $1.00 for postage and handling (Check made payable to Lederle Laboratories) to Caltrate Information Kit, Lederle Promotional Center, 2200 Bradley Hill Rd., Blauvelt, NY 10913.

Fermentation Information: Get "The Story of Fermentation," free from the Educational Services Department, Pfizer International, Inc., 235 East 42nd Street, New York, NY 10017.

Develop Better Study Habits: Learn to study better for school with "Studying Tips & Hints" from Cliff Notes, Inc., P.O. Box 80728, Dept. SV-047, Lincoln, NE 68501.

Fire Prevention Chart: Get a free fire prevention chart from Liberty Mutual Insurance, Public Relations Department,

175 Berkeley Street, Boston, Massachusetts 02117.

Packing the Right Way: Learn to pack for a trip the right way. Learn what to bring and how to pack it, along with security tips. Write to ASTA Fulfillment Dept., 1101 King Street, Alexandria, VA 22314.

How Paper is Made: "Make Paper From Trees." Send for this free booklet from the Forest Service, U.S. Department of Agriculture, Washington, D.C. 20250.

Exercises to Relieve Back Pain: Relieve yourself from lower-back pain with 10 doctor-recommended exercises in this free booklet called "Getting The Upper Hand On Lower-Back Pain." Write to Porter & Novelli, 303 E. Wacker Dr., Chicago, IL 60601.

Fire Prevention: Learn to prevent fires, formulate escape plans, and how to get help with "Your House Is On Fire" (#AA-2982) offered by Aetna Insurance, Public Relations Department, 151 Farmington Ave., Hartford, CT 06156.

Grandma's Molasses Recipes: Free recipe book from Grandma's Molasses, Molasses Information Network, P.O. Box 9179, Morristown, NJ 07960. Ask for: Free Recipe Booklet.

Caring for Your Teeth: To receive a free booklet called "An Ounce Of Prevention," that tells you how to take care of your teeth, write to the American Dental Hygenists Association, 444 N. Michigan Ave. (#3400), Chicago, IL 60611.

Your Rights to Obtain Credit: Find out your rights if you have ever been denied credit. Write to the Federal Trade Commission, Consumer Inquiries, Pennsylvania Ave. & 6th Street N.W., Washington, D.C. 20580.

Breast Examination Card: Get a free breast examination card to help you with early detection of any potentially cancerous lumps. Send a business size S.A.S.E. to First Response BSE Card, P.O. Box 562, Gibbstown, NJ 08027.

How to Face the Death of a Loved One: Learn what to do when faced with the death of a loved one. This free booklet called "My Duty" can help. Write to Clark Grave Vault Co., Columbus, OH 43201.

Tamper Free Foods & Medicine: Make sure the foods and medicines that you buy are tamper-free with this free booklet that shows you how. Write to U.S. Pharmacopeial Convention, 12601 Twinbrook Pkwy., Rockville, MD 20852.

Solve Washing & Drying Problems: Get a free booklet on how to solve your washing and drying problems. Write to The Maytag Company, Home Service Dept., Newton, Iowa, 50208.

Aloe Vera Samples: Get a free sample of "Aloe Vera Magic." A special moisturizing creme from the plant of the same name. Send $1.00 for postage and handling to Jason Natural Products (Aloe Vera Magic Sample) 8468 Warner Dr., Culver City, CA 90232-2484.

Babysitters Telephone Guide: "Telephone Tips For Babysitters" is a great folder for recording all of the phone numbers a baby-sitter will need. Ask your local telephone company for a free folder.

Free Aplets & Cotlets: Get a free sample of Aplets & Cotlets - The 100% pure fruit & nut candy. Made with pure apples and apricots, large walnuts, and with no preservatives. Just send $1.00 for postage and handling (Refunded with 1st purchase from their catalog) to Aplets & Cotlets, P.O. Box "C", Cashmere, WA 98815.

Guide to Feeding Newborns: Get "The Newborn

Feeding Guide" when you send $.50 for postage to Evenflo Products, 771 No. Freedom St., Ravenna, OH 44266.

Calorie & Carbohydrate Guide: Get a free Calorie Counter & Carbohydrate Guide from Hollywood Diet Bread, 1747 Van Buren St., Hollywood, Florida 33020.

Poison Ivy Poster: Teachers, get a free poster that illustrates and describes Poison Ivy. Write to Ivy Corp., Box 596, West Caldwell, NJ 07006.

Free Health Coloring Book: Get a free 26-page coloring book called "The ABC's of Good Oral Health," From the American Dental Association, 211 E. Chicago Ave., Chicago, IL 60611. Be sure to send $.25 for postage.

Paper Plant Tour Booklet: Get this free booklet that takes you on a tour of a paper plant. Write to Educational Services Department,, Hammermill Papers, Erie, Pennsylvania 16512. Ask for: "From Forest Tree To Fine Papers."

Free Bumper Sticker: Get a free "Skateboard Bumper Sticker" and a booklet on skateboard safety tips by writing to Roller Sports, 1855 Cassat Ave., Jacksonville, Florida 32210.

Camping Information: If you want to go camping out in the wild, don't do it before you write to the Office of Public Inquiries, National Park Service, 18th & "C" Streets N.W., Washington, D.C. 20240, for some free maps and information.

FREE RECIPES

Write to any of the addresses below and you'll get lots of delicious recipes to impress your family with.

Minute Brown Rice-Recipes: Promotional Services Center, P.O. Box 789, Kankakee, IL 60902-0789. Ask for:13 recipes for "Minute" Instant Brown Rice.

Best Foods Co., Consumer Services Department, International Plaza, Englewood, NJ 07632. Ask for: "Best Foods Recipe Collection."

The California Apricot Advisory Board, 1280 Boulevard Way Room #107, Walnut Creek, CA 94595. Ask for: Apricot Recipes.

Sun-Maid Raisin Growers of CA, Kingsburg, CA 93631. Ask for: Raisin Recipe Booklet.

Halibut Association of North America, 309 Maritime Bldg., 911 Western Ave., Seattle, WA 98104. Ask for:Halibut Recipes.

Healthy Appetite Guide, P.O. Box 1214, Grand Rapids, MN 55745-1214. Send a business size S.A.S.E. and ask for: Healthy Appetite Guide.

Nestle Test Kitchens, 100 Bloomingdale Rd., White Plains, NY 10605. Ask for: chocolate lovers cookbooks.

Hiram Walker Co., P.O. Box 33006, Detroit, MI 48232. Ask for: Cordial Liquor Recipes.

Dannon Company, 22-11 38th Avenue, Long Island City, NY 11101. Ask for: "Favorite Yogurt Recipes."

Rice Council, Box 740121, Houston, TX 77274. Send a business size S.A.S.E. and ask for: "Light, Lean & Low Fat" recipe booklet.

Velveeta Cookbook, Box 833, South Holland, IL 60473. Ask for: Cheese Recipes.

Wilson & Company, 4545 Lincoln Blvd., Oklahoma City, OK 73105. Ask for: "Masterpiece Ham Recipes."

Kikkoman International, P.O. Box 784, San Francisco, CA 94101. Ask for: Kikkoman Recipe Collection.

Ragu Foods, Inc., 33 Benedict Place, Greenwich, CT 06830. Ask for: "Authentic Italian Pasta Recipes."

LaCHOY, Archibald, OH 43502. Ask for: Chinese Food Recipes.

Idaho Potato Commission, P.O. Box 1068, Boise, Idaho 83701. Ask for: Idaho Potato Tips & Recipes Booklet.

California Raisin Advisory Board, Box 5172, Fresno, CA 93755, Send $.25 for postage and ask for "Tasty Recipes Made With Raisins."

Recipe Book Offer, P.O. Box 347, Ayer, MA 01432. Send $.25 for postage.

Sioux Honey Association, P.O. Box 388, Sioux City, Iowa 51102. Send $.25 for postage and ask for "Honey Magic Recipes."

Celebrate with Campbell's Soup Recipe Book, P.O. Box 1232, Bensalem, PA 19020. Send a business size S.A.S.E. and ask for: Recipes using Campbell's Soup.

Ann Pillsbury Kitchens, The Pillsbury Co., Minneapolis, Minn. 55402. Ask for: list of free educational books.

Dole's Quick & Easy Recipes, P.O. Box 7758, San Francisco, CA 94120. Send a business size S.A.S.E. for your request.

Mazola Anniversary Cookbook, Box 307, Coventry, CT 06238. Send $.50 for postage and ask for "75 Years of Good

Cooking."

Fish & Seafood, Consumer Information Center, Pueblo, CO 81009. Send $.50 for postage and ask for "Fish and Seafood Made Easy."

Veg-All Recipes, The Larsen Company, P.O. Box 19026, Greenbay, WI 54307-9026.

Pace Recipe Cards, P.O. Box 169, El Paso, TX 79977.

FREE THINGS FOR SPORTS FANS

Football fans you can receive free teams photos and decals from your favorite team. Just send a postcard asking for a a Fan Mail Package.

San Diego Chargers Public Relations Department, 9449 Friars Road, San Diego, CA 92120.

Pittsburgh Steelers Public Relations Department, 300 Stadium Circle, Pittsburgh, PA 15212.

New England Patriots Public Relations Department, Sullivan Stadium on Rt. "One," Foxboro, MA 02035.

Denver Broncos Public Relations Department, 5700 Logan Street, Denver, CO 80216.

Phoenix Cardinals Public Relations Department, 51 West 3rd Street, Tempe, AZ 85281.

Los Angeles Rams Public Relations Department, 2327 W.Lincoln Avenue, Anaheim, CA 92801.

Dallas Cowboys Public Relations Department,
One Cowboys Parkway, Irving, TX 75063.

Tampa Bay Buccaneers Public Relations Department,
One Buccaneer Place, Tampa, FL 33607.

Minnesota Vikings Public Relations Department,
9520 Viking Drive, Eden Prairie, MN 55344.

Los Angeles Raiders Public Relations Department,
332 Center Street, El Segundo, CA 90245.

New York Jets Public Relations Department,
598 Madison Avenue, New York, N.Y. 10022.

San Francisco '49ers Public Relations Department,
4949 Centennial Blvd., Santa Clara, CA 95054.

Miami Dolphins Public Relations Department,
2269 NW 199th Street, Miami, FL 33056.

Kansas City Chiefs Public Relations
Department, One Arrowhead Drive,
Kansas City, MO 64129.

Orleans Saints Public Relations Department,
1500 Poydras Street, New Orleans, LA 70112.

Cleveland Browns Public Relations Department,
Cleveland Stadium Tower B, Cleveland, OH 44114.

Indianapolis Colts Public Relations Department,
7001 West 56th Street, Indianapolis, IN 46253.

Detroit Lions Public Relations Department,
1200 Featherstone Road, Pontiac, MI 48057.

Chicago Bears Public Relations Department,

250 North Washington, Lake Forest, IL 60045.

Atlanta Falcons Public Relations Department,
Hwy I-85 and Suwanee Road, Suwanee, GA 30174.

Cincinnati Bengals Public Relations Department,
200 Riverfront Stadium, Cincinnati, OH 45202.

Philadelphia Eagles Public Relations Department,
Veterans Stadium, Philadelphia, PA 19148.

Green Bay Packers Public Relations Department,
1265 Lombardi Avenue, Green Bay, WI 54307-0628.

Buffalo Bills Public Relations Department,
One Bills Drive, Orchard Park, N.Y. 14127.

New York Giants Public Relations Department,
Giants Stadium, East Rutherford, NJ 07073.
Seattle Seahawks Public Relations Dept.,
11220 N.E. 53rd Street, Kirkland, WA 98033.

Free NHL Fan-Mail Package: Get a free fan-mail package from your favorite NHL team. Send a business size S.A.S.E. to any of the teams below and they'll send you back a package full of team decals and photos of the team's stars.

Boston Bruins Public Relations Department,
150 Causeway St., Boston, MA 02114.

Buffalo Sabres Memorial Stadium,
140 Main Street, Buffalo, NY 14202.

Chicago Black Hawks Public Relations,
1800 W. Madison, Chicago, IL 60612.

Detroit Red Wings Public Relations,
600 Civic Center Dr., Detroit, MI 48226.

Hartford Whalers Public Relations Department,
242 Trumbull St., Hartford, CT 06103.

Los Angeles Kings Public Relations,
Forum Box 10, Inglewood, CA 90306.

Minnesota North Stars Met Center,
7901 Cedar Avenue South, Bloomington, MN 55425.

New York Islanders, Nassau Vet Coliseum,
Hempstead Turnpike, Uniondale, NY 11553.

New York Rangers, Madison Square Garden,
Four Penn Plaza, New York, NY 10001.

Philadelphia Flyers Public Relations,
Spectrum-Pattison, Philadelphia, PA 19148.

Pittsburgh Penguins Public Relations,
Civic Arena Gate 7, Pittsburgh, PA 15219.

St. Louis Blues Public Relations Department,
5700 Oakland Ave., St. Louis, MO 63110.

Washington Capitals Public Relations,
Capital Centre, Landover, MD 20786.

TRAVEL INFORMATION AND FREE THINGS FROM STATES

Free Maps Posters For States: You can get lots of free information about the following states including brochures, maps, posters, etc. Just write to the addresses below and you are on your way.

Illinois Department of Conservation, Division of Parks, Room 100, State Office Building, Springfield, IL 62706.

Iowa Development Commission, 250 Jewett Bldg.,
Des Moines, Iowa 50309.

Georgia Tourist Information Department,
P.O. Box 1776, Atlanta, GA 30301.

Idaho Travil Council, 700 West State Street,
Boise, ID 83720.

Arizona Highway Department,
2039 West Lewis Ave., Phoenix, AZ 85009.

Arkansas Publicity & Parks Commission,
State Capitol, Little Rock, Arkansas

Travel Division, Department of Public Information,
Capitol Annex, Frankfort, Kentucky 40601.

Lincoln Birthplace National Historic Site, Rt. One,
Hodgenville, Kentucky 42748.

Hawaii Visitors Bureau, Suite 801,
Waikiki Business Plaza, Honolulu, Hawaii 96815.

State of Alabama Bureau of Information,
Montgomery, Alabama 36104.
Pennsylvania Historical Commission,
Box 232, Harrisburg, Pennsylvania 17108.

Missouri Division of Commerce,
Jefferson City, Missouri 65101.

Connecticut Department of Commerce,
210 Washington Street, Hartford, CT 06106.

Massachusetts Department of Commerce,
State Office Building, 100 Cambridge Street,

Boston, Massachusetts 02202.

Florida Development Commission,
Tallahassee, Florida 32304.

Pocono Vacation Bureau, 100 Main St.,
Stroudsburg, PA 18360.

Vermont State Chamber of Commerce,
Montpelier, Vermont 05602.

New Jersey Department of Commerce,
Tourism & Travel CN826, Trenton, NJ 08625.

State of Michigan Tourist Council,
Stevens T. Mason Bldg., Lansing, Michigan 48926.

Oregon Travel Information Division,
State Highway Department, Salem, Oregon 97310.

Pennsylvania Dutch Tourist Bureau,
P.O. Box 1558, Lancaster, PA 17604.

Cape Cod Chamber of Commerce,
Hyannis, Mass. 02601.

Wyoming Travel Commission, 2320 Capitol Ave.,
Cheyenne, Wyoming 82001.

Hawaiian Airlines, Honolulu International
Airport, Box 9008, Honolulu, Hawaii 96820.

Iowa State Conservation Commission,
East 7th and Court Avenue,
Des Moines, Iowa 50308.

Texas Highway Department, Travel & Information Division,
P.O. Box 5064, Austin, TX 78703.

Washington D.C. Visitor's Bureau,
1212 New York Ave. NW. Washington, D.C. 20005.

Colorado Board of Tourism, 1625 Broadway ,
Denver, CO 80202-4729.

New Mexico Department of Development,
State Capitol, Santa Fe, New Mexico 87501.

State of Ohio Highway Department,
Columbus, OH 43215.

Maine Tourist Bureau, 142 Free St.,
Portland, Maine 04101.

Tourist Division, Maryland Department of Economic
State Office Building, Annapolis, MD 21404.

Alaska Travel Division, Pouch "E",
Juneau, Alaska 99801.

Montana Highway Commission, Tourist Department,
Box 1730, Wheat Building, Helena, Montana 59601.

Indiana Tourist Division, 334 State House,
 Indianapolis, Indiana 46204.

Ohio Chamber of Commerce,
820 Huntington Bank Bldg., Columbus, OH 43215

Hawaii Visitor's Bureau, 441 Lexington Ave.,
New York, NY 10017.

Mississippi Industrial Board,
P.O. Box 849, Jackson, Miss. 39205.

Nebraska Department of Roads, Information Section,
Capitol Bldg., Lincoln, Nebraska 68509.

Delaware State Development Department,
45 The Green, Dover, Delaware 19901.

Oklahoma Industrial Development Commission,
500 Will Rogers Memorial Bldg.,
Oklahoma City, Okla. 73105.

State of Nebraska Parks Commission,
Lincoln, Nebraska 68509.

Connecticut State Highway Department,
P.O. Drawer "A", Wethersfield, Conn. 06109

Utah U.S. Department of Agriculture,
Forest Service, Ogden, Utah

Florida Board of Parks, Tourist Division,
Tourist Bureau, 499 Biscayne Blvd., Miami, Fla. 33132.

Greater South Dakota Association, Box 806,
Pierre, South Dakota 57501.

South Carolina State Development Board,
Box 927, Columbia, S.C. 29202.

Arizona Office of Tourism,
1480 E. Bethany Home Road, Phoenix, AZ 85014.

Louisiana Tourist Commission,
666 No. Foster Dr., Baton Rouge, LA 70821

New York Convention and Visitors Bureau,
2 Columbus Circle, New York, NY 10019.

West Virginia Department of Commerce,

Tourist Division, State Capitol, Charleston,
West Virginia 25305.

Wisconsin Conservation Department,
Madison, WI 53701.

Pennsylvania Department of Commerce, Tourist Division,
Harrisburg, Pennsylvania 17120.

Virginia State Travel Service,
Ninth Street Office Bldg., Richmond, VA 23219.

Colorado Visitor's Bureau, Hospitality Center,
225 West Colfax, Denver, CO 80202.

Nevada Department of Economic Development,
Carson City, Nevada 89701.

Texas Parks and Wildlife Department, Austin, TX 78701.

Minnesota:Division of Publicity,
State Office Building, St. Paul, Minn. 55101.

Michigan Travel Bureau,
P.O. Box 30226, Lansing, Michigan 48909.

Spokane Chamber of Commerce,
1020 W. Riverside Ave., Spokane, WA 99201.

Office of Public Information,
Department of Forests & Waters,
Box 1467, Harrisburg, Pennsylvania 17120.

State of Oklahoma, Department of Highways,
Jim Thorpe Bldg., Oklahoma City, OK 73105.

State of New York Conservation Dept.,
Bureau of Forest Recreation, Albany, NY 12226.

Boston Chamber of Commerce, Visitors Information,
125 High Street, Boston, Massachusetts 02110.

San Francisco Convention & Visitors Bureau,
1375 Market St., San Francisco, CA 94103.

San Diego Convention & Visitors Bureau,
1200 Third Ave., Suite 824, San Diego, CA 92101.

Wisconsin State Tourist Bureau, State Office Bldg.,
Madison, WI 53702.

Maine Department of Economic Development,
State House, Augusta, Maine 04330.

TRAVEL INFORMATION AND VACATIONS GUIDES

Maps & information about Various Countries: Get free information about many countries, that includes maps and brochures, and maybe even some posters. Just write to any of the addresses listed below, and you will be on your way.

Canadian Government Travel Bureau, Tourist Division,
Ottawa, Canada.

Province of Quebec, Department of Tourism,
Fish & Game, 12 Rue St., Anne, Quebec, P.Q. Canada.

New Brunswick Travel Bureau, P.O. Box 1030,
Fredericton, New Brunswick, Canada.

Nova Scotia Travel Bureau, Halifax,
 Nova Scotia, Canada.

British Columbia Province; Government Travel Bureau,
Victoria, B.C., Canada.

Greater Vancouver Visitors Bureau, 650 Burrard St.,
Vancouver 1, B.C., Canada.

Saskatchewan; Tourist Development Branch,
Dept. of Industry & Commerce,
Pewer Building, Regina Saskatchewan, Canada.

Ontario Ministry of Tourism, Queens Park,
Toronto, Ontario, Canada M7A-2E5.

Manitoba; Tourist Development Branch,
Winnepeg, Manitoba, Canada.

Northwest Territories Tourist Office,
400 Laurier Ave. West, Ottawa, Ontario, Canada.

Newfoundland; Tourist Development Office,
St. Johns, Newfoundland, Canada.

Alberta; Government Travel Bureau,
Edmonton, Alberta, Canada.

Prince Edward Island; Travel Bureau,
Charlottetown, P.E.I., Canada.

The Yukon; Department of Travel & Publicity,
Whitehorse, Yukon, Canada.

Information on Latin America/The Alliance for Progress;
Department of Information and Public Affairs,
Organization of American States,
Washington, D.C., 20006.

France; French National Railroads,

Tourist Department, 610 Fifth Avenue, New York,
NY 10020.

Thailand; The Royal Thai Embassy,
Public Relations Attache, Washington 8, D.C.

Israel Government Tourist Office,
350 Fifth Avenue, New York, NY 10118.

Mexico; Sanborn's, P.O. Drawer 1210, McAllen, TX 78501.

Romania; Romanian Embassy, Washington, D.C. 20008.

Spain; Iberia Air Lines, 97-77 Queens Blvd.,
Rego Park, NY 11374.

Japan National Tourist Organization,
45 Rockefeller Plaza, New York, NY 10020.

Holland; KLM Royal Dutch Airlines,
437 Madison Ave., New York, NY 10022.

Scandinavia Overseas Service,
444 Madison Ave., New York, NY 10022

Argentina; Embassy of Argentina,
1600 New Hampshire Ave., Washington, D.C.

Belgium; Belgian National Tourist Office,
745 Fifth Ave., New York, NY 10022.

Greece; Greek National Tourist Office,
645 Fifth Ave., New York, NY 10022.

Sicily; Italian Government, Travel Department,
626 Fifth Ave., New York, NY 10020.

Republic of Mali (Africa); Embassy of the Republic of Mali,

2130 "R" Street N.W., Washington 8, D.C.

Ireland; Irish Tourist Board, 681 Market St.,
San Francisco, CA 94105.

Indonesian Consulate General, Information Section,
5 East 68th Street, New York, NY 10021.

New Zealand Consulate General, Suite 530,
630 Fifth Ave., New York, NY 10020.

Consulate General of Guatemala,
57 Park Ave., New York, NY 10016.

Embassy of Nicaragua,
1627 New Hampshire Ave., Washington, D.C.

Mexican Government Tourism Office,
405 Park Ave., Suite 1203, New York, NY 10022.

Dominican Republic;
1270 Avenue of America's, New York, NY 10020.

Philippine Islands; Embassy of the Philippines,
1617 Massachusetts Ave. N.W., Washington, D.C.

Ecuador Embassy, 2535 15th Street N.W.,
Washington, D.C. 20009.

Austrian Embassy, 2343 Massachusetts Ave.
N.W., Washington, D.C. 20008.

Swiss National Tourist Office, Swiss Federal Railways,
608 Fifth Ave., New York, NY 10020.

Portuguese National Tourist Office,
570 Fifth Ave., New York, NY 10036.

Lebanon; Tourist Counselor, Embassy of Lebanon,
Park Sheraton Hotel, "A-400" Washington, D.C. 20008.

Egyptian Government Tourist Office,
630 Fifth Ave., New York, NY 10020.

Trinidad Tourist board,
400 Madison Ave., New York, NY 10017.

Morocco; Royal Air Maroc,
680 Fifth Ave., New York, NY 10019.

Commonwealth of Puerto Rico,
734 15th Street N.W., Washington, D.C. 20005.

Bulgarian Tourist Office,
50 East 42nd Street, New York, NY 10017.

Turkish Tourism and Information Office,
821 United Nations Plaza, New York, NY 10017.

Chilean Embassy, 1736 Massachusetts Ave. N.W.,
Washington, D.C. 10017

Danish Information Office, 75 Rockefeller Plaza,
New York, NY 10019.

Labrador Tourist Bureau, Confederation Building,
St.Johns, Newfoundland

Yugoslav State Tourist Office, 630 Fifth Ave.,
New York, NY 10020.

Finnish Chamber of Commerce, 540 Madison Ave.,
New York, NY 10022.

Columbia Information Service, 140 East 57th Street,
New York, NY 10022.

Consulate General of Switzerland, 444 Madison Ave.,
New York, NY 10022.

Panama Canal Co., Balboa Heights, Canal Zone.

Irish Tourist Office, 590 Fifth Ave., New York, NY 10036.

Nigerian Consulate General, 575 Lexington Ave.,
New York, NY 10022.

Consulate General of Lithuania,
6147 South Artesian Ave., Chicago, IL 60629.

Government of India, Tourist Office,
30 Rockefeller Plaza, #15, New York, NY 10112.

Australian News & Information Bureau,
636 Fifth Ave., New York, NY 10020.

Quantas Airline, Education Department,
542 Fifth Ave., New York, NY 10036.

Consulate General of the Phillipines,
556 Fifth Ave., New York, NY 10036.

Japan National Tourist Organization,
360 Post Street, San Francisco, CA 94108.

Commonwealth of Puerto Rico,
304 Park Avenue South, New York, NY 10010.

British Travel Association,
680 Fifth Ave., New York, NY 10019.

British Information Services,
845 Third Avenue, New York, NY 10022.

Embassy of Nigeria, 2201 "M" Street N.W.,
Washington, D.C. 20037.

Brazilian Embassy, 3007 Whitehaven St. N.W.
Washington, D.C. 20008.

Embassy of Pakistan, 2315 Massachusetts Ave. N.W.,
 Washington, D.C. 20017

Consulate General of the Republic of China,
801 Second Ave., New York, NY 10017.

Italian Government, Travel & Tourist Department,
630 Fifth Ave., New York, NY 10111.

Consulate General of Chile, 809 United Nations Plaza,
New York, NY 10017.

National Tourist Office of West Germany,
747 Third Ave., New York, NY 10017.

Russia; Information Dept., Embassy of the U.S.S.R.,
1706 18th Street N.W., Washington, D.C. 20009.
 Or, Intourist, 630 Fifth Avenue, New York, NY 10020.

Japan Air Lines, Tourist Information Dept.,
655 Fifth Avenue, New York, NY 10022.

French Embassy, Information Division, 972 Fifth Ave.,
New York, NY 10021.

The Embassy of Israel,
Washington, D.C. Or, Israel Government,
Tourist Office 350 Fifth Ave., New York, NY 10001.

Latvian Legation, 4325 17th Street N.W.,
Washington, D.C. 20011.

Norwegian Information Service,
825 Third Avenue, New York, NY 10022.

Embassy of the Republic of Iraq,
1801 "P" Street N.W., Washington, D.C. 20036.

Mexican Embassy, 2829 16th Street N.W.,
Washington, D.C. 20009.

Luxembourg Consulate General, Tourist office,
One Dag Hammarskjold Plaza, New York, NY 10017.

Venezuela Embassy, Information Bureau,
2437 California Street N.W., Washington, D.C. 20008.

Norwegian Information Service,
Norwegian Embassy,
3401 Massachusetts Ave. N.W., Washington, D.C. 20007.

Aruba Tourist Bureau, 521 Fifth Avenue,
12th Floor, New York, NY 10175.

Ivory Coast Embassy, 2424 Massachusetts Ave. N.W.,
Washington, D.C. 20008.

Italian Government Travel Office, 630 Fifth Ave.,
New York, NY 10020.

Embassy of El Salvador,
2308 California Street N.W., Washington, D.C.

Austrian Information Service,
31 East 69th Street, New York, NY 10021.

Information Service of India,
Embassy of India, Washington, D.C., 20008.

German Democratic Republic to the U.N.,
58 Park Ave., New York, NY 10016.

Belgian Government, Information Center,
50 Rockefeller Plaza, New York, NY 10020.

Columbian National Tourist Board,
140 East 57th Street, New York, NY 10022.

Barbados Tourist Board, 800 Second Avenue,
New York, NY 10017.

Argentine Consulate General, 12 West 56th Street,
New York, NY 10019.

Consulate General of Jamaica, 200 Park Avenue,
New York, NY 10017.

Consulate General of Pakistan,
12 East 65th Street, New York, NY 10021.

Bermuda Department of Tourism, 630 Fifth Ave.,
New York, NY 10020.

THE WHOLESALE BARGAINS FREE STUFF GUIDE

Index